Deck Officer Study G

2010 - 2011 EDITION

*Preparation for the United States Coast Guard
Merchant Marine License Examinations*

VOLUME 1
DECK GENERAL

Edited by:

CAPTAIN JOSEPH S. MURPHY, II
Professor, Department of Marine Transportation
Massachusetts Maritime Academy

Academy Publishing Company
6 Munroe Parkway
Wareham, MA 02571

ISBN 1-881349-07-1 (Volume 1)
ISBN 1-881349-02-0 (6 Volume Set)
Printed in the United States

TABLE OF CONTENTS

DECK GENERAL - VOLUME 1

PART 1 - MARLINESPIKE SEAMANSHIP

PART 1 - MARLINESPIKE SEAMANSHIP

PART 2 - CARGO HANDLING & STOWAGE

PART 2 - CARGO HANDLING & STOWAGE

PART 3 - BASIC PRINCIPLES OF WATCHKEEPING

PART 3 - WATCHKEEPING PROCEDURES

Basic Principles of Watchkeeping (Emergency Operations)

PART 4 - ANCHORING & MOORING

Anchors & Ground Tackle

Anchor Nomenclature

Anchoring Procedures

Mooring Procedures

Anchor Computations

PART 5 - SHIPHANDLING & MANEUVERING

PART 5 - SHIPHANDLING & MANEUVERING

PART 6 - TOWING OPERATIONS

PART 7 - SHIP STABILITY & DAMAGE CONTROL

PART 8 - SHIP CONSTRUCTION

PART 8 - SHIP CONSTRUCTION

PART 8 - SHIP CONSTRUCTION

PART 9 - SHIP'S BUSINESS

PART 9 - SHIP'S BUSINESS

PART 10 - GREAT LAKES

PREFACE

GOAL
The *Deck Officer Study Guide* was compiled to assist prospective deck license candidates enrolled in a structured curriculum or studying independently with their preparation for the following U. S. Coast Guard Merchant Marine license examinations and open-book renewal exercises:

License Examinations:
*   Master   Oceans-Near Coastal-Inland-Great Lakes, Any Gross Tons
*   Chief Mate   Oceans-Near Coastal-Inland-Great Lakes, Any Gross Tons
*   Second Mate   Oceans-Near Coastal-Inland-Great Lakes, Any Gross Tons
*   Third Mate/OICNW   Oceans-Near Coastal-Inland-Great Lakes, Any Gross Tons
*   Master & Mate   Limited License, All Routes, All Tonnage Groups

Review & Renewal Exercises:
*   Comprehensive Renewal Exercise, All Grades of License
*   Rules of the Road Exercise, All Grades of License

Certification Examinations:
*   Able Seaman/Lifeboatman, All Grades of Certification

PURPOSE
The U. S. Coast Guard posts the Merchant Marine examination question bank on the Internet which constitutes publication of the questions in the public domain. This information is made available to afford the public an opportunity to review and comment upon the questions' clarity and accuracy. The data base file contains the U. S. Coast Guard questions for all grades of license. The Merchant Marine examination bank is not an examination study guide. It is merely a question and answer file which divides the deck license questions up into five generic topic areas. The questions are not organized into specific categories and appear in random fashion.

The *Deck Officer Study Guide* eliminates the need for computer know-how and expensive computer equipment. Each volume of the *Deck Officer Study Guide* substantially reorganizes the sequence of the examination questions into clear-cut sections for each of the five deck disciplines. The objective of this effort is to provide you with quick access to definitive areas of required expertise in order to accelerate systematic study and stimulate cognitive learning. Each section of the *Deck Officer Study Guide* isolates the key concepts affording you an opportunity for a comprehensive self-testing program. This methodology defines your individual starting point for additional research and remedial skill development.

COMPREHENSIVENESS
The primary reference source consulted during the compilation of the *Deck Officer Study Guide* was the U. S. Coast Guard Merchant Marine question bank. The multiple choice questions in this publication are the actual questions which will appear on the current series of Merchant Marine license examination modules and renewal exercises. During the collation of this publication, more than 15,000 U. S. Coast Guard multiple choice questions, answers and associated references were analyzed and regrouped into specific examination subjects. **See: Merchant Mariner Info Center; Deck Exam Info; Deck Exam Questions (http://www.uscg.mil/STCW/)**

ACCURACY

For all questions requiring a mathematical or process solution, the correct answers have been determined by using the most commonly accepted method for solving such problems. A candidate using that method for solving the problem correctly should find an answer that corresponds exactly with his or her answer. A candidate using an alternate but valid method should choose the answer that is closest to his or her answer. Certain questions may contain a specific tolerance which is given in parentheses following the statement. The tolerance applies to that statement alone. There is never an intended or implied connection between any two questions in any part of this book nor on any section of the deck license examination. A concerted effort has been made to produce a study guide which is accurate and reflects current scholarship. This effort is especially difficult in many areas of marine science and technology because reference texts often provide conflicting opinions on individual issues. The aim of the *Deck Officer Study Guide* is to reflect on those differences and to consider alternative theories or interpretations. Ambiguities or inconsistencies are always brought to the immediate attention of the U. S. Coast Guard at the National Maritime Center (NMC-4B) in Arlington, VA. Your assistance and input is both solicited and vital to this effort because deference has been given to the U. S. Coast Guard's keyed answer in all cases throughout this publication.

TEXT ARRANGEMENT

The *Deck Officer Study Guide* is designed to be *"User Friendly"*. It provides quick access to definitive subject areas and/or key concepts. The body of the text is organized into the following seven distinct volumes:

- VOLUME 1   Deck General
- VOLUME 2   Navigation General
- VOLUME 3   Deck Safety
- VOLUME 4   Rules of the Road
- VOLUME 5   Navigation Problems Parts "A" & "B"
- VOLUME 6   Deck Examination Illustration Book (COMDTPUB P16721.6A)
- VOLUME 7   Lifeboatman (Lifeboatman Examination Only)

The seven volumes address the subject matter embodied in all sections of the current Merchant Marine license examination modules for all grades of deck license. The arrangement and content of each section was determined by utilizing the U. S. Coast Guard's examination specifications, as detailed in Table 46 CFR 10.910-2, *"License Codes"*.

The arrangement format for *Volume 1, Deck General* presents each question with a sequential number which indicates both the volume number and a number unique to each question, next the U.S. Coast Guard database question number, followed by an appropriate Rule reference, the applicable system of Rules, a stem, which supplies needed information and poses the question, and four possible answers. The U. S. Coast Guard's keyed answer to each question in the *Volume 1, Deck General* is indicated by the anchor symbol "⚓".

040338/RR00272   **RULE 9 (b)**

BOTH INTERNATIONAL & INLAND Two vessels are meeting as shown in a narrow channel. Vessel "A" is a sailing vessel. Vessel "B" is a power-driven vessel which can safely navigate only within the channel. Vessel "B" sounds the danger signal. Vessel "A" shall _____. See Illustration DIAGRAM 37

- A.   maintain course and speed
- ⚓ B.   not impede the passage of vessel "B"
- C.   sound one prolonged followed by two short blasts
- D.   have the right of way

ILLUSTRATIONS

Some of the questions in this publication require the use of an illustration or diagram to answer the question correctly. All of the illustrations and diagrams are contained in COMDTPUB P16721.6A, *Merchant Marine Deck Examination Illustration Book, January 1992 edition. Volume 6, Deck Examination Illustration Book* of the *Deck Officer Study Guide* is a reproduction of COMDTPUB P16721.6A. If a question requires the use of an illustration or diagram, it will be specifically stated in the lead-in sentence or stem of the question.

040338/RR00272   **RULE 9 (b)**
BOTH INTERNATIONAL & INLAND Two vessels are meeting as shown in a narrow channel. Vessel "A" is a sailing vessel. Vessel "B" is a power-driven vessel which can safely navigate only within the channel. Vessel "B" sounds the danger signal. Vessel "A" shall _____. **SEE ILLUSTRATION: DIAGRAM 37**
   A. maintain course and speed
⚓ B. not impede the passage of vessel "B"
   C. sound one prolonged followed by two short blasts
   D. have the right of way

The Deck General illustrations have been included in this volume.

REFERENCES

Deck Examination Reference Texts have been cited whenever possible. Refer to and review the list of *Deck Examination Reference Texts* contained in *Volume 1, Deck General* of the *Deck Officer Study Guide*. **Preference has been given to the Examination Room Reference texts which are always preceded by an asterisk (*).** Use the <u>examination room</u> reference books as desk companions while studying and during self-testing exercises. Listed references may appear as an abbreviation or code. A table following the Preface in *Volume 1, Deck General of the Deck Officer Study Guide* lists the abbreviations and codes in alphabetical order and identifies the title of the reference. Some of the references listed are no longer available. As new questions are developed, they are drawn from current references. Over time, older references go out of print or are revised. If new reference material is published the U. S. Coast Guard reviews the questions in current use to ensure that they are still valid. The entire contents of any authorized Deck Examination Reference text may be used during all parts of the license examination with the exception of Rules of the Road during which NO reference material of any kind may be used.

MERCHANT MARINE EXAMINATION QUESTION STRUCTURE

All of the deck license examination modules are randomly generated. The examination questions do not follow in the same question sequence as those found in the *Deck Officer Study Guide*. Therefore, you must <u>NEVER</u> memorize lists of answers. This technique will not produce the desired results. The U. S. Coast Guard computer system is not programmed with an answer randomization capability but many of the questions in the test bank use identical question stems and/or similar answers with the answers rearranged in a different sequence; therefore, you must <u>NEVER</u> memorize answers by letter identity alone. New questions and updated examination modules will be generated by the U. S. Coast Guard in order to reflect changes in national and international regulations, shipboard procedures, or evolutionary changes in the marine industry. You must always be prepared to demonstrate your proficiency and knowledge of the subject matter rather than your mastery of the rote memorization of the questions themselves.

DECK LICENSE EXAMINATION GUIDANCE

The *Guide for Administration of Merchant Marine Deck Examinations (Deck Guide)*, (June 2009) and a table of *Deck Examination Subjects* outline the examination administration procedures, module rotation, and basic module structure for various grades of deck license. The U.S. Coast Guard Regional Examination Centers (RECs) are allowed some degree of latitude with regard to the administration of examinations. **You should personally confirm the module sequence, starting times and dates at the Regional Exam Center (REC) well in advance of your test day. See: Merchant Mariner Info Center; Deck Exam Info; Deck Exam Guide (http://www.uscg.mil/nmc/deck_exams.asp).**

*The Guide for Administration of Merchant Marine Deck Examinations (Deck Guide), (*June 2009*)* should be consulted on line at the address above. The assessment guidelines will help you to be better prepared. We fear things in direct proportion to our ignorance of them. The more you know about your exam and your rights the better off you will be.

The *Deck Examination Subjects Table* is designed to provide prospective license applicants with a detailed explanation of what subject areas may potentially appear in specific examination module. Be advised that, identical subject areas appear in different examination sections for various grades of license. Not every topic listed for a module will appear on every test, and different forms of a module can have different areas of emphasis. U. S. Coast Guard's examination specifications, as detailed in Table 46 CFR 10.910-2, "*License Codes*" contain the end caption:

"Any other subject considered necessary to establish the applicant's proficiency."

This catch-all statement has been rather liberally interpreted by the U. S. Coast Guard Merchant Marine Examination Branch to mean: *"No holds barred - Anything goes!"*

ACKNOWLEDGMENTS

A practical study guide of this scope and depth must acknowledge many debts - to other study guides of this and former generations, to maritime educators, marine scholars and authorities who have worked so diligently to improve the educational standards and professional skills of American Licensed Deck Officers.

The names of the scholars which follow have contributed primarily because of their commitment to the diffusion of knowledge. A preface is superfluous in respect of a work with such obvious purpose as this; but some acknowledgments are truly in order.

A collective acknowledgment of indebtedness is gratefully made; to my colleagues, one and all, from the Department of Marine Transportation at the Massachusetts Maritime Academy for their support, expertise and helpful suggestions made in informal conversations.

I am particularly grateful to:

Department of Marine Transportation, Massachusetts Maritime Academy
- CAPT. Jim Fitzpatrick, Associate Professor
- CAPT. Dave Mackey, Professor
- CAPT. Pat Modic, Professor
- CAPT. Ed Bruce, Senior Laboratory Instructor
- CAPT. Kurt DeCicco, Laboratory Instructor

Department of Marine Transportation, Maine Maritime Academy
- CAPT. Andy Chase
- CAPT. Ralph Pundt
- CAPT. Sam Teel
- CAPT. Peg Brandon

Department of Marine Transportation, California Maritime Academy
- CAPT. Jim Buckley
- CAPT. Paul Lyeda
- CAPT. Tuuli Messer-Bookman

Department of Marine Transportation, New York Maritime College
- CAPT. Rick Smith
- CAPT. Dennis Frederick

Department of Marine Transportation, Great Lakes Maritime College
- RADM. John Tanner, President
- CAPT. Mike Surgalski

Department of Marine Transportation, U.S. Merchant Marine Academy
- CAPT. Bob Meurn
- CAPT. George Sandberg
- CAPT. Dan Hunt

for their continuing scholarship, valued counsel and years of dedication to Marine Science; and most of all, To my students at the Massachusetts Maritime Academy who have contributed ideas through their work and classroom discussions.

The opinions and guidance, herein, are my own; none of the mentioned contributors bears any responsibility for any of the material contained in this book.

JOSEPH S. MURPHY, II
Massachusetts Maritime Academy

U.S.C.G. Regional Examination Centers (REC)

See: STCW Website, Merchant Mariner Information Center, Regional Examination Center Locations.
http://www.uscg.mil/nmc/rec_information.asp

ALASKA, Anchorage - ANCMS
(907) 271-6736

U.S. Coast Guard, Marine Safety Office (REC)
800 E. Dimond Blvd.; Suite 3-227
Anchorage, AK 99515

ALASKA, Juneau - JUNMS
(907) 463-2458

U.S. Coast Guard, Marine Safety Office (REC)
9105 Mendenhall Mall Road, Suite 170
Mendenhall Mall
Juneau, AK 99801-8545

CALIFORNIA, San Francisco - SFCMS
(510) 637-1124

U.S. Coast Guard, Marine Safety Office (REC)
Oakland Federal Building, North Tower
1301 Clay Street, Room 180N
Oakland, CA 94612-5200

CALIFORNIA, L.A./Long Beach - LOSMS
(562) 495-1480

U.S. Coast Guard, Marine Safety Office (REC)
501 W, Ocean Blvd., Suite 6200
Long Beach, CA 90802

FLORIDA, Miami - MIAMS
(305) 536-6548/6874

U.S. Coast Guard, Marine Safety Office (REC)
Claude Pepper Federal Building, 6th Floor
51 S.W. First Avenue
Miami, FL 33130-1608

HAWAII, Honolulu - HONMS
(808) 522-8264

U.S. Coast Guard, Marine Safety Office (REC)
433 Ala Moana Blvd., Pier 4
Honolulu, HI 96813-4909

LOUISIANA, New Orleans - NEWMS
(985) 624-5700

U.S. Coast Guard, Marine Safety Office (REC)
4250 Highway 22, Suite F
Mandeville, LA 70471

MARYLAND, Baltimore - BALMS
(410) 962-5132

U.S. Coast Guard, Marine Safety Office (REC)
U.S. Custom House, Room 420
40 South Gay Street
Baltimore, MD 21202-4022

MASSACHUSETTS, Boston - BOSMS
(617) 223-3040

U.S. Coast Guard, Marine Safety Office (REC)
455 Commercial Street
Boston, MA 02109-1045

MISSOURI, St. Louis - SLMMS
(314) 269-2504

U.S. Coast Guard, Marine Safety Office (REC)
1222 Spruce Street, Room 7.105
St. Louis, MO 63103-2846

NEW YORK, New York - NYCMS
(212) 668-7492

U.S. Coast Guard, Marine Safety Office (REC)
Battery Park Bldg.; 1 South Street
New York, NY 10004-1466

OHIO, Toledo - TOLMS
(419) 418-6010

U.S. Coast Guard, Marine Safety Office (REC)
420 Madison Ave., Suite 700
Toledo, OH 43604-1265

U.S.C.G. Regional Examination Centers (REC)

OREGON, Portland - PORMS
(503) 231-2296

U.S. Coast Guard, Marine Safety Office (REC)
911 NE 11th Avenue, Room 637
Portland, OR 97232-4169

SOUTH CAROLINA, Charleston - CHAMS
(843) 720-3250
(800) 826-1511

U.S. Coast Guard, Marine Safety Office (REC)
196 Tradd Street
Charleston, SC 29401-1899

TENNESSEE, Memphis - MEMMS
(901) 544-3297

U.S. Coast Guard, Marine Safety Office (REC)
200 Jefferson Avenue, Suite 1301
Memphis, TN 38103-2300

TEXAS, Houston - HOUMS
(713) 948-3350

U.S. Coast Guard, Marine Safety Officer (REC)
8876 Gulf Freeway. Suite 200
Houston, TX 77017-6595

WASHINGTON, Puget Sound - SEAMS
(206) 202-7327

U.S. Coast Guard, Marine Safety Office (REC)
915 Second Avenue, Room 194
Seattle, WA 98174-1067

Deck Examination Reference Texts & Materials

<u>**MATERIALS ALLOWED IN THE EXAM ROOM**</u>

The following reference texts and materials will be provided by the Coast Guard at the Regional Examination Center (REC) for use by license candidates for all grades of license.

1. Merchant Marine Deck Examination Illustration Book (COMDTPUB P16721.6A) January 1992 Edition
2. Nautical Almanac
3. Reprints from the 1983 Tide & Tidal Current Tables (COMDTPUB P16721.46)
    - Part 1: 1983 Tide Tables (Atlantic Coast of N. America)
    - Part 2: 1983 Tidal Current Tables (Atlantic Coast of N. America)
4. Sight Reduction Tables for Marine Navigation, H.O. Pub. No. 229, Vol. 2, Latitudes 15°-30°, Inclusive
5. American Practical Navigator, Pub No. 9, Volume II, 1981 Edition
6. International Code of Signals, H.O. Pub. No. 102, 1969 Edition, Revised 1993
7. Reprints from the Light List Lists and Coast Pilots (COMDTPUB P16721.38)
    - Part 1: Block Island and Eastern Long Island Sound
        - Section A: Light List - Volume I (blue pages)
        - Section B: Coast Pilot - 2 (white pages)
    - Part 2: Chesapeake Bay Entrance and Approaches
        - Section A: Light List - Volume II (yellow pages)
        - Section B: Coast Pilot - 3 (green pages)
8. Light List Volume V - Mississippi River
9. U.S. Coast Pilot, Volume 1 (Northern Right Whales)
10. U.S. Coast Pilot, Volume 4 (Northern Right Whales)
11. U.S. Coast Pilot, Volume 5 (Latest edition - Rivers & Western Rivers modules only)
12. U.S. Coast Pilot, Volume 6 (Latest edition - Great Lakes modules only)
13. U.S. Coast Pilot, Volume 7 (Latest edition - Rivers & Rivers other than Western Rivers modules only)
14. * Radio Navigational Aids Pub. No. 117
15. Chemical Data Guide for Bulk Shipment by Water CIM 16616.6A, 1990 edition
16. * Code of Federal Regulations §
    - A. * 33 CFR Parts 1 to 124, Navigation Rules, Anchorages, Bridges
    - B. * 33 CFR Parts 125 to 199, Oil Pollution, and Navigation Safety Regulations
    - C. * 46 CFR Parts 1 to 40, Tanker Regulations, Manning Requirements
    - D. * 46 CFR Parts 41 to 69, Marine Engineering and Load Line Regulations
    - E. * 46 CFR Parts 70 to 89, Passenger Vessel Regulations
    - F. * 46 CFR Parts 90 to 139, Cargo and Miscellaneous Vessels Regulations
    - G. * 46 CFR Parts 140 to 155, Dangerous Cargo Regulations
    - H. * 46 CFR Parts 156 to 165, Manning & Equipment Specifications (Subpart Q)
    - I. * 46 CFR Parts 166 to 199, Small Passenger Vessel Regulations
    - J. * 46 CFR 200-499, Maritime Administration, Great Lakes
    - K. * 49 CFR Parts 100 to 177, Transportation of Hazardous Material
17. Operating Manual DEEP DRILLER (COMDTPUB P16721.29) MODU examinations
18. Operating Manual COASTAL DRILLER (COMDTPUB P16721.30) MODU examinations
19. Stability Data Reference Book (COMDTPUB P16721.31) August 1989 Edition
20. Guidance Manual for Loading the M/V GRAND HAVEN (COMDTPUB P16721.32) (Great Lakes-AGT)
21. Ship's Code Card WS TA B-0-7 (4-92)
22. Ship's Weather Observations WS FORM B-81 (08-96)

All parts of the above license examination reference materials may be used on every section of the deck license examination with the exception of Rules of the Road during which no reference material of any kind may be used.

* *The effective date is the latest date available.*

Deck Examination Reference Texts & Materials

The following charts and miscellaneous materials are required in the examination room for us by license candidates:

TEST MATERIALS

1. Training Chart No. 12221-TR, Chesapeake Bay and Approaches
2. Training Chart No. 12354-TR, Eastern Long Island
3. Training Chart No. 13205-TR, Block Island Sound and Approaches
4. Maneuvering Board WOBZP 5090
5. Great Circle Tracking Chart WOXZC 5270
6. Great Circle Tracking Chart WOXZC 5274
7. Position Plotting Sheet VPO SX001 - Universal
8. Position Plotting Sheet 923 (Latitudes 17°- 24°)
9. Position Plotting Sheet 924 (Latitudes 23°- 30°)
10. Stability Worksheets (Locally reproduced)
11. Radar Plots (Locally reproduced for Radar Module)
12. Chart 18531, Columbia River
13. Maps of the Mississippi River (Cairo to the Gulf)

CANDIDATES MAY PROVIDE

1. Rude Star Finder or equivalent
2. Plotting Instruments: i.e. Dividers, triangles, Nautical Slide Rule
3. Calculators. Applicants may use calculators but not preprinted forms during the examinations. All calculators must meet the following standards:
   - It must not use pre-programmed strips or chips or any other pre-programmed device which may be inserted into the calculator.
   - It may not be a permanently programmed, specialty computer such as a navigation computer. Computers capable of generating trigonometric functions, logs and anti-logs, squares, cubes, and the roots thereof are acceptable provided they meet the other requirements.
   - Any manually programmable calculator without simple erasure capability is not permitted.

Deck Reference Library

The following is a list of the charts, reference publications and text books currently in use by the Deck Examination Team at the U.S. Coast Guard National Maritime Center, as of April 2007.

ANCHORING

TITLE	PUBLISHER	AUTHOR
Anchoring and Mooring	Sheridan House	Gree
The Complete Book of Anchoring and Mooring	Cornell Maritime Press	Hinz
The Oil Rig Moorings Handbook	Brown, Son & Ferguson	Vendrell
The Use of Anchors in Offshore Petroleum Operations	Gulf Publishing Co.	Peuch
Anchoring and Mooring	Sheridan House	Gree
The Complete Book of Anchoring and Mooring	Cornell Maritime Press	Hinz
The Oil Rig Moorings Handbook	Brown, Son & Ferguson	Vendrell
The Use of Anchors in Offshore Petroleum Operations	Gulf Publishing Co.	Peuch

CARGO OPERATIONS - DRY CARGO

TITLE	PUBLISHER	AUTHOR
MPS Crane Operator	Navy Cargo Handling Battalion One	
Cranes and Derricks	McGraw Hill	Shapiro
General Information for Grain Loading	National Cargo Bureau	
Code of Safe Practice for Cargo Stowage and Securing	(IMO)	
Code of Safe Practice for Solid Bulk Cargoes	(IMO)	
Guidelines for the Preparation of the Cargo Securing Manual (MSC Circ. 745)	(IMO)	
Cargo Handling	Marine Education Textbooks	Immer
Marine Cargo Operations	John Wiley & Sons	Sauerbier & Meurn
Notes on Cargo Work	Stanford Maritime	Kemp and Young
Thomas' Stowage	Brown, Son & Ferguson	Thomas
Notes on Cargo Work	Sheridan House	Kemp and Young
T-ACS 4 Class Mission Operations Handbook	Naval Sea Systems Comd.	

CARGO OPERATIONS - LIQUID CARGO

TITLE	PUBLISHER	AUTHOR
Ballast Water Management	(IMO)	
Bunkering Sample Guide	(IMO)	
Chemical Data Guide for Bulk Shipment by Water (COMDTINST M16616.6)	U.S. Coast Guard	
Inert Gas Systems	(IMO)	
International Safety Guide for Oil Tankers and Terminals	Witherby & Co. Ltd.	ICS, OCIMF & IAPH
Manual for the Safe Handling of Flammable and Combustible Liquids (CG-174)	U.S. Coast Guard	
Manual on Oil Pollution	(IMO)	
MARPOL 73/78 - 2006	(IMO)	
Tanker Handbook for Deck Officers	Brown, Son & Ferguson	Baptist
Tanker Operations	Cornell Maritime Press	Huber (formerly Marton)

Deck Reference Library

COMMUNICATIONS

TITLE	PUBLISHER	AUTHOR
Global Maritime Distress and Safety System (GMDSS) Handbook	(IMO)	CD-Rom version 2.0
IMO Performance Standards for Global Maritime Distress and Safety Systems	(IMO)	
International Code of Signals (Pub. No. 102)	(NGIA)	
Language of the Western Rivers	U.S. Coast Guard	
Maritime Radio Users Handbook	R.T.C.M.	
Radio Navigational Aids (Pub. No. 117)	(NGIA)	

DICTIONARIES

TITLE	PUBLISHER	AUTHOR
Encyclopedia of Nautical Knowledge	Cornell Maritime Press	McEwen & Lewis
International Maritime Dictionary	Van Nostrand Reinhold Co.	DeKerchove
Webster's Third New International Dictionary	Merriam-Webster	Gove

FIRE FIGHTING

TITLE	PUBLISHER	AUTHOR
Fire Fighting Manual for Tank Vessels (CG-329)	U.S. Coast Guard	
Marine Fire Fighting	IFSTA Fire Protection Pub.	
Marine Fire Prevention, Firefighting and Fire Safety	U.S. Maritime Administration	

LAWS & REGULATIONS

TITLE	PUBLISHER	AUTHOR
Business and Law for the Shipmaster	Brown, Son & Ferguson	Hopkins
Chartering and Charter Parties	Cornell Maritime Press	Cooley
International Maritime Dangerous Goods (IMDG) Code	(IMO)	
Master's Handbook on Ship's Business	Cornell Maritime Press	Messer
Navigation and Vessel Inspection Circulars (NVICs)	U.S. Coast Guard	
Purser's Handbook	Cornell Maritime Press	Armstrong
Safety of Life at Sea Manual (2004)	(IMO)	
Shipmaster's Handbook on Ship's Business	Cornell Maritime Press	Martin & Aragon
The Business of Shipping	Cornell Maritime Press	Kendall
The Law of Seamen	Lawyers Co-Operative Pub.	Norris
Title 33 Code of Federal Regulations (Navigation on Navigable Waters)	Government Printing Office	
Title 46 Code of Federal Regulations (Shipping)	Government Printing Office	
Title 47 Code of Federal Regulations, Part 80 (Stations in the Maritime Services)	Government Printing Office	
Title 49 Code of Federal Regulations, Subchapter C (Hazardous Materials Regulations)	Government Printing Office	
Title 50 Code of Federal Regulations (Marine Mammals)	Government Printing Office	
Titles 33, 46, 47, 49 & 50 of the U.S.C. (All Applicable Sections)	Government Printing Office	
United States Code Annotated Title 46, Subtitle II	West Publishing Co.	

Deck Reference Library

MEDICAL CARE

TITLE	PUBLISHER	AUTHOR
Community First Aid and Safety	American Red Cross	
Heartsaver CPR	American Heart Association	
International Medical Guide for Ships	World Health Organization	
The Ship's Medicine Chest and Medical Aid at Sea	U.S. Public Health Service	

METEOROLOGY

TITLE	PUBLISHER	AUTHOR
Heavy Weather Guide	Naval Institute Press	Kotch
Marine Surface Weather Observations	National Weather Service	
Meteorology	McGraw-Hill	Donn
Notes on Meteorology	Stanford Maritime	Kemp and Young
Weather for the Mariner	Naval Institute Press	Kotch

MOBILE OFFSHORE DRILLING UNITS (MODUs)

TITLE	PUBLISHER	AUTHOR
Floating Drilling Equipment and its Use	Gulf Publishing Co.	Sheffield
Practical Introduction to Anchor Handling and Supply Vessel Operations	Clarkson Research Services	Ritchie
Rotary Drilling Unit I Lesson 10: Safety on the Rig Unit V Lesson 1: Wind, Waves and Weather Unit V Lesson 2: Spread Mooring Systems Unit V Lesson 3: Buoyancy, Stability and Trim Unit V Lesson 4: Jacking Systems and Rig Moving Procedures Unit V Lesson 6: Vessel Inspection and Maintenance Unit V Lesson 7: Helicopter Safety Unit V Lesson 8: Offshore Crane Operations Unit V Lesson 9: Life Offshore	University of Texas at Austin	Petroleum Extension Service
The Best in Dynamic Positioning Automation, & Power, & Propulsion	Oilfield Publications Limited	Bray
The Jack-Up Drilling Platform	Gulf Publishing Co.	Boswell

NAVIGATIONAL CHARTS

TITLE	PUBLISHER	AUTHOR
Flood Control and Navigation Maps (Mississippi River)	U.S. Army Corps of Engineers	
Chart No. 1 - Nautical Chart Symbols and Abbreviations	(NGIA)	
Coastal Charts 12221, 12354 and 13205	National Ocean Service	
Harbor Chart 18531 (Columbia River)	National Ocean Service	
Pilot Charts	(NGIA)	

Deck Reference Library

NAVIGATIONAL REFERENCE PUBLICATIONS

TITLE	PUBLISHER	AUTHOR
Light List (COMDTPUB P16502)	U.S. Coast Guard	
LORAN-C User Handbook (COMDTPUB P16562.6)	U.S. Coast Guard	
Nautical Almanac	U.S. Naval Observatory	
Pub. No. 117 - Radio Navigational Aids	(NGIA)	
Pub. No. 226 - Handbook of Magnetic Compass Adjustment	(NGIA)	
Pub. No. 229 - Sight Reduction Tables	(NGIA)	
Pubs. No. 110 & 111 - List of Lights	(NGIA)	
Sailing Directions - Enroute	(NGIA)	
Sailing Directions - Planning Guide	(NGIA)	
Star Finder (No. 2102-D)	Weems & Plath	Rude & Collins
Tidal Current Tables	National Ocean Service	
Tide Tables	National Ocean Service	
United States Coast Pilots	National Ocean Service	

NAVIGATIONAL EQUIPMENT PERFORMANCE STANDARDS

TITLE	PUBLISHER	AUTHOR
IMO Performance Standards for: Automatic Identification Systems Automatic Radar Plotting Aids Electronic Chart Display Information Systems Global Position Systems Radar	(IMO)	

NAVIGATIONAL TEXTBOOKS

TITLE	PUBLISHER	AUTHOR
American Practical Navigator (Pub. No. 9)	(NGIA)	Bowditch
Automatic Radar Plotting Aids Manual	Cornell Maritime Press	Bole & Jones
Dutton's Navigation and Piloting	Naval Institute Press	Cutler
GPS - A Guide to the Next Utility	Trimble Navigation	Hurn
Mariner's Gyro-Navigation Manual	Cornell Maritime Press	O'Hara
Radar and ARPA Manual	Heinemann-Newnes	Bole & Dineley
Radar Navigation Manual (Pub. No. 1310)	(NGIA)	
The River Radar Manual	The River School	Kline
The Use of Radar at Sea	Naval Institute Press	Wylie
Using GPS	Sheridan House	Dixon

RULES OF THE ROAD

TITLE	PUBLISHER	AUTHOR
Navigation Rules COMDTINST M16672.2D	U.S. Coast Guard	
Farwell's Rules of the Nautical Road	Naval Institute Press	Bassett & Smith
Nautical Rules of the Road	Cornell Maritime Press	Farnsworth & Young

Deck Reference Library

SAFETY

TITLE	PUBLISHER	AUTHOR
FAO/ILO/IMO Document for Guidance on Training & Cert. of Fishing Vessel. Personnel	(IMO) 2001 edition	
Gulf Coast Fishing Vessel Safety Manual	National Council of Fishing Vessel Safety & Insurance	
Manual for the Safe Handling of Flammable and Combustible Liquids (CG-174)	U.S. Coast Guard	
The Deckhand's Manual	Inland Waterways Safety Service	
Vessel Safety Manual	North Pacific Fishing Vessel Owners' Association	

SEAMANSHIP

TITLE	PUBLISHER	AUTHOR
American Merchant Seaman's Manual	Cornell Maritime Press	Cornell & Hoffman
Chapman Piloting, Seamanship & Small Boat Handling	Hearst Marine Books	Maloney
Knight's Modern Seamanship	Van Nostrand Reinhold Co.	Noel
Merchant Marine Officer's Handbook	Cornell Maritime Press	Turpin & MacEwen
Nicholl's Seamanship and Nautical Knowledge	Brown, Son & Ferguson	Cockroft
Seamanship Notes	Sheridan House	Kemp and Young
Seamanship Notes	Stanford Maritime	Kemp and Young
Seamanship Techniques Volumes 1 and 2	Sheridan House	D.J. House
Seamanship Techniques	Heinemann-Newnes	House
The Boatswain's Manual	Sheridan House	Miller

SHIPHANDLING

TITLE	PUBLISHER	AUTHOR
Auxiliary Sail Vessel Operations	Cornell Maritime Press	Chase
Basic Shiphandling	Stanford Maritime	Willerton
Behavior and Handling of Ships	Cornell Maritime Press	Hooyer
Naval Shiphandling	Naval Institute Press	Crenshaw
Practical Ship-Handling	Brown, Son & Ferguson	Armstrong
Ship Handling in Narrow Channels	Cornell Maritime Press	Plummer
Shiphandling for the Mariner	Cornell Maritime Press	MacElrevey
Shiphandling with Tugs	Cornell Maritime Press	Reid
This Is Sailing	Hearst Marine Books	Creagh-Osborne

SHIP CONSTRUCTION

TITLE	PUBLISHER	AUTHOR
Introduction to Steel Shipbuilding	McGraw-Hill	Baker
Merchant Ship Construction	Sheridan House	Pursey
Modern Ships	Cornell Maritime Press	LaDage
Ship Construction	Sheridan House	Eyres
Ship Construction, Sketches and Notes	Stanford Maritime	Kemp and Young

STABILITY

TITLE	PUBLISHER	AUTHOR
Ship Stability	Butterworth-Heinemann	Derrett
Stability and Trim for the Ship's Officer	Cornell Maritime Press	LaDage & VanGemert

Deck Reference Library

SURVIVAL

TITLE	PUBLISHER	AUTHOR
A Practical Guide to Lifeboat Survival	Naval Institute Press	Center for Survival
How to Survive on Land and Sea	Naval Institute Press	Craighead
Lifesaving Appliances - 2003	(IMO)	
Survival Guide for the Mariner	Cornell Maritime Press	Meurn
The Captain's Guide to Liferaft Survival	Sheridan House	Cargal
Water Survival Guide	Harry Lundeberg School of Seamanship	

TOWING

TITLE	PUBLISHER	AUTHOR
Modern Towing	Cornell Maritime Press	Blank
Primer of Towing	Cornell Maritime Press	Reid
Tugs, Towboats and Towing	Cornell Maritime Press	Brady

WATCHSTANDING

TITLE	PUBLISHER	AUTHOR
Int. Aeronautical and Maritime Search and Rescue Manual	(IAMSAR)	
Safety of Life At Sea (SOLAS)	IMO	
Watchstanding Guide for the Merchant Officer	Cornell Maritime Press	Meurn

Deck Reference Library Codes

CODE	REFERENCE
ABMAN	ABLE SEAMAN MANUAL
ABS	AMERICAN BUREAU OF SHIPPING
ALMANAC	THE NAUTICAL ALMANAC
AMSM	AMERICAN MERCHANT SEAMAN'S MANUAL
API RP 2D	AMERICAN PETROLEUM INSTITUTE
APPNDX	APPENDIX
ARAGON	SHIPMASTER'S HANDBOOK ON SHIP'S BUSINESS
ARMSTRONG	PURSER'S HANDBOOK
ARPA	AUTOMATIC RADAR PLOTTING AIDS MANUAL
ART	ARTICLE
BAKER	INTRODUCTION TO STEEL SHIPBUILDING
BAPTIST	TANKER HANDBOOK FOR DECK OFFICERS
BOWD 1 & 2	AMERICAN PRACTICAL NAVIGATOR, VOLUME I AND II
BRADY	TUGS, TOWBOATS, AND TOWING
CFR	CODE OF FEDERAL REGULATIONS
CG-174	A MANUAL FOR THE SAFE HANDLING OF FLAMMABLE AND COMBUSTIBLE LIQUIDS AND OTHER HAZARDOUS PRODUCTS
CHAP	CHAPTER
CHAPMAN	PILOTING, SEAMANSHIP AND SMALL BOAT HANDLING
CHART NO. 1	NAUTICAL CHART SYMBOLS AND ABBREVIATIONS
CHASE	AUXILIARY SAIL VESSEL OPERATIONS
CHEM. DATA GUIDE	CHEMICAL DATA GUIDE FOR BULK SHIPMENT BY WATER
CHS	CARGO HANDLING
D'ARCANGELO	GUIDE TO SOUND SHIP STRUCTURE
DECKHAND MANUAL	THE DECK HAND'S MANUAL
DEKERCHOVE	INTERNATIONAL MARITIME DICTIONARY
DERRETT	SHIP STABILITY FOR MASTER AND MATES
DMAHTC	DEFENSE MAPPING AGENCY/HYDROGRAPHIC/TOPOGRAPHIC CENTER
DONN	METEOROLOGY
DUTTON'S	NAVIGATION AND PILOTING
ENCY/ NAUT KNOW	ENCYCLOPEDIA OF NAUTICAL KNOWLEDGE
EXPL	EXPLANATION OF TABLES
EYRES	SHIP CONSTRUCTION
FARWELL'S	FARWELL'S RULES OF THE NAUTICAL ROAD
FVSM	FISHING VESSEL SAFETY MANUAL
GLIN	GREAT LAKES ICE NAVIGATION
GLOSS	GLOSSARY
GLWLF	GREAT LAKES WATER LEVEL FACTS (PUBLISHED BY ARMY CORPS OF ENGINEERS DETROIT DISTRICT)
GSSS	A GUIDE TO SOUND SHIP STRUCTURES
H.O. 102	INTERNATIONAL CODE OF SIGNALS (REV. 1981)
H.O. 226	HANDBOOK OF MAGNETIC COMPASS ADJUSTMENT
H.O. 229	SIGHT REDUCTION TABLES, VOLUME 2 - LATITUDES 15°-30°
HMT	HULL MAINTENANCE TECHNICIAN
HOOYER	BEHAVIOR AND HANDLING OF SHIPS
HOPKINS	BUSINESS AN LAW AND THE SHIPMASTER
ICCMS	INTERNATIONAL CONVENTIONS AND CONFERENCES ON MARINE SAFETY
IMCO	INTERNATIONAL CONVENTION ON STANDARDS OF TRAINING, CERTIFICATION AND WATCH-KEEPING AND SEAFARERS (1978)
IMMER	CARGO HANDLING
IOTTSG	INTERNATIONAL SAFETY GUIDE FOR OIL TANKERS AND TERMINALS

CODE	REFERENCE
KEMP CARGO	NOTES ON CARGO WORK
KEMP CONST.	SHIP CONSTRUCTION SKETCHES AND NOTES
KEMP MET	NOTES ON METEOROLOGY
KEMP SEA	SEAMANSHIP NOTES
KENDELL	THE BUSINESS OF SHIPPING
KNIGHTS	KNIGHTS MODERN SEAMANSHIP
KOTSCH	WEATHER FOR THE MARINER
LADAGE/GEORGE	STABILITY AND TRIM FOR THE SHIP'S OFFICER
LBMAN	LIFEBOATMAN MANUAL
MACELREVEY	SHIPHANDLING FOR THE MARINER
MARAD	U.S. MARITIME ADMINISTRATION
MARTIN	SHIPMASTER'S HANDBOOK
MARTON/HUBER	TANKER OPERATIONS
MBLLFGL	MONTHLY BULLETIN OF LAKE LEVELS
MCO	MARINE CARGO OPERATIONS
MERSAR	MERCHANT SHIP SEARCH AND RESCUE MANUAL M16130.1
MFPFFS	MARINE FIRE PREVENTION AND FIREFIGHTING SAFETY
MILLER	THE BOATSWAIN'S MANUAL
MMOH	MERCHANT MARINE OFFICER'S HANDBOOK
MODSHIPS	MODERN SHIPS
MRT	MARINE RADIOTELEPHONE USERS HANDBOOK
MSRS	MERCHANT SHIP SEARCH & RESCUE MANUAL
NICHOLLS	NICHOLLS'S CONCISE GUIDE, VOLUME 2
NICHOLS	SEAMANSHIP AND NAUTICAL KNOWLEDGE
NORRIS	THE LAW OF SEAMEN
NPFVOA	VESSEL SAFETY MANUAL
NVIC	NAVIGATION AND VESSEL INSPECTION CIRCULARS
NWS	NATIONAL WEATHER SERVICE
O'HARA	MARINER'S GYRO-NAVIGATION MANUAL
ORMH	OIL RIG MOORING HANDBOOK
OSBOURNE	THIS IS SAILING
PETEX (UNITS 1-10)	ROTARY DRILL
PLANT	FORMULA FOR THE MARINER
PLUMMER	SHIPHANDLING WITH IN NARROW CHANNELS
PRIMER	A PRIMER OF OFFSHORE OPERATIONS
PTS	PRINCIPLES OF TANKER SAFETY
PUB 117	RADIO NAVIGATION AIDS
PUB 1310	RADAR NAVIGATION MANUAL
PUECH	THE USE OF ANCHORS IN OFFSHORE PETROLEUM OPERATIONS
PURSEY	MERCHANT SHIP CONSTRUCTION
REID	PRIMER OF TOWING
ROR	NAUTICAL RULES OF THE ROAD
SAUERBIER	MARINE CARGO OPERATIONS
SEATECH	SEAMANSHIP TECHNIQUES, VOLUME 1 AND 2
SHIP	PRACTICAL SHIPHANDLING
SHIPHAND	SHIPHANDLING FOR THE MARINER
SHIPS MED CHEST	THE SHIP'S MEDICINE CHEST AND MEDICAL AID AT SEA
SOLAS	INTERNATIONAL CONVENTION FOR SAFETY OF LIFE AT SEA (1974)
SURVIVE	HOW TO SURVIVE ON LAND AND SEA
SWIT	SHIPHANDLING WITH TUGS

Deck Reference Library Codes

CODE	REFERENCE
T-	TABLE
TABAK	CARGO CONTAINERS
THOMAS	THOMAS' STOWAGE
TIDAL CURRENT TABLE	1983 TIDAL CURRENT TABLES ATLANTIC COAST OF NORTH AMERICA
TIDE TABLE	1983 TIDE TABLES EAST COAST OF NORTH AND SOUTH AMERICA
TORMH	THE OIL RIG MOORINGS HANDBOOK
USCP	UNITED STATES COAST PILOT
WATERCRAFT	WATERCRAFT AMERICA MANUAL
WILLERTON	BASIC SHIPHANDLING
WOOLCOTT	LIQUIFIED PETROLEUM GAS TANKER PRACTICE
WSM	WATER SURVIVAL MANUAL
WYLIE	THE USE OF RADAR AT SEA

Deck Examination Subjects

Examination Topic	Master Management Level	Chief Mate/Master Management Level	2nd Mate Operational Level	3rd Mate/OICNW Operational Level
NAVIGATION AND POSITION DETERMINATION:				
OCEAN TRACK PLOTTING				
Middle Latitude Sailing	Nav. Probs.	CNAV	Nav. Probs.	CNAV
Mercator Sailing	Nav. Probs.	CNAV	Nav. Probs.	CNAV
Parallel Sailing	Nav. Probs.	CNAV	Nav. Probs.	CNAV
Great Circle Sailing	Nav. Probs.	CNAV	Nav. Probs.	CNAV
Composite Sailing (Voyage Plan)	Nav. Probs.	CNAV	Nav. Probs.	CNAV
ETA	Nav. Probs.	CNAV	Nav. Probs.	CNAV
RESTRICTED WATER NAVIGATION				
Distance Off		TNAV	Nav. Probs.	TNAV
Special Case Bearing Problems		TNAV	Nav. Probs.	TNAV
Fix or Running Fix		TNAV	Nav. Probs.	TNAV
Dead Reckoning		TNAV	Nav. Probs.	TNAV
Chart Navigation (Plot Exercise)		CHART PLOT		CHART PLOT
CELESTIAL OBSERVATIONS				
Observed Altitude Sextant Altitude Corrections	Nav. Probs.	CNAV	Nav. Probs. General	CNAV
Special Cases: High Altitude Observations	Nav. Probs.	CNAV		
Low Altitude Observations	Nav. Probs.	CNAV		
Back Sight	Nav. Probs.	CNAV		
Latitude by Polaris	Nav. Probs.	CNAV	Nav. Probs.	CNAV
Latitude by Meridian Transit Upper/Lower Transit (Any Body)	Nav. Probs.	CNAV		CNAV
Latitude by Meridian Transit Ex-Meridian Upper/Lower Transit (Any Body)	Nav. Probs.	CNAV	Nav. Probs.	
Latitude by Meridian Transit (Sun Only)	Nav. Probs.		Nav. Probs.	CNAV
Fix or Running Fix (Any Body)	Nav. Probs.	CNAV	Nav. Probs.	CNAV
Fix or Running Fix (Sun Only)				
Star Identification - Major Stars	Nav. Probs.	CNAV	Nav. Probs.	CNAV
Star Identification - Minor Stars	Nav. Probs.	CNAV	Nav. Probs.	CNAV
Star Selection	Nav. Probs.	CNAV	Nav. Probs.	CNAV

License Codes (46 CFR 10.910-2)

Examination Topic	Master Management Level	Chief Mate/Master Management Level	2nd Mate Operational Level	3rd Mate/OICNW Operational Level
TIME OF CELESTIAL PHENOMENA				
Time of Meridian Transit Upper & Lower Limb (Any Body)	Nav. Probs.	CNAV		
Time of Meridian Transit (Sun Only)			Nav. Probs.	CNAV
Second Estimate of Meridian Transit	Nav. Probs.	CNAV		
Zone Time of Sun Rise/Set/Twilight	Nav. Probs.	CNAV	Nav. Probs.	CNAV
DETERMINATION OF COMPASS ERROR				
Azimuth (Any Body)	Nav. Probs.	CNAV	Nav. Probs.	CNAV
Azimuth (Sun Only)		TNAV		TNAV
Amplitude (Any Body)	Nav. Probs.	CNAV	Nav. Probs.	CNAV
Amplitude (Sun Only)		TNAV		TNAV
Deviation Table Construction	Nav. Probs.	TNAV	Nav. Probs.	TNAV
Terrestrial Observations Visual Ranges		TNAV	Nav. Probs.	TNAV
Magnetic Compass Error/Correction	Nav. Probs.	TNAV	Nav. Probs.	TNAV
Gyro Compass Error/Correction	Nav. Probs.	TNAV	Nav. Probs.	TNAV
TERRESTRIAL OBSERVATIONS				
Electronic Navigation: Radio Time Signal	Nav. Probs.	TNAV	Nav. Probs.	TNAV
Radar Navigation		CHART PLOT	Nav. Probs.	CHART PLOT
Fathometer		CHART PLOT	Nav. Probs.	CHART PLOT
Restricted Visibility Navigation	ALL	ALL	ALL	ALL
Electronic Navigation Systems	Part 1	Nav. General	General	Nav. General
Chart Projections	Part 1	Nav. General	General	Nav. General
Chart Construction	Part 1	Nav. General	General	Nav. General
Navigation Publications & Notice to Mariners	Part 1	Nav. General	General	Nav. General
Nautical Astronomy	Part 1	Nav. General	General	Nav. General
Navigation Definitions	Part 1	Nav. General	General	Nav. General
Instruments & Accessories	Part 1	Nav. General	General	Nav. General
AIDS TO NAVIGATION				
U.S. Buoyage Systems	Part 1	Nav. General	General	Nav. General
IALA A & B Buoyage Systems	Part 1	Nav. General	General	Nav. General
Fixed Lights & Daymarks	Part 1	Nav. General	General	Nav. General

Deck Examination Subjects

Examination Topic	Master Management Level	Chief Mate/Master Management Level	2nd Mate Operational Level	3rd Mate/OICNW Operational Level
MISCELLANEOUS				
Fuel Conservation	Nav. Probs.	TNAV		
Speed by RPM	Nav. Probs.	TNAV	Nav. Probs.	TNAV
Apparent Slip Computations	Nav. Probs.	TNAV	Nav. Probs.	TNAV
SEAMANSHIP				
Marlinespike Seamanship			General	Deck General
Purchases, Blocks & Tackle			General	Deck General
Small Boat Handling Under Oars & Sail			General	Deck General
WATCHKEEPING				
International Rules (72 COLREGS)	Rules of the Road	Rules of the Road	Rules of the Road	Rules of the Road
Both International (72 COLREGS) & Inland Navigation Rules	Rules of the Road	Rules of the Road	Rules of the Road	Rules of the Road
Inland Navigation Rules	Rules of the Road	Rules of the Road	Rules of the Road	Rules of the Road
Basic Principles of Watchkeeping	Part 1	Deck General Safety	General	Deck General Safety
Navigation Safety Regulations	Part 1	Safety	General	Deck General Safety
RADAR EQUIPMENT	Part 1	Safety	General	Safety
Radar Observer Certificate	**REQUIRED**	**REQUIRED**	**REQUIRED**	**REQUIRED**
COMPASS MAGNETIC & GYRO				
Principles of Gyro Compass	Part 1	Nav. General	General	Nav. General
Gyro Controlled Systems	Part 1	Nav. General	General	Nav. General
Operation & Care of Main Gyro Systems	Part 1	Nav. General	General	Nav. General
Principles of Magnetic Compass	Part 1	Nav. General	General	Nav. General
Magnetic Compass Adjustment	Part 1	Nav. General	General	Nav. General
METEOROLOGY & OCEANOGRAPHY				
Characteristics of Weather Systems		Nav. General	General	Nav. General
Synoptic Weather Charts & Reports		Nav. General	General	Nav. General
Ocean Current Systems		Nav. General	General	Nav. General
TIDES & TIDAL CURRENTS				
Extensive Tidal Effects	Part 1	Nav. General		
Terms & Definitions		Nav. General	General	Nav. General
Tide & Tidal Current Publications		TNAV	General	TNAV
Tide & Tidal Current Calculations		TNAV	General	TNAV

License Codes (46 CFR 10.910-2)

Examination Topic	Master Management Level	Chief Mate/Master Management Level	2nd Mate Operational Level	3rd Mate/OICNW Operational Level
SHIP MANEUVERING AND HANDLING				
Approaching pilot vessel or station	Part 1	Deck General		
Shiphandling in rivers & estuaries	Part 1	Deck General	General	Deck General
Maneuvering in Shallow Water	Part 1	Deck General	General	Deck General
Interaction with Bank & Passing Ships	Part 1	Deck General	General	Deck General
Berthing & Unberthing	Part 1	Deck General		
Anchoring & Mooring		Deck General	General	Deck General
Dragging, Clearing Fouled Anchors		Deck General	General	Deck General
Dry-docking with & without Prior Damage		Deck General		
Heavy Weather Operations		Deck General		
Maneuvering for Launching Lifeboats/Rafts		Deck General		
Receiving Survivors From Lifeboats/Rafts		Deck General	General	Deck General Safety
Maneuvering Diagram & Nomenclature		Deck General	General	Deck General
Determination of Maneuvering Characteristics		Deck General		
Wake Reduction & Propulsion		Deck General		
Ice Operations & Navigation	Part 1	Deck General		
Towing Operations		Deck General	General	Deck General
SHIP STABILITY, CONSTRUCTION, & DAMAGE CONTROL				
Principles of Ship Construction		Deck General	General	Deck General
Vessel Structural Members		Deck General	General	Deck General
Principles of Trim & Stability	Part 2	Safety	General	Safety
IMO Ship Stability Recommendations	Part 2	Safety		
Stability, Trim & Stress Calculations	Part 2	Safety	General	
Principles of Damage Control	Part 2	Safety	General	Safety
Damage Control Techniques	Part 2	Deck General		
Change in Draft Due to Density	Part 2	Safety		
SHIP POWER PLANTS				
Marine Power Plant Operating Principles		Safety		
Ship's Auxiliary Machinery		Safety		
Marine Engineering Terms		Safety		

Deck Examination Subjects

Examination Topic	Master Management Level	Chief Mate/Master Management Level	2nd Mate Operational Level	3rd Mate/OICNW Operational Level
CARGO HANDLING AND STOWAGE				
Bulk/Dry Cargo Stowage & Security including Cargo Gear		Deck General	General	Deck General
Dry Cargo Loading & Discharging Operations		Deck General	General	Deck General
International Regulations for Cargoes (IMDG Codes)	Part 1	Deck General		
Dangerous Cargo Regulations	Part 1	Deck General	General	Deck General Safety
Hazardous Cargo Regulations	Part 1	Deck General	General	Deck General Safety
Tank Vessel Cargo Operations & Safety		Deck General	General	Deck General
Tank Vessel Piping Systems		Deck General	General	Deck General
Tank Vessel Pumping Systems		Deck General	General	Deck General
Cargo Oil Terms & Definitions		Deck General	General	Deck General
Ballast, Tank Cleaning & Gas Freeing Operations		Deck General	General	Deck General Safety
Load on Top Procedures		Deck General	General	Deck General
Inert Gas Systems Crude Oil Washing Operations		Deck General	General	Deck General Safety
FIRE PREVENTION AND FIRE FIGHTING APPLIANCES				
Organization of Fire Drills		Safety	General	Safety
Classes & Chemistry of Fire		Safety	General	Safety
Basic Firefighting Techniques & Fire Prevention		Safety	General	Safety
Firefighting Systems		Safety	General	Safety
Firefighting Equipment & Regulations		Safety	General	Safety
EMERGENCY PROCEDURES				
Ship Beaching Precautions		Deck General		
Actions Prior To & After Grounding		Deck General		
Refloating a Grounded Vessel		Deck General		
Collision		Deck General		
Temporary Repairs		Deck General	General	Safety
Passenger & Crew Safety		Deck General	General	Safety
Fire or Explosion		Deck General	General	Safety
Abandon Ship Procedures		Deck General	General	Safety
Emergency Steering		Deck General	General	
Rescuing Survivor From Ship & Aircraft Disasters		Deck General	General	Safety
Man Overboard Procedures		Deck General	General	Safety
Emergency Towing Operations	Part 1	Deck General	General	Deck General

License Codes (46 CFR 10.910-2)

Examination Topic	Master Management Level	Chief Mate/Master Management Level	2nd Mate Operational Level	3rd Mate/OICNW Operational Level
MEDICAL CARE				
First Aid		Safety	General	
International Medical Guide for Ships		Safety		
Ship's Medicine Chest & Medical Aid at Sea		Safety		
International Code of Signals Medical Codes		Safety	General	Safety
First Guide for Accidents with Dangerous Goods		Safety	General	Safety
MARITIME LAW & INTERNATIONAL LAW				
International Convention on Load Lines	Part 1	Safety		
SOLAS	Part 1	Safety		
MARPOL 73/78	Part 1	Safety	General	Safety
International Health Regulations	Part 1	Safety		
International Instructions for Ship/Passenger/Crew/Cargo Safety	Part 1	Safety		
MARITIME LAW & NATIONAL LAW				
Load Line Regulations	Part 1	Deck General		
Certificates & Documentation of Vessels	Part 1	Deck General	General	Safety
Rule & Regulations for Inspected Vessels	Part 1	Safety	General	Safety
Ship's Sanitation & Health	Part 1	Safety		
Pollution Prevention Regulations	Part 1	Safety	General	Safety
Pilotage	Part 1	Safety		
Licensing & Certification of Seamen	Part 1	Safety	General	Safety
Shipment, & Discharge of Seamen, Manning of Vessels	Part 1	Deck General		
Title 46 U.S. Code - Captain of the Port Regulations, Vessel Traffic Service Procedures for the Route Desired	Part 1	Safety		
SHIPBOARD MANAGEMENT AND TRAINING				
Personnel Management	Part 1	Deck General		
Shipboard Organization	Part 1	Deck General		
Required Crew Training	Part 1	Deck General		
Ship Sanitation	Part 1	Deck General		
Vessel Alteration/Repair (Hot Work)	Part 1	Deck General		
General Safety Practices	Part 1	Safety	General	Safety

Deck Examination Subjects

Examination Topic	Master	Chief Mate/Master	2nd Mate	3rd Mate/OICNW
	Management Level	Management Level	Operational Level	Operational Level
SHIP'S BUSINESS				
Chartering	Part 1	Deck General		
Liens & Salvage	Part 1	Deck General		
Marine Insurance	Part 1	Deck General		
Entry & Clearance Procedures	Part 1	Deck General		
Vessel Certificates & Documents Required	Part 1	Deck General	General	Deck General Safety
COMMUNICATIONS				
International Code of Signals		Safety	General	Safety
Methods of Transmission Flashing Light		Safety	General	Safety
Radiotelegraphy Procedures		Safety	General	Safety
Radiotelephone Procedures		Safety	General	Safety
Flag Hoist Procedures		Safety	General	Safety
Distress & Emergency Signals		Safety	General	Safety
Distress Signals Emergency Signals Special Signals Medical Signals Storm Signals Wreck Signals Aircraft Signals Submarine Signals Letter Signals National Identity Signals		Safety	General	Safety
Flashing Light Certificate	**REQUIRED**	**REQUIRED**	**REQUIRED**	**REQUIRED**
LIFESAVING				
Survival at Sea		Safety	General	Safety
Lifesaving Appliance Regulations		Safety	General	Safety
Lifesaving Appliance Operation		Safety	General	Safety
SEARCH AND RESCUE				
IMO Merchant Ship SAR Manual (MERSAR)	Part 1	Safety		
AMVER	Part 1	Safety		
Any Other Subject Considered Necessary to Establish the Applicant's Proficiency	ALL	ALL	ALL	ALL

46 CFR 10.910 Subjects for deck officer endorsements.

Table 10.910-1 gives the codes used in table 10.910-2 for all deck officers. Table 10.910-2 indicates the examination subjects for each endorsement, by code number. Figures in the body of the table, in place of the letter "x", refer to notes.

Table 10.910–1 Codes for Deck Officer Endorsements

Deck Officer Endorsements:

1. Master, Oceans/near coastal, any gross tons.
2. Chief mate, oceans/near coastal, any gross tons.
3. Master, oceans/near coastal, 500/1,600 gross tons.
4. Second mate, oceans/near coastal, any gross tons.
5. Third mate, oceans/near coastal, any gross tons.
6. Mate, oceans/near coastal, 500/1,600 gross tons.
7. Master, oceans/near coastal, and mate, near coastal, 200 gross tons (includes master, near coastal, 100 gross tons).
8. Operator, uninspected passenger vessels, near coastal.
9. Operator, uninspected passenger vessels, Great Lakes/inland.
10. Apprentice mate, towing vessels, ocean (domestic trade) and near-coastal routes.
11. Apprentice mate (steersman), towing vessels, Great Lakes and inland routes.
12. Steersman, towing vessels, Western Rivers.
13. Master, Great Lakes/inland, or master, inland, any gross tons.
14. Mate, Great Lakes/inland, any gross tons.
15. Master, Great Lakes/inland, 500/1,600 gross tons.
16. Mate, Great Lakes/inland, 500/1,600 gross tons.
17. Master or mate, Great Lakes/inland, 200 gross tons (includes master, Great Lakes/inland, 100 gross tons).
18. Master, rivers, any gross tons.
19. Master, rivers, 500/1,600 gross tons.
20. Mate, rivers, 500/1,600 gross tons.
21. Master or mate, rivers, 200 gross tons (includes master, rivers, 100 gross tons).
22. Master, uninspected fishing industry vessels, oceans/near coastal.
23. Mate, uninspected fishing industry vessels, oceans/near coastal.
24. First class pilot.

Deck Examination Topics	1	2	3	4	5	6	7	8	9	10	11	12	13	14	15	16	17	18	19	20	21	22	23	24
Navigation and position determination:																								
Ocean Track Plotting:																								
Middle Latitude Sailing	1	1		1	1																			
Mercator Sailing	X	X		1	1																			
Great Circle Sailing	1	1		1																				
Parallel Sailing	1	1		1	1																			
ETA	X	X	1	X	X																			
Piloting:																								
Distance Off		X	X	X	X	X	X	X	X	X	X		X	X	X	X	X					X	X	X
Bearing Problems		X	X	X	X	X	X	X	X	X	X		X	X	X	X	X					X	X	X
Fix or Running Fix		X	X	X	X	X	X	X	X	X	X		X	X	X	X	X					X	X	X
Chart Navigation		X	X	X	X	X	X	X	X	X	X	2	X	X	X	X	X	2	2	2	2	X	X	X
Dead Reckoning		X	X	X	X	X	X	X	X	X	X		X	X	X	X	X					X	X	X
Celestial Observations:																								
Special Cases (High/low Altitude, Back sight)	1																							
Latitude by Polaris	1	1	1	1																				
Latitude by Meridian Transit	1																							
Lat. by Meridian Transit (Sun Only)	X	X	1	X	X	1	1		1													1	1	
Fix or Running Fix (Any Body)	X	X	1	X																		1		
Fix or Running Fix (Sun Only)				X	1	1			1														1	
Star Identification	1	1	1	1																				
Star Selection	1	X	1	X																			1	
Times of Celestial Phenomena:																								
Time of Meridian Transit	1																							
Time of Meridian Transit (Sun Only)	X	X	1	X	X	1	1		1													1	1	
Second Estimate Meridian Transit	1																							
Zone Time Sun Rise/Set/Twilight	X	X	1	1	1	1	1		1													1	1	
Speed by RPM	X	X		X									3											
Fuel Conservation	X	X											3											
Electronic Navigation	X	X	X	X	X	X	X	X	X	X	X		X	X	X	X	X					X	X	X
Instruments and Accessories	X	X	X	X	X	X	X	X	X	X	X	X	X	X	X	X	X	X	X	X	X	X	X	X
Aids to Navigation	X	X	X	X	X	X	X	X	X	X	X	X	X	X	X	X	X	X	X	X	X	X	X	X
Charts, Publications, and Notices to Mariners	X	X	X	X	X	X	X	X	X	X	X	X	X	X	X	X	X	X	X	X	X	X	X	X
Nautical Astronomy & Navigation Definitions	X	X		X	X																			
Chart Sketch																								4

License Codes (46 CFR 10.910-2)

Deck Examination Topics	1	2	3	4	5	6	7	8	9	10	11	12	13	14	15	16	17	18	19	20	21	22	23	24
Seamanship:																								
Marlinspike Seamanship				X	X	X	X	X	X	X	X	X		X		X	X	X	X	X	X	X	X	X
Purchases, Blocks and Tackle				X	X	X	X			X	X	X		X		X	X	X	X	X	X	X	X	X
Small Boat Handling Under Oars or Sail				X	X								X	X										
Watchkeeping:																								
COLREGS	X	X	X	X	X	X	X	X	5	X	5		5	5	5	5	5					X	X	5
Inland Navigational Rules	X	X	X	X	X	X	X	X	X	X	X	X	X	X	X	X	X	X	X	X	X	X	X	X
Basic Principles, Watchkeeping	X	X	X	X	X	X	X			X	X	X	X	X	X	X	X	X	X	X				
Navigation Safety Regulations (33 CFR 164)	X	X		X	X								X	X			X					6	6	6
Radar Equipment:																								
Radar Observer Certificate	X	X	X	X	X	X	1				1		X	X			X					X	X	X
Compass-Magnetic and Gyro:																								
Principles of Gyro Compass	X	X	X	X	X								X	X	X	X						X	X	
Principles of Magnetic Compass	X	X	X	X	X	X						X	X	X	X	X	X	X	X	X	X	X	X	X
Magnetic Compass Adjustment	X	X											X	X										
Gyro Compass Error/Correction	X	X	X	X	X	X	7				X	X	X	X	X	X	7					X	X	X
Magnetic Compass Error/Correction	X	X	X	X	X	X	X	X	X	X	X		X	X	X	X	X					X	X	X
Determination of Compass Error:																								
Azimuth (Any Body)	X	X		1																				
Azimuth (Sun Only)		1		X	1	1				1			3									1	1	
Amplitude (Any Body)	X																							
Amplitude (Sun Only)		X	1	X	1	1				1			3									1	1	
Deviation Table Construction	X	X	1	X	X								3											
Terrestrial Observation		X	X	X	X	X	X	X	X	X	X		X	X	X	X	X					X	X	X
Gyro Controlled Systems	X	X	X	X		X																		
Operation & Care of Main Gyro Systems	X	X	X	X		X																		
Meteorology and Oceanography:																								
Characteristics of Weather Systems		X	X	X	X	X	X	X	X	X	X	X	X	X	X	X	X	X	X	X	X	X	X	X
Ocean Current Systems		X	X	X	X																	X	X	
Weather Charts and Reports		X	X	X	X		X			X												X		
Tides and Tidal Currents:																								
Extensive Tidal Effects	X	X	X																					
Terms and Definitions		X	X	X	X	X	X	X	X	X	X		X	X	X	X	X					X	X	X
Publications		X	X	X	X	X	X	X	X	X	X		X	X	X	X	X					X	X	X
Calculations		X	X	X	X	X	X	X	X	X	X		X	X	X	X	X					X	X	X

Deck Examination Topics	1	2	3	4	5	6	7	8	9	10	11	12	13	14	15	16	17	18	19	20	21	22	23	24
Ship Maneuvering and Handling:																								
Approaching Pilot Vessel or Station	X	X	X			X																		X
Shiphandling in Rivers, Estuaries	X	X	X		X	X	X	X	X	X	X	X	X	X	X	X	X	X	X	X	X	X		X
Maneuvering in Shallow Water	X	X	X		X	X	X	X	X	X	X	X	X	X	X	X	X	X	X	X	X	X		X
Interaction with Bank/Passing Ship	X	X	X		X	X	X	X	X	X	X	X	X	X	X	X	X	X	X	X	X	X		X
Berthing and Unberthing	X	X	X		X	X	X						X	X	X		X	X	X		X	X		X
Anchoring and Mooring		X	X	X	X	X	X	X	X	X			X	X	X	X	X					X	X	X
Dragging, Clearing Fouled Anchors		X	X	X	X	X	X						X	X	X	X	X					X		
Drydocking, with & without Prior Damage		X	X																					
Heavy Weather Operations		X	X				X	X	X								X					X	X	
Maneuvering for Launching of Lifeboats and Liferafts in Heavy Weather		X	X				X			X			X		X							X	X	
Receiving Survivors From Lifeboats/Liferafts		X	X				X			X	X													
General: Turn Circle, Pivot Point, Advance and Transfer				X	X	X	X	X	X	X	X	X	X	X	X	X	X	X	X	X	X	X	X	X
Determine Maneuvering Characteristics of Major Vessel Types		X		X	X																			
Wake Reduction		X	X				X	X	X	X	X	X	X	X	X	X	X	X	X	X	X	X		X
Ice Operations/Ice Navigation	X	X	X			X				X	X	X	X	3	X	3								
Towing Operations		X	X	X	X	X	X			X	X	X		X		X	X	X	X	X	X			
Ship Stability, Construction, and Damage Control:																								
Principles of Ship Construction		X	X	X	X		X			X	3	X	3	X	X	X								
Trim and Stability	X	X	X	X	X	X	X			X	X	X	X	3	X	3	X	X	X		X	X	X	
Damage Trim and Stability	X	X	X			X	7																	
Stability, Trim, and Stress Calculation	X	X	X	X			7																	
Vessel Structural Members		X	X	X	X	X	7							X	X	3	7							
IMO Ship Stability Recommendations	X	X																						
Damage Control	X	X	X			X		7									7							
Change in Draft Due to Density	X	X																						
Ship Power Plants:																								
Marine Power Plant Operating Principles		X	X				7						X		X		7	X	X					
Ships' Auxiliary Machinery		X	X									X			X			X	X					
Marine Engineering Terms		X	X			7						X		X			7	X	X					
Small Engine Operations and Maintenance							X	X	X								X			X				

License Codes (46 CFR 10.910-2)

Deck Examination Topics	1	2	3	4	5	6	7	8	9	10	11	12	13	14	15	16	17	18	19	20	21	22	23	24
Cargo Handling and Stowage:																								
Cargo Stowage and Security, Including Cargo Gear		X	X	X	X	X	7						X	X	X	X	7	X	X	X				
Loading and Discharging Operations		X	X	X	X	X							X	X	X	X		X	X	X				
International Regulations for Cargoes (IMDG code)	X	X	X																					
Dangerous/Hazardous Cargo Regulations	X	X	X	X	X	X							X	X	X	X		X	X	X				
Tank Vessel Safety		X	X	X	X	X							X	X	X	X		X	X	X				
Cargo Piping and Pumping Systems		X	X	X	X	X							X	X	X	X		X	X	X				
Cargo Oil Terms and Definitions		X	X	X	X	X							X	X	X	X		X	X	X				
Ballasting, Tank Clean., & Gas Free Ops		X	X	X	X	X						X	X	X	X		X	X	X					
Load on Top Procedures		X	X	X	X	X						X	X	X	X		X	X	X					
Barge Regulations (Operations)										X	X	X												
Fire Prevention and Firefighting Appliances:																								
Organization of Fire Drills		X	X	X	X	X	X			X	X	X	X	X	X	X	X	X	X	X	X	X	X	
Classes and Chemistry of Fire		X	X	X	X	X	X	X	X	X	X	X	X	X	X	X	X	X	X	X	X	X	X	
Firefighting Systems		X	X	X	X	X	X			X	X	X	X	X	X	X	X	X	X	X	X	X	X	

1. For ocean routes only.
2. River chart navigation only.
3. Topic covered only on Great Lakes specific module(s) taken for "Great Lakes and inland" routes.
4. Including recommended courses, distances, prominent aids to navigation, depths of waters in channels and over hazardous shoals, other important features of the route, such as character of the bottom. The OCMI may accept chart sketching of only a portion or portions of the route for long or extended routes.
5. Take COLREGS if license not limited to non-COLREG waters.
6. For officer endorsements over 1600 gross tons.
7. For officer endorsements over 100 gross tons.
8. Sail vessel safety precautions, rules of the road, operations, heavy weather procedures, navigation, maneuvering, and sailing terminology. Applicants for sail/auxiliary sail endorsements to master, mate or operator of uninspected passenger vessels are also tested in the subjects contained in this addendum.

DECK GENERAL

VOLUME 1

FIBER LINE CONSTRUCTION & USE

MANILA LINE

010001/DG00774 **KNIGHTS**
The strongest of the natural fibers is _____.
A. cotton
B. hemp
⚓ C. manila
D. sisal

MARLINE

010002/DG00784 **MMOH**
Marline is _____.
A. four-stranded sisal line
B. three-stranded cotton line
C. sail twine
⚓ D. two-stranded hemp cord

010003/DG02642 **SEATECH**
Which line is two-stranded, left-handed small stuff?
A. Houseline
⚓ B. Marline
C. Ratline
D. Lagline

COTTON LINE

010004/DG00794 **KNIGHTS**
White Line is made from _____.
⚓ A. cotton
B. hemp
C. manila
D. sisal

NATURAL FIBER LINE SIZE

010005/DG00804 **AMSM**
Line is called "small stuff" if its circumference is less than _____.
A. 1/2"
B. 3/4"
C. 1"
⚓ D. 1-3/4"

010006/DG00824 **AMSM; KNIGHTS**
The larger sizes of manila line are measured by their _____.
A. radius
B. diameter
⚓ C. circumference
D. weight per foot

NATURAL FIBER LINE LAY

010007/DG00644 **AMSM**
The "lay" of a line refers to _____.
A. its normal location of stowage
⚓ B. the direction of twist in the strands
C. the manner in which it is coiled
D. the manner in which it is rigged

010008/DG02462 **SEATECH**
Which term describes a part of a natural fiber line?
A. Twines
⚓ B. Fibers
C. Lays
D. Lacings

010009/DG02456 **SEATECH**
Which term describes a part of a natural fiber line?
A. Lacings
B. Lays
⚓ C. Strands
D. Twines

010010/DG00864 **KNIGHTS**
During the manufacture of line, yarns are twisted together in the _____.
⚓ A. opposite direction from which the fibers are twisted together to form strands
B. same direction the fibers are twisted to form strands
C. opposite direction from which the fibers are twisted together to form the line
D. opposite direction from which the fibers are twisted together forming cables

010011/DG00814 **KNIGHTS**
In the manufacture of line, plant fibers are twisted together to form _____.
A. cable
B. line
C. strands
⚓ D. yarns

010012/DG02464 **SEATECH**
Which term describes a part of a natural fiber line?
⚓ A. Yarns
B. Twines
C. Lacings
D. Lays

010013/DG01186 **SEATECH**
Which term describes a rope in which three right-handed strands are laid up left-handed?
A. Soft-laid
B. Hard-laid
C. Shroud laid
⚓ D. Hawser-laid

010014/DG02602   **SEATECH**
As you hold a piece of manila line vertically in front of you, the strands run from the lower right to the upper left. Which type of line is this?
A. Plain-laid
B. Shroud-laid
⚓ C. Left-hand laid
D. Water-laid

010015/DG02562   **SEATECH**
As you hold a piece of manila line vertically in front of you, the strands run from the lower left to the upper right. Which type of line is this?
⚓ A. Right-hand laid
B. Cable-laid
C. Sennet-laid
D. Water-laid

010016/DG00764   **MMOH**
Roundline is a _____.
A. four-stranded, left- or right-handed line
⚓ B. three-stranded, right-handed line
C. three-stranded, left-handed line
D. small tarred hempline of three strands laid left-handed

NATURAL FIBER LINE COILING

010017/DG00964   **AMSM**
To coil a left-hand laid rope, you should coil the line in _____.
A. a clockwise direction only
⚓ B. a counterclockwise direction only
C. an alternating clockwise and counterclockwise direction
D. either a clockwise or a counterclockwise direction

010018/DG00994   **KNIGHTS**
Manila lines in which the strands are right-hand laid _____.
⚓ A. should be coiled in a clockwise direction
B. should be coiled in a counterclockwise direction
C. may be coiled either clockwise or counterclockwise
D. should never be coiled

010019/DG00684   **KNIGHTS**
Right-laid line should be coiled _____.
⚓ A. clockwise
B. counterclockwise
C. either clockwise or counterclockwise
D. on a reel

010020/DG00984   **AMSM**
To coil a right-laid rope, you should coil the line in _____.
⚓ A. a clockwise direction
B. a counterclockwise direction
C. alternating clockwise and counterclockwise directions
D. either a clockwise or counterclockwise directions

010021/DG00954   **CHAPMAN**
In order to correctly open a new coil of manila line, you should _____.
A. pull the tagged end from the top of the coil
⚓ B. pull the tagged end through the eye of the coil
C. secure the outside end and unroll the coil
D. unreel the coil from a spool

010022/DG01004   **CHAPMAN**
Uncoiling manila line improperly can result in a(n) _____.
A. number of fishhooks
⚓ B. kink in the line
C. 50% loss of efficiency of the line
D. increase in deterioration of the line

010023/DG00894   **CHAPMAN**
When taking a length of new manila rope from the coil, you should _____.
A. mount the coil so it will turn like a spool and unreel from the outside
B. roll the coil along the deck and allow the rope to fall off the coil
⚓ C. lay the coil on end with the inside end down, then pull the inside end up through the middle of the coil
D. lay the coil on end with the inside end up then unwind the rope from the outside of the coil

NATURAL FIBER LINE STOWAGE

010024/DG00874   **CHAPMAN**
Which type of line would have the LEAST resistance to mildew and rot?
⚓ A. Manila
B. Nylon
C. Dacron
D. Polypropylene

010025/DG01024   **AMSM**
A natural fiber rope can be ruined by dampness because it may _____.
⚓ A. rot
B. shrink
C. stretch
D. unlay

010026/DG00904   **CHAPMAN**

In order to help protect a natural fiber rope from rotting, the line must be _____.

A. dried, and stowed in a place with adequate ventilation
B. stowed in a hot, moist compartment
C. stowed on deck at all times
D. stowed in any compartment

NATURAL FIBER LINE MAINTENANCE

010027/DG00914   **CHAPMAN**

When natural fiber rope gets wet, the _____.

A. overall strength of the line will decrease
B. line shrinks in length
C. line will become more elastic
D. line will be easier to handle

010028/DG01014   **AMSM**

In order to detect rot in manila lines, you should _____.

A. feel the surface of the line for broken fibers
B. measure the reduction in circumference of the line
C. observe any mildew on the outer surface
D. open the strands and examine the inner fibers

010029/DG00934   **CHAPMAN**

Which method is used to detect rot in manila lines?

A. Opening the strands and examining the inner fibers
B. Measuring the reduction in circumference of the line
C. Observing for the appearance of mildew on the outer surface
D. Feeling the surface of the line for broken fibers

010030/DG00754   **KNIGHTS**

Which method is used to detect rot in manila lines?

A. Feeling the surface of the line for broken fibers
B. Measuring the reduction in circumference of the line
C. Observing for the appearance of mildew on the outer surface
D. Opening the strands and examining the inner fibers

010031/DG00944   **KNIGHTS**

When caring for natural-fiber line, you should NEVER _____.

A. dry the line before stowing it
B. lubricate the line
C. protect the line from weather
D. slack off taut lines when it rains

010032/DG00744   **KNIGHTS**

When using natural-fiber rope, you should NEVER _____.

A. dry the line before stowing it
B. reverse turns on winches periodically to keep out kinks
C. try to lubricate the line
D. use chafing gear

NYLON LINE

010033/DG01134   **KNIGHTS**

The critical point in nylon line elongation is about _____.

A. 20%
B. 30%
C. 40%
D. 50%

010034/DG01094   **BASIC SHIP**

Which statement is TRUE with respect to the elasticity of nylon mooring lines?

A. Nylon can stretch over forty percent without being in danger of parting.
B. Nylon can be elongated by one-hundred percent before it will part.
C. Nylon will part if it is stretched any more than twenty percent.
D. Under load, nylon will stretch and thin out but will return to normal size when free of tension.

010035/DG00923   **KNIGHTS**

An advantage of nylon rope over manila rope is that nylon rope _____.

A. can hold a load even when a considerable number of the yarns have been abraded
B. can be stored on deck, exposed to sunlight
C. can be used in conjunction with wire or spring-lay rope
D. gives audible warning of overstress whereas manila does not

010036/DG00694   **KNIGHTS**

An advantage of nylon rope over manila rope is that nylon rope _____.

A. can be used in conjunction with wire or spring-lay rope
B. can be stored on decks exposed to sunlight
C. can hold a load even when a considerable amount of the yarns have been abraded
D. gives audible warning of overstress whereas manila does not

010037/DG01264   **CHAPMAN**
Which type of line is best able to withstand sudden shock loads?
A. Polypropylene
⚓ B. Nylon
C. Dacron
D. Manila

010038/DG01174   **CHAPMAN**
Compared to manila line, size for size, nylon line _____.
A. has less strength than manila line
⚓ B. has more strength than manila line
C. is equivalent to manila line
D. will rot quicker than manila line

010039/DG01104   **KNIGHTS**
Nylon line can be dangerous because it _____.
A. breaks down when wet
B. kinks when wet
C. is not elastic
⚓ D. stretches

010040/DG01254   **AMSM**
Under identical load conditions, nylon, when compared with natural fiber line, will stretch _____.
A. less and have less strength
B. more and have less strength
⚓ C. more and have greater strength
D. less and have greater strength

010041/DG01234   **AMSM**
Which type of line will stretch the most when under strain?
A. Polypropylene
B. Dacron
⚓ C. Nylon
D. Manila

010042/DG01884   **BRADY**
Which material makes the strongest mooring line?
A. Sisal
B. Manila
⚓ C. Nylon
D. Polypropylene

010043/DG01885   **BRADY**
Which rope has the greatest breaking strength?
A. Manila
⚓ B. Nylon
C. Polyester
D. Polypropylene

010044/DG01190   **U.S. NAVAL INSTITUTE**
A normal safe working load for used nylon rope in good condition is _____.
A. 10% of its breaking strain
⚓ B. 25% of its breaking strain
C. 33% of its breaking strain
D. 50% of its breaking strain

010045/DG01274   **KNIGHTS**
If given equal care, nylon line should last how many times longer than manila line?
A. Three
B. Four
⚓ C. Five
D. Six

010046/DG01244   **KNIGHTS; *46 CFR 33.10-10**
Nylon line is NOT suitable for _____.
A. towing
⚓ B. lashings
C. stoppers
D. mooring lines

DACRON & POLYESTER LINE

010047/DG01054   **AMSM**
Which mooring line has the least elasticity?
⚓ A. Dacron
B. Nylon
C. Esterlene
D. Polypropylene

010048/DG01890   **BRADY**
Which synthetic rope has the greatest breaking strength?
A. Polyethylene
⚓ B. Polyester
C. Polyglycine
D. Polypropylene

POLYPROPYLENE LINE

010049/DG01164   **KNIGHTS**
Which type of line floats?
A. Dacron
B. Nylon
C. Old manila
⚓ D. Polypropylene

010050/DG01194   **CHAPMAN**
What type of line melts easiest?
A. Wire
B. Dacron
C. Nylon
⚓ D. Polypropylene

LAY OF SYNTHETIC LINE

010051/DG00674   **KNIGHTS**
Stuffer-braid rope has _____.
⚓ A. a yarn core
   B. no core
   C. three strands
   D. 12 threads

010052/DG01154   **KNIGHTS**
Which line would be least likely to kink?
⚓ A. Braided
   B. Left-handed laid
   C. Right-handed laid
   D. Straight laid

SYNTHETIC LINE COILING

010053/DG01074   **KNIGHTS**
A new coil of nylon line should be opened by _____.
   A. pulling the end up through the eye of the coil
   B. taking a strain on both ends
   C. uncoiling from the outside with the coil standing on end
⚓ D. unreeling from a spool

010054/DG01184   **KNIGHTS**
A new coil of nylon line should be opened by _____.
   A. pulling the end up through the eye of the coil
   B. uncoiling from the outside with the coil standing on end
   C. taking a strain on both ends
⚓ D. unreeling from a spool

SYNTHETIC LINE STOWAGE

010055/DG01064   **CHAPMAN**
Which factor is most likely to impair the strength and durability of synthetic line?
   A. Dry rot
   B. Mildew
⚓ C. Sunlight
   D. Washing with mild soap

WIRE ROPE CONSTRUCTION & USE

WIRE ROPE SIZE

010056/DG01584   **AMSM**
The size of wire rope is determined by the _____.
   A. number of strands
   B. number of wires in each strand
   C. circumference
⚓ D. diameter

WIRE ROPE STRANDS & NOMENCLATURE

010057/DG01524   **AMSM**
A mooring line is described as being 6x24, 1-3/4 inch wire rope. What do the above numbers refer to?
   A. Strands, yarns, circumference
⚓ B. Strands, wires, diameter
   C. Wires, yarns, diameter
   D. Strands, circumference, wires

010058/DG01514   **AMSM**
A 6x12, two-inch wire rope has _____.
   A. 12 strands and a two-inch diameter
   B. 12 strands and a two-inch circumference
⚓ C. 6 strands and a two-inch diameter
   D. 6 strands and a two-inch circumference

010059/DG01354   **AMSM**
A 6x19 wire rope would be _____.
   A. 6 inches in diameter and 19 fathoms long
   B. 6 inches in circumference with 19 strands
⚓ C. 6 strands with 19 wires in each strand
   D. 19 strands with 6 wires in each strand

010060/DG01495   **AMSM**
A common class of wire rope is the 6 x 37 class. What does the 37 represent?
   A. Number of wires in the inner core
   B. Number of strands per wire rope
   C. Tensile strength of the wire
⚓ D. Number of wires per strand

WIRE ROPE CORE

010061/DG01544   **AMSM**
The main function of the core of a wire rope is to _____.
   A. give flexibility
⚓ B. support the strands laid around it
   C. allow some circulation around the strands
   D. allow lubrication inside the rope

010062/DG02347   **AMSM**
What is an advantage of having wire rope with a fiber core over that of a wire rope of the same size with a wire core?
   A. Fiber core rope offers greater strength.
⚓ B. Fiber core rope offers greater flexibility.
   C. Fiber core rope can be used at higher operating temperatures.
   D. Fiber core rope is the only type authorized for cargo runners.

LAY OF WIRE

010063/DG01464   **AMSM**

When talking about wire rope, the lay of the wire is the _____.

⚓ A. direction wires and strands are twisted together
B. number of strands in the wire
C. direction the core is twisted
D. material used in the core

010064/DG00654   **KNIGHTS**

A rope made of a combination of wire and fiber is known as _____.
A. independent
B. lang lay
C. preformed
⚓ D. spring lay

010065/DG02365   **AMSM**

A six-strand composite rope made up of alternate fiber and wire strands around a fiber core is called _____.

⚓ A. spring lay
B. lang lay
C. cable lay
D. alternate lay

010066/DG01434   **AMSM**

In the manufacture of wire rope, if the wires are shaped to conform to the curvature of the finished rope before they are laid up, the rope is called _____.
A. composite
B. left-lay
C. improved
⚓ D. preformed

GALVANIZING WIRE ROPE

010067/DG01394   **AMSM**

Galvanizing would be suitable for protecting wire rope which is used for _____.
A. cargo runners
⚓ B. stays
C. topping lifts
D. All of the above

010068/DG01574   **AMSM**

Wire rope is galvanized to _____.
⚓ A. protect it from corrosion due to contact with saltwater
B. make it bend more easily
C. increase its strength
D. increase its circumference

010069/DG01404   **AMSM**

Galvanizing would not be suitable for protecting wire rope which is used for _____.
⚓ A. cargo runners
B. mooring wires
C. shrouds
D. stays

USE OF WIRE ROPE

010070/DG03464   **PETEX**

The ultimate or maximum strength of a wire rope is referred to as the _____.
A. operating strength
B. working load
⚓ C. breaking strength
D. lifting load

010071/DG01589   **ENCY. NAUT. KNOW.**

Why is 6 x 19 class wire rope more commonly used for cargo runners than the more flexible 6 x 37 wire rope?
⚓ A. It resists abrasion better.
B. It is longer.
C. It hugs the winch drum better.
D. It is less expensive.

010072/DG01305   **AMSM**

What is an advantage of the 6 x 19 class of wire rope over the 6 x 37 class of wire rope of the same diameter?
A. Greater holding power
B. Better for towing
C. More resistance to elongation
⚓ D. More resistance to corrosion

010073/DG01112   **AMSM; PETEX V**

What is an advantage of the 6 x 37 class of wire rope over the 6 x 19 class of wire rope of the same diameter?
⚓ A. Greater flexibility
B. More resistance to corrosion
C. More resistance to elongation
D. Lower weight per foot

010074/DG01414   **AMSM**

A wire rope that has been overstrained will show _____.
A. a bulge in the wire where the strain occurred
⚓ B. a decrease in diameter where the strain occurred
C. a kink in the wire where the strain occurred
D. no visible effects of an overstrain

010075/DG02288   **AMSM**

What will cause wire rope to fail?
A. Operating the winch too fast
B. Using a sheave 9 times the wire's diameter
C. Kinking
⚓ D. All of the above

010076/DG02305　　　　　　　　　**AMSM**
Which will cause a wire rope to fail?
A. Using a medium graphite grease as a lubricant
B. Operating a winch too slow
⚓ C. Using a sheave with an undersized throat
D. A sheave diameter of 24 times the wire's diameter

WIRE ROPE MAINTENANCE

010077/DG01344　　　　　　　　　**KNIGHTS**
When working with wire rope, which must be considered?
A. Metal sheaves should be lined with wood or leather.
⚓ B. It needs better care than hemp or manila.
C. It should be lubricated annually.
D. The diameter of a sheave over which a rope is worked should be ten times that of the rope.

010078/DG02275　　　***46 CFR 04.05-1; KNIGHTS**
When inspecting wire rope before a hoisting operation, one must look for _____.
A. fishhooks
B. kinks
C. worn spots
⚓ D. All of the above

010079/DG00417　　　　　　　　　**KNIGHTS**
When inspecting wire rope that has been in use for some time, one must look for _____.
A. fishhooks
B. kinks
C. worn spots
⚓ D. All of the above

010080/DG01534　　　　　　　　　**AMSM**
Which statement(s) is(are) TRUE concerning wire rope?
⚓ A. Wire rope should be condemned if the outside wires are worn to one-half their original diameter.
B. Wire rope should be condemned if the fiber core appears moist.
C. Wire rope which is right-hand laid should be coiled counterclockwise to prevent kinking.
D. All of the above

010081/DG03544　　　　　　　　　**BRADY**
Wire rope should be renewed when the _____.
A. outer wires are rusted
⚓ B. outer wires are worn to half their original diameter
C. inner core appears dry
D. certification period expires

010082/DG00927　　　　　　　　**AMSM; BRADY**
Sluicing or slushing wire rope _____.
A. prevents internal and external rust and corrosion
B. reduces chafing and increases its useful service life
C. reduces internal friction within the wire
⚓ D. All of the above

010083/DG01564　　　　　　　　　**AMSM**
What is the main reason to slush a wire rope?
A. Keep the wire soft and manageable
⚓ B. Lubricate the inner wires and prevent wear
C. Prevent kinking
D. Prevent rotting

010084/DG01444　　　　　　　　　**AB MAN**
If kinking results while wire rope is being coiled clockwise, you should _____.
A. coil it counterclockwise
B. not coil it
⚓ C. take a turn under
D. twist out the kinks under a strain

010085/DG02264　　　　　　　　　**BRADY**
When you "end for end" a wire rope, you _____.
A. cut off the free end and bitter end of the rope
B. splice two wire ropes together
⚓ C. remove the wire rope from the drum and reverse it so that the free end becomes the bitter end
D. remove the wire rope from the drum and turn it over, so the wire bends in the opposite direction

MARLINESPIKE SEAMANSHIP

MISCELLANEOUS MARLINESPIKE EQUIPMENT
BOSUN'S CHAIR

010086/DG00394　　　　　　　**ENCY. NAUT. KNOW.**
The rope which is rove from the truck to be used with a bos'n's chair is called a _____.
⚓ A. gantline
B. life line
C. strop
D. whip

010087/DG01103　　　　　　　　　**HOUSE**
What should you inspect to be sure that it is safe to go aloft in a bosun's chair?
A. The gantline
B. The tail block
C. The chair and bridle
⚓ D. All of the above

010088/DG01093   **HOUSE**
When rigging a bosun's chair, a tail block or lizard is used to _____.
A. guide the bosun's chair down a stay when applying a protective coating
B. run paint or tools up to a sailor in a chair with a heaving line
C. keep a bosun's chair from swinging with the ship's motion
⚓ D. reeve the gantline through

010089/DG01072   **HOUSE**
The normal and safest way for a sailor in a bosun's chair to be raised aloft is _____.
A. for the sailor to pull himself aloft and then make fast with a bosun's chair hitch
⚓ B. manually by two or three sailors heaving away on deck
C. by taking the gantline to a winch drum and heaving away with the winch
D. by fairleading the gantline with a snatch block and pulling with a cargo runner

010090/DG01091   **HOUSE**
Which of the following statements concerning the rigging and use of bosun's chairs is TRUE?
A. When riding a stay, make sure that the bow of the shackle passes through the becket of the bridle.
⚓ B. Always have the chair hoisted manually.
C. The lowering hitch should always be made before getting into the chair.
D. Always secure the gantline to the chair with a clove hitch.

010091/DG00945   **NICHOLLS**
After having been pulled aloft in a bosun's chair on a mast, you must now make yourself fast in the chair prior to painting the mast. You should first _____.
A. have the sailor on deck make the hauling part fast to a cleat on the mast
B. make the tail of the line leading from the becket bend fast to a padeye on the mast
⚓ C. seize the hauling part and the standing part firmly in one hand to support your weight
D. frap yourself to the mast to take the strain off the hauling part

010092/DG01067   **HOUSE**
The normal and safest way for a sailor to be lowered in a bosun's chair when descending vertically is _____.
⚓ A. for that sailor to feed the hauling part through a bosun's chair hitch
B. to lead the hauling part to a cleat on the mast and slacking the sailor down
C. by taking several turns of the gantline on a winch drum and then lower the sailor by backing off on the winch
D. by leading the bight of the hauling part to a rail and taking several turns, then slacking away with the bight

010093/DG01063   **NICHOLLS**
You have been pulled aloft in a bosun's chair rigged to a mast that you intend to paint. You are now supporting your weight by seizing the hauling part and the standing part of the gantline in one hand. Your next procedure in securing the bosun's chair is to _____.
A. secure the tail of the standing part leading from the becket bend to the mast
⚓ B. dip the bight of the hauling part around your back and up in front of you to form the hitch
C. take a strain on the hauling part by having it led to the gypsy head on a winch
D. secure the standing part of the gantline to the hauling part by taking turns of marlin and tying off

010094/DG02073   **MILLER**
You are preparing to lubricate standing rigging on your vessel. When rigging a bosun's chair on a stay with a shackle, _____.
A. connect the shackle to the bosun's chair with a hook
⚓ B. never allow the shackle pin to ride on the stay
C. run the gantline through the shackle and then make fast to the bosun's chair
D. tie the bitter end of the gantline to the shackle before shackling it to the bosun's chair

010095/DG01073   **HOUSE**
You are preparing to slush a stay on your vessel by lowering yourself down the stay in a bosun's chair. The proper way to do this is to ride down the stay on a riding shackle _____.
A. with the pin of the shackle riding on the stay
⚓ B. with the pin of the shackle through the chair's bridle eye
C. with a hook attaching the chair to the riding shackle
D. connected to a second shackle on the chair

010096/DG01085 HOUSE

Which of the following statements concerning the rigging of bosuns' chairs and their use is TRUE?

A. Always secure the gantline to the chair with a bowline.

B. Always have the chair hoisted with at least three turns on a winch drum.

⚓ C. Any tools, paint pots etc. should be secured by lanyards.

D. When riding a stay, make sure that the bow of the shackle passes through the becket of the bridle.

STAGING

010097/DG01135 AMSM

What equipment is customarily used when seamen are working on a stage rigged over the side of a vessel?

A. Jacob's ladder

B. Manropes

C. Heaving lines

⚓ D. All of the above

010098/DG01121 HOUSE

What should be readily available on deck while seamen are working over the side on a stage?

⚓ A. Ring buoy

B. Fire extinguisher

C. First aid kit

D. Stokes basket

010099/DG01133 AMSM

To properly rig the downhaul to your stage for lowering, you must _____.

A. take only figure eights around the horns

⚓ B. take 2 or 3 round turns around the stage and then belay the downhaul around the horns

C. take 2 round turns around the stage and then dip the third turn to form a clove hitch

D. pass the downhaul through the bridle formed by the standing part and then take round turns

010100/DG01105 HOUSE

You are rigging a stage over the ship's side to serve as a working platform. For stability of the stage, the downhaul to one end of the stage and the downhaul to the other end, which are used for lowering the stage, should be led _____.

A. both to the inboard side of the stage

B. both to the outboard side of the stage

⚓ C. one to the inboard and the other to the outboard

D. either both to the inboard or both to the outboard side of the stage

010101/DG01107 HOUSE

You are rigging a stage over the vessel's side and are securing the downhaul with lowering turns at your end of the stage. When finished, the remainder of the line should be _____.

⚓ A. lowered down into the water

B. coiled on the stage with the bitter end on the bottom

C. coiled on the stage with the bitter end on top

D. coiled on deck to be slacked down by a seaman as needed

010102/DG01137 C. H. WRIGHT

When lowering manropes alongside a stage rigged over the side of a vessel, they should be allowed to trail in the water _____.

A. to easily remove the kinks that form in the lines

B. to allow the seamen on the stage to know the direction and strength of the current

⚓ C. to provide the seaman something to hold onto if he or she falls from the stage into the water

D. only for short periods of time since they will become waterlogged and be very heavy to pull up

010103/DG01120 C. H. WRIGHT

A stage should only be rigged _____.

A. over the bow or stern of a vessel

B. over the flat sides of a vessel

⚓ C. over the open water

D. over the dockside

010104/DG01106 HOUSE

A vessel is underway with a work stage rigged over the side. A seaman may work on the stage, but only when _____.

A. wearing a life jacket

B. wearing a safety harness secured to the stage

C. wearing both a life jacket and a safety harness secured to the stage

⚓ D. the vessel is not making way

HOOKS

010105/DG00262 AMSM

Mousing a cargo hook with marline or small line _____.

A. increases the lifting capacity of the hook

B. protects the hook from the sling ring

⚓ C. prevents the sling ring from coming out of the hook

D. All of the above

010106/DG00237   **KNIGHTS**

The latch of a safety hook _____.
- A.   increases the strength of the hook
- ⚓ B.   prevents the sling ring from coming out of the hook if the strain is abruptly eased
- C.   prevents the sling ring from coming out of the hook if there is a strain on the sling ring
- D.   All of the above

010107/DG01760   **ENCY. NAUT. KNOW.**

A hook that will release quickly is a _____.
- A.   longshore hook
- B.   margin hook
- C.   marginal hook
- ⚓ D.   pelican hook

010108/DG01329   **AMSM**

A pelican hook _____.
- ⚓ A.   can be released while under strain
- B.   is used for boat falls
- C.   is used for extra heavy loads
- D.   is used for light loads only

010109/DG00265   **AMSM**

Which statement is TRUE about hooks and shackles?
- A.   Hooks are stronger than shackles of the same diameter.
- ⚓ B.   Shackles are stronger than hooks of the same diameter.
- C.   Hooks and shackles of the same diameter are of equal strength.
- D.   All the above may be true, depending on the hook's or shackle's overall length.

JACOB'S LADDER

010110/DG00454   **INT. MARITIME DICTIONARY**

A rope ladder with wooden rungs is a _____.
- A.   drop ladder
- B.   life ladder
- ⚓ C.   Jacob's ladder
- D.   jury ladder

SHACKLES

010111/DG02451   **BRADY**

A safety shackle is identified by its _____.
- A.   shape
- ⚓ B.   pin
- C.   certification stamp
- D.   color code

CANVAS

010112/DG01663   **AMSM**

A bench hook is used for _____.
- A.   handling of cargo cases
- B.   hanging oilskins
- ⚓ C.   sewing canvas
- D.   splicing small stuff

010113/DG01673   **ENCY. NAUT. KNOW.**

A sail hook is used for _____.
- A.   hoisting a windsail
- B.   parceling
- ⚓ C.   sewing canvas
- D.   testing canvas

010114/DG01683   **AMSM**

Herringbone is a term associated with _____.
- A.   anchoring
- B.   mooring
- ⚓ C.   sewing
- D.   splicing

MOORING LINES

BOW & STERN LINES

010115/DG02013   **CHAPMAN**

A mooring line that checks forward motion of a vessel at a pier is a _____.
- A.   bow line
- B.   forward bow line
- ⚓ C.   stern line
- D.   stern breast line

010116/DG01793   **AMSM**

The lines led forward from the bow and aft from the stern when a vessel is moored to the dock are _____.
- ⚓ A.   bow and stern lines
- B.   breast lines
- C.   halyards
- D.   warps

SPRING LINE

010117/DG02063   **AMSM**

A "spring line" is _____.
- A.   any wire rope used for mooring
- B.   a fire-warp
- ⚓ C.   a mooring line running diagonally to the keel
- D.   a mooring line perpendicular to the keel

010118/DG02069   **AMSM**

A "spring line" is a _____.
- A.   mooring line made of spring lay wire rope
- ⚓ B.   mooring line running diagonally to the keel
- C.   mooring line parallel to the keel
- D.   wire rope used for securing an anchor buoy

010119/DG02053   **AMSM**

A mooring line leading 45° to the keel, used to check forward or astern movement of a vessel, is called a _____.

  A. spring line
  B. warp line
  C. bow line
  D. breast line

010120/DG02033   **AMSM**

A spring line leads _____.

  A. fore and aft from the ship's side
  B. to the dock at a right angle to the vessel
  C. through the bull nose or chock at the bow
  D. through the chock at the stern

010121/DG02590   **CHAPMAN**

Which method of adjusting mooring lines is MOST useful for leaving a boat free to rise and fall with the tide?

  A. Crossing the spring lines
  B. Slacking all forward running lines while keeping all after running lines taut
  C. Doubling up on spring or breast lines
  D. Slacking bow and stern lines

010122/DG01783   **AMSM**

Which mooring line is likely to undergo the most strain when docking a ship under normal conditions?

  A. Bow line
  B. Breast line
  C. Spring line
  D. Stern line

BREAST LINE

010123/DG01743   **AMSM; KNIGHTS**

A mooring line leading at nearly right angles to the keel is a _____.

  A. bow line
  B. breast line
  C. spring line
  D. stern line

010124/DG02023   **AMSM**

A mooring line leading at nearly right angles to the keel is a _____.

  A. spring line
  B. bow line
  C. stern line
  D. breast line

010125/DG02043   **CHAPMAN; AMSM**

A mooring line that prevents a vessel from moving sideways away from the dock is a _____.

  A. bow line
  B. breast line
  C. stern line
  D. spring line

010126/DG02353   **AMSM**

Which mooring line prevents sideways motion of a vessel moored to a pier?

  A. A line led forward from the bow
  B. A line led aft from the bow
  C. A line led in the same direction as the keel
  D. A line led at a right angle to the keel

MOORING TERMS & NOMENCLATURE

010127/DG00314   **ENCY. NAUT. KNOW.**

Avast means _____.

  A. let go
  B. pull
  C. slack off
  D. stop

010128/DG00434   **ENCY. NAUT. KNOW.**

To "belay" a line means to _____.

  A. coil it down
  B. heave it taut
  C. stow it below
  D. secure it to a cleat

010129/DG01933   **AMSM**

When checking a mooring line, you should _____.

  A. ensure the bight is not fouled between the ship and the dock by taking up slack
  B. pay out slack smartly and keep free for running
  C. secure more turns to hold the line against any strain, then clear the area
  D. surge the line so that it maintains a strain without parting

010130/DG02059   **AMSM**

You are handling a mooring line and are instructed to "Check the line". What should you do?

  A. Ensure the bight is not fouled by taking up slack.
  B. Pay out the line smartly and keep it free for running.
  C. Secure the line by adding more turns.
  D. Surge the line so it maintains a strain without parting.

010131/DG00414   ENCY. NAUT. KNOW.
To "ease" a line means to _____.
A. cast off
B. double up so that one line does not take all the strain
⚓ C. pay out line to remove most of the tension
D. slack it off quickly

010132/DG01943   AMSM
In order to pay out or slack a mooring line which is under strain, you should _____.
A. sluice the line
⚓ B. surge the line
C. stopper the line
D. slip the line

010133/DG00304   ENCY. NAUT. KNOW.
To warp a vessel means to _____.
A. anchor the vessel
B. bring the head into the wind
C. clean the decks
⚓ D. move the vessel by hauling on lines

MOORING EQUIPMENT

010134/DG00594   INT. MARITIME DICTIONARY
A bollard is found on the _____.
A. beach
B. deck
⚓ C. pier
D. towed vessel

010135/DG00444   ENCY. NAUT. KNOW.
A metal object on the pier resembling a tree stump and made to receive mooring lines is a _____.
A. bight
⚓ B. bollard
C. chock
D. camel

010136/DG02489   INT. MARITIME DICTIONARY
A post on a dock or wharf used to secure mooring lines or hawsers is called a _____.
A. bitt
⚓ B. bollard
C. cleat
D. capstan

010137/DG01823   ENCY. NAUT. KNOW.
Chafing gear _____.
A. reduces and prevents corrosion of standing rigging
B. prevents corrosion of running rigging
⚓ C. reduces and prevents wear caused by the rubbing of one object against another
D. protects the body against extreme cold

010138/DG00125   CHAPMAN
Chafing gear is normally used _____.
A. for portable fenders
B. for ground tackle
C. on the inside of the hawsepipe
⚓ D. on mooring lines

010139/DG02003   CHAPMAN
Chafing gear is used to _____.
A. anchor the boat
B. pick up heavy loads
⚓ C. protect fiber rope from abrasion
D. strengthen mooring lines

010140/DG00097   AMSM
Chafing gear should be placed _____.
⚓ A. at all wearing points of mooring lines
B. at the bitter ends of all standing rigging
C. around running rigging
D. on wire rope only

010141/DG01963   CHAPMAN
What should you do to a line to prevent fraying where it passes over the side of the vessel?
A. Worm that part of the line.
B. Splice that part of the line.
⚓ C. Cover it with chafing gear.
D. Install a cleat.

010142/DG01983   CHAPMAN
When a line is subject to wear where it passes through a mooring chock, it should be _____.
A. wormed, parceled, and served
B. wrapped with heavy tape
⚓ C. wrapped with chafing gear
D. wrapped in leather

010143/DG01844   ENCY. NAUT. KNOW.
A wooden float placed between a ship and a dock to prevent damage to both is called a _____.
⚓ A. camel
B. dolphin
C. rat guard
D. wedge

010144/DG01936   INT. MARITIME DICTIONARY
A "gypsy" or "gypsyhead" is a _____.
A. punt used for painting over the side
B. small, reciprocating steam engine
⚓ C. spool-shaped drum fitted on a winch
D. swinging derrick

010145/DG02016　　　　　　　　　　AMSM
The revolving drum of a winch used to haul lines is called a _____.
A. bull gear
⚓ B. gypsyhead
C. spanner
D. wildcat

010146/DG01852　　　　　　　　　　AMSM
What is normally used to pass a mooring line to a dock?
A. Distance line
B. Gantline
⚓ C. Heaving line
D. Tag line

010147/DG01856　　　　　　　　　　AMSM
When passing a hawser to the dock you would first use what line?
A. Gantline
⚓ B. Heaving line
C. Preventer
D. Warp

010148/DG01634　　　　　　　　　CHAPMAN
A monkey fist is found on a _____.
⚓ A. heaving line
B. lead line
C. manrope
D. mooring line

010149/DG04063　　　　　　　　　　AMSM
The knot at the end of the heaving line used to pass the towing hawser is called a _____.
⚓ A, monkey's fist
B. ball or baseball knot
C. heaving knot
D. three strand Turk's head

010150/DG00854　　　　　　　　　　AMSM
A piece of small stuff (small line) secured to an object to prevent it from going adrift is a _____.
⚓ A. lanyard
B. keeper
C. noose
D. stopper

010151/DG01913　　　　　　　　　　AMSM
An example of a messenger is a _____.
A. fairlead
⚓ B. heaving line
C. stay
D. warp

010152/DG00354　　　　　ENCY. NAUT. KNOW.
A "stopper" is _____.
⚓ A. a short length of line used for temporarily holding another line
B. a snatch block for handling a topping lift
C. an engine order telegraph
D. the brake on a cargo winch

010153/DG02203　　　　　　　　　　AMSM
A Chinese stopper (two lines) will hold best when you _____.
A. fasten the bitter ends to the mooring line with half hitches
⚓ B. twist the ends together and hold them in the direction of the pull
C. twist the ends together and hold them in the direction opposite to the pull
D. twist the ends together and hold them at right angles to the mooring line

010154/DG01193　　　　　　　　　　AMSM
The main advantage of a Chinese stopper over the one line stopper is that it _____.
⚓ A. will not jam on the mooring line
B. is stronger
C. is easier to use when under heavy tension
D. is safer to use when under heavy tension

010155/DG01114　　　　　　　　　KNIGHTS
What type of stopper would you use on a nylon mooring line?
A. Chain
⚓ B. Nylon
C. Manila
D. Wire

010156/DG01214　　　　　　　　　KNIGHTS
Which statement is TRUE about nylon line?
A. Manila line will usually last longer than nylon line.
B. Nylon line is excellent for use in alongside towing.
C. A normal safe working load will stretch nylon line 50%.
⚓ D. Nylon stoppers should be used with nylon line.

010157/DG01224　　　　　　　　　KNIGHTS
Which is NOT a recommended practice when handling nylon line?
A. Nylon lines which become slippery because of oil or grease should be scrubbed down.
⚓ B. Manila line stoppers should be used for holding nylon hawsers.
C. When easing out nylon line, keep an extra turn on the bitt to prevent slipping.
D. Iced-over nylon lines should be thawed and drained before stowing.

010158/DG01989   **AMSM**

If you were to pass a stopper on a wire rope, what should the stopper be made of?
- A. Wire
- B. Manila
- C. Nylon
- ⚓ D. Chain

010159/DG01374   **KNIGHTS**

Which type of stopper should be used to stop off wire rope?
- ⚓ A. Chain
- B. Manila
- C. Polypropylene
- D. Wire

MOORING LINE STOWAGE

010160/DG02510   **CHAPMAN**

Mooring lines should be turned end-for-end occasionally. This is because _____.
- A. a line is weakened by constantly pulling on it in one direction
- ⚓ B. normal wear on the line is thus distributed to different areas
- C. it prevents the line from kinking or unlaying
- D. it prevents permanent misalignment of the line's internal strands

010161/DG00424   **ENCY. NAUT. KNOW.**

Faking a line means to _____.
- ⚓ A. arrange it on deck in long bights
- B. coil it down on deck
- C. put a whipping on it
- D. stow it below

010162/DG01993   **AMSM**

The usual method of arranging a line on deck so that it will run out easily without kinking or fouling is _____.
- A. coiling the line
- ⚓ B. faking down the line
- C. flemishing the line
- D. racking the line

010163/DG02570   **AMSM**

When a line is laid down in loose, looping figure-eights, it is said to be _____.
- ⚓ A. faked
- B. flemished
- C. coiled
- D. chined

010164/DG00704   **AMSM**

Laying out a line in successive circles flat on deck with the bitter end in the center is known as _____.
- A. coiling
- B. faking
- ⚓ C. flemishing
- D. lining

010165/DG02520   **AMSM**

When a line is spirally coiled about its end and lying flat on deck, it is said to be _____.
- A. coiled
- B. faked
- ⚓ C. flemished
- D. seized

010166/DG00664   **AMSM**

Coiling new rope against the lay, bringing the lower end up through the center of the coil, then coiling with the lay, in order to remove the kinks, is known as _____.
- A. coiling
- B. faking
- C. flemishing
- ⚓ D. thoroughfooting

HANDLING MOORING LINES

010167/DG02580   **CHAPMAN**

You want to double the strength of a mooring line by using two lines. To accomplish this, the second line must _____.
- A. be 1-1/2 times the diameter of the first
- B. be married to the first
- C. not cross the first
- ⚓ D. be of the same length

010168/DG01903   **AMSM**

When securing a manila line to a bitt what is the minimum number of round turns you should take before figure-eighting the line?
- A. None
- ⚓ B. 1
- C. 2
- D. 3

010169/DG01996   **AMSM**

Which method should be used to secure a manila line to bitts?
- A. A round turn on the bitt farthest from the strain and then figure eights
- ⚓ B. A round turn on the bitt closest to the strain and then figure eights
- C. Figure eights and then a round turn at the top of both bitts
- D. Only figure eights are necessary on both bitts

010170/DG00423   HOUSE
When securing a synthetic line to a bitt what is the minimum number of round turns you should take before figure-eighting the line?
A. None
B. 1
⚓ C. 2
D. 3

010171/DG00422   HOUSE
Which method should be used to secure a synthetic fiber line to two bitts?
⚓ A. Two round turns on the bitt closest to the strain and then figure eights
B. Two round turns on the bitt farthest from the strain and then figure eights
C. Figure eights and then a round turn at the top of both bitts
D. Only figure eights are necessary on both bitts

010172/DG01208   AMSM
When making a wire fast to bitts it is recommended that you _____.
A. use only figure eights
B. take 2 round turns around one bitt, then make figure eights
⚓ C. take 3 round turns around both bitts, then make figure eights
D. alternate round turns and figure eights around both bitts

010173/DG01883   CHAPMAN; AMSM
The most common method of securing a line to a cleat is a _____.
A. half hitch, then round turns
⚓ B. round turn, then figure eights
C. figure eight, then round turns
D. figure eight, then half hitches

010174/DG00117   CHAPMAN
If two mooring lines are to be placed on the same bollard, which method is BEST?
A. Place the eye from the forward line on the bollard and then place the eye from the second line directly over the first.
B. It makes no difference how the lines are placed.
⚓ C. Place the eye from either line on the bollard, and then bring the eye of the other line up through the eye of the first, and place it on the bollard.
D. Place both eyes on the bollard, in any manner, but lead both lines to the same winch head on the vessel and secure them on the winch.

010175/DG01462   CHAPMAN
Two mooring lines may be placed on the same bollard and either one cast off first if _____.
⚓ A. the eye of the second line is dipped
B. the mooring lines are doubled
C. the bollard has two horns
D. one of the lines is a breast line

010176/DG01973   CHAPMAN
Which statement is TRUE about placing the eyes of two mooring lines on the same bollard?
A. Put one line at the low point and one at the high point of the bollard so they don't touch.
⚓ B. Take the eye of the second line up through the eye of the first line before putting the second line on the bollard.
C. Never put two mooring lines on the same bollard.
D. The mooring line forward should be put on the bollard first.

010177/DG00100   AMSM
Which statement is ALWAYS true?
⚓ A. Keep clear of any line that is under a strain.
B. A line will creak, make snapping sounds, and smoke before it parts.
C. Only synthetic lines will snap back after parting.
D. Stepping on the bight of a line is safer than stepping in the bight of a line.

010178/DG00101   AMSM
You can safely step in the bight of a line _____.
A. when it is not under strain
B. if both ends are made fast
C. in an emergency
⚓ D. at no time

010179/DG00095   AMSM
You should keep clear of _____.
⚓ A. any line under a strain
B. lines that are paying out
C. lines that are coiled down only
D. None of the above are correct

010180/DG01953   AMSM
What is likely to occur when you are surging synthetic mooring lines on the gypsyhead during mooring operations?
A. The lines may jam and then jump off the gypsyhead.
B. If there is sudden strain on the line, the man tending the line may be pulled into the gypsyhead.
C. The lines' surging may cause the vessel to surge.
⚓ D. The heat generated may cause the lines to temporarily fuse to the gypsyhead.

010181/DG02025   **AMSM**
What is the chief hazard encountered when surging synthetic mooring lines on the gypsyhead during operations?
A. If there is sudden strain, the man tending the line may be pulled into the gypsyhead.
B. The lines may jam and then jump off the gypsyhead.
C. The lines' surging may cause the vessel to surge.
⚓ D. The heat generated may cause the lines to temporarily fuse to the gypsyhead.

010182/DG01763   **AMSM**
You are in charge while handling a synthetic hawser on a capstan. The hawser has a heavy strain and you wish to avoid the hawser's slipping on the capstan drum. Which action should you take?
⚓ A. Back off on the capstan a bit and have the seaman take several more turns on the drum.
B. Have the seaman take a strain on the hawser and carefully have several turns added on the drum.
C. Have more than one seaman hold a good strain on the hawser and continue to heave easy.
D. While continuing to heave slowly on the capstan, have the seaman take several more turns on the drum.

010183/DG00044   **AMSM**
You are using an automatic tension winch by yourself. If you get caught in the turns of the line as they lead into the gypsyhead _____.
A. the safety cutout will stop the winch before you're injured
B. the line will part and snap back
⚓ C. you may be pulled into the winch and injured or killed
D. None of the above are correct

DIAGRAM D019DG

010184/DG01788   **AMSM**
Which position shown is the most dangerous when tying up? See Diagram D019DG
⚓ A. I
B. II
C. III
D. IV

DIAGRAM D044DG

010185/DG01567   **AMSM**
The mooring line shown as "A" is called a(n) _____. See Diagram D044DG
A. after breast line
B. after spring line
C. onshore stern line
⚓ D. offshore stern line

010186/DG00083   **AMSM**
The mooring line labeled "A" as shown is called a(n) _____.
⚓ A. offshore stern line
B. onshore stern line
C. after spring line
D. after breast line

010187/DG00617   **AMSM**
In illustration D044DG, the mooring line labeled "A" is called a(n) _____. See Diagram D044DG
A. onshore stern line
⚓ B. offshore stern line
C. after breast line
D. after spring line

010188/DG01012   **AMSM**
In illustration D044DG, the mooring line labeled "A" is called a(n) _____. See Diagram D044DG
A. after breast line
B. after spring line
⚓ C. offshore stern line
D. inshore stern line

010189/DG00147   **AMSM**
In illustration D044DG, the mooring line labeled "B" is called a(n) _____. See Diagram D044DG
⚓ A. inshore stern line
B. offshore stern line
C. after spring line
D. after breast line

010190/DG00642   **AMSM**
In illustration D044DG, the mooring line labeled "B" is called a(n) _____. See Diagram D044DG
A. offshore stern line
⚓ B. inshore stern line
C. after spring line
D. after breast line

010191/DG01102   **AMSM**
In illustration D044DG, the mooring line labeled "B" is called a(n) _____. See Diagram D044DG
A. after breast line
B. after spring line
⚓ C. inshore stern line
D. offshore stern line

010192/DG01635   **AMSM**
In illustration D044DG, the mooring line labeled "B" is called a(n) _____. See Diagram D044DG
A. after breast line
B. after spring line
C. offshore stern line
⚓ D. inshore stern line

010193/DG01689　　　　　　　　AMSM
The mooring line shown as "C" is called a _____.
See Diagram D044DG
A.　stern line
B.　spring line
C.　shore line
⚓ D.　breast line

010194/DG00127　　　　　　　　AMSM
In illustration D044DG, the mooring line labeled "C" is called a _____. See Diagram D044DG
⚓ A.　breast line
B.　shore line
C.　spring line
D.　stern line

010195/DG00673　　　　　　　　AMSM
In illustration D044DG, the mooring line labeled "C" is called a _____. See Diagram D044DG
A.　shore line
⚓ B.　breast line
C.　spring line
D.　stern line

010196/DG01185　　　　　　　　AMSM
As shown, the mooring line labeled "C" is called a _____. See Diagram D044DG
A.　stern line
B.　spring line
⚓ C.　breast line
D.　shore line

010197/DG00043　　　　　　　　AMSM
In illustration D044DG, the mooring line labeled "D" is called a(n) _____. See Diagram D044DG
⚓ A.　after spring line
B.　forward spring line
C.　waist breast line
D.　stern line

010198/DG00677　　　　　　　　AMSM
In illustration D044DG, the mooring line labeled "D" is called a(n) _____. See Diagram D044DG
A.　forward spring line
⚓ B.　after spring line
C.　waist breast line
D.　stern line

010199/DG01312　　　　　　　　AMSM
In illustration D044DG, the mooring line labeled "D" is called a(n) _____. See Diagram D044DG
A.　stern line
B.　forward spring line
⚓ C.　after spring line
D.　waist breast line

010200/DG01814　　　　　　　　AMSM
In illustration D044DG, the mooring line labeled "D" is called a(n) _____. See Diagram D044DG
A.　stern line
B.　forward spring line
C.　waist breast line
⚓ D.　after spring line

010201/DG00017　　　　　　　　AMSM
The mooring line labeled "E" is called a(n) _____. See Diagram D044DG
⚓ A.　bow spring line
B.　aft spring line
C.　forward breast line
D.　bow line

010202/DG00582　　　　　　　　AMSM
In illustration D044DG, the mooring line labeled "E" is called a(n) _____. See Diagram D044DG
A.　after spring line
⚓ B.　bow spring line
C.　forward breast line
D.　bow line

010203/DG00925　　　　　　　　AMSM
In illustration D044DG, the mooring line labeled "E" is called a(n) _____. See Diagram D044DG
A.　bow line
B.　after spring line
⚓ C.　bow spring line
D.　forward breast line

010204/DG01499　　　　　　　　AMSM
In illustration D044DG, the mooring line labeled "E" is called a(n) _____. See Diagram D044DG
A.　bow line
B.　forward breast line
C.　after spring line
⚓ D.　bow spring line

010205/DG00007　　　　　　　　AMSM
The mooring line labeled "F" is called a _____.
See Diagram D044DG
⚓ A.　breast line
B.　bow line
C.　forward spring line
D.　None of the above

010206/DG00721　　　　　　　　AMSM
The mooring line labeled "F" is called a _____.
See Diagram D044DG
A.　bow line
B.　forward spring line
⚓ C.　breast line
D.　None of the above

010207/DG00475 AMSM
In illustration D044DG, the mooring line labeled "F" is called a _____. See Diagram D044DG
A. bow line
⚓ B. breast line
C. forward spring line
D. None of the above

010208/DG00013 AMSM
In illustration D044DG, the mooring line labeled "G" is called a(n) _____. See Diagram D044DG
⚓ A. inshore bow line
B. offshore bow line
C. forward breast line
D. forward spring line

010209/DG00535 AMSM
In illustration D044DG, the mooring line labeled "G" is called a(n) _____. See Diagram D044DG
A. offshore bow line
⚓ B. inshore bow line
C. forward breast line
D. forward spring line

010210/DG00817 AMSM
In illustration D044DG, the mooring line labeled "G" is called a(n) _____. See Diagram D044DG
A. forward spring line
B. forward breast line
⚓ C. inshore bow line
D. offshore bow line

010211/DG01475 AMSM
As shown, the mooring line labeled "G" is called a(n) _____. See Diagram D044DG
A. forward spring line
B. offshore bow line
C. forward breast line
⚓ D. inshore bow line

010212/DG00192 AMSM
The mooring line labeled "H" is called a(n) _____. See Diagram D044DG
⚓ A. offshore bow line
B. onshore bow line
C. offshore spring line
D. forward breast line

010213/DG00682 AMSM
The mooring line labeled "H" is called a(n) _____. See Diagram D044DG
A. forward breast line
⚓ B. offshore bow line
C. offshore spring line
D. onshore bow line

010214/DG01392 AMSM
In illustration D044DG, the mooring line labeled "H" is called a(n) _____. See Diagram D044DG
A. forward breast line
B. offshore spring line
⚓ C. offshore bow line
D. onshore bow line

010215/DG02050 AMSM
In illustration D044DG, the mooring line labeled "H" is called a(n) _____. See Diagram D044DG
A. forward breast line
B. offshore spring line
C. onshore bow line
⚓ D. offshore bow line

KNOTTING SEIZINGS & WHIPPINGS

FIGURE EIGHT

010216/DG01794 AMSM
A "figure eight" knot is used to _____.
A. be a stopper
B. shorten a line
C. join lines of equal size
⚓ D. keep a line from passing through a sheave

010217/DG01804 CHAPMAN
Instead of whipping an end of a line, a temporary means of preventing the line from unraveling is to tie a

_____.
A. becket bend
B. blackwall hitch
⚓ C. figure-eight knot
D. square knot

SHEEPSHANK

010218/DG01714 KNIGHTS
A "sheepshank" is used to _____.
A. keep a line from fraying
B. join lines of unequal size
C. stop off a line
⚓ D. shorten a line

SHEET BEND

010219/DG01774 CHAPMAN
Which knot is used to attach two different sized lines together?
A. Granny knot
⚓ B. Sheet bend
C. Square knot
D. Thief knot

010220/DG00605   **CHAPMAN; HOUSE**
You would properly secure a gantline to a bosun's chair with a _____.
A. fisherman's bend
B. bowline
⚓ C. double sheet bend
D. double blackwall hitch

TIMBER HITCH

010221/DG01624   **AMSM**
Which kind of hitch should you use to secure a spar?
A. Blackwall hitch
B. Stage hitch
⚓ C. Timber hitch
D. Two half hitches

FISHERMAN'S BEND

010222/DG01463   **CHAPMAN**
On a small boat, which knot is best suited for attaching a line to the ring of an anchor?
A. Clove hitch
B. Figure-eight knot
⚓ C. Fisherman's bend
D. Overhand knot

BECKET BEND

010223/DG01493   **CHAPMAN**
The knot used to join two lines of different diameter is a _____.
A. square knot
B. carrick bend
⚓ C. becket bend
D. sheepshank

010224/DG01614   **AMSM**
Which bend or knot is used to tie a small line to a larger one?
⚓ A. Becket bend
B. Bowline
C. Clove hitch
D. Lark's head

CARRICK BEND

010225/DG01473   **AMSM**
The "carrick bend" is used to _____.
A. add strength to a weak spot in a line
⚓ B. join two hawsers
C. be a stopper to transfer a line under strain
D. join lines of different sizes

010226/DG01483   **AMSM**
The knot used to join two lines or two large hawsers for towing is called a _____.
A. square knot
⚓ B. carrick bend
C. sheet bend
D. bowline

010227/DG01654   **AMSM**
Which knot should be used to bend two hawsers together for towing?
⚓ A. Double carrick bend
B. Fisherman's bend
C. Heaving line bend
D. Rolling hitch

ROLLING HITCH

010228/DG01644   **AMSM**
A rolling hitch can be used to _____.
A. make a temporary eye
B. mouse a hook
⚓ C. secure a line around a spar
D. shorten a line

010229/DG01784   **AMSM**
The "rolling hitch" could be used to _____.
A. join two lines of different sizes
B. join two lines of equal sizes
C. add strength to a weak spot in a line
⚓ D. act as a stopper to transfer a line under strain

BOWLINE

010230/DG01724   **AMSM**
A "bowline" is used to _____.
A. join lines of equal size
⚓ B. form a temporary eye (loop) at the end of a line
C. be a stopper
D. keep a line from fraying

010231/DG01863   **AMSM**
If a mooring line should part while you are tying up at a dock, you should make a temporary eye by tying a _____.
A. becket bend
B. clove hitch
⚓ C. bowline
D. square knot

010232/DG01117   **HOUSE**
The knot used to form the bridle at the standing part of a gantline rigged to a stage is a _____.
A. sheet bend
B. carrick bend
C. fisherman's bend
⚓ D. bowline

010233/DG01914   **CHAPMAN; AMSM**
You need to make a fixed loop at the end of a line in order to use the line as a mooring line. You have insufficient time to make a splice. Which knot should you use?
A. Clove Hitch
B. Fisherman's Bend
⚓ C. Bowline
D. Round-turn and two half hitches

FRENCH BOWLINE

010234/DG01513   **AMSM**
Which knot is suitable for hoisting an unconscious person?
A. Bowline in a bight
⚓ B. French bowline
C. Fisherman's loop
D. Spider hitch

010235/DG00129   **AMSM**
Which knot is suitable for hoisting an unconscious person?
A. Bowline on a bight
B. Fisherman's loop
⚓ C. French bowline
D. Spider hitch

010236/DG01503   **AMSM**
Which knot should be used to send a man over the side when he may have to use both hands?
A. Bowline
⚓ B. French bowline
C. Bowline on a bight
D. Running bowline

010237/DG01604   **AMSM**
Which knot would serve best as a safety sling for a person working over the side?
A. Bowline on a bight
⚓ B. French bowline
C. Jug sling
D. Lifting hitch

HALF HITCH

010238/DG01734   **CHAPMAN**
Which knot reduces the strength of a line by the LEAST amount?
A. Carrick bend
B. Square knot
C. Sheet bend
⚓ D. Bowline

MARLINE HITCH

010239/DG01142   **AMSM**
The hitch used to secure the standing part of a gantline to the horns of a stage is a _____.
⚓ A. marlinespike hitch
B. clove hitch
C. blackwall hitch
D. Killick hitch

010240/DG01143   **AMSM**
When rigging a stage, the standing part should be fastened to the horns of a stage with which of the following hitches?
A. Clove hitch
B. Timber hitch
⚓ C. Marlinespike hitch
D. Double blackwall hitch

SQUARE KNOT

010241/DG01764   **CHAPMAN**
The "square knot" is used for _____.
A. forming temporary eyes in lines
⚓ B. joining two lines of equal size
C. keeping line from unlaying or fraying
D. joining two lines of different size

SEIZING

010242/DG01664   **KNIGHTS**
A method used to make an eye in a bight of line where it cannot be spliced is known as _____.
A. braiding
B. plaiting
⚓ C. seizing
D. serving

010243/DG01684   **AMSM**
Temporary seizings on wire rope are made with _____.
A. marline
B. sail twine
C. tape
⚓ D. wire

010244/DG01674   **KNIGHTS**
Which is NOT a type of seizing?
A. Flat seizing
B. Racking seizing
C. Throat seizing
⚓ D. Tube seizing

010245/DG02990   **AMSM**

When cutting regular-lay wire rope, what is the minimum number of seizings to be placed on each side of the cut?

A. One
B. Two, and three on rope diameters over 1 inch
⚓ C. Three, and more on larger diameter wire ropes
D. Four

010246/DG02960   **KNIGHTS**

When cutting wire rope, seizings are put on each side of the cut. The seizings prevent the wire from unlaying and also _____.

⚓ A. maintain the original balance of the tension in the wires and strands
B. prevent moisture from entering between the wires at the cut end
C. forces lubricant from the core to protect the raw, cut end
D. All of the above

WHIPPINGS

010247/DG01694   **KNIGHTS**

A "whipping" is _____.

A. a messenger
B. a stopper for nylon line
C. a U-bolt for securing a cargo whip to the winch drum
⚓ D. turns of twine around a rope end

010248/DG00834   **KNIGHTS**

A whipping on a fiber line _____.

⚓ A. keeps the ends from fraying
B. strengthens it
C. protects your hands
D. becomes part of a splice

010249/DG01704   **KNIGHTS**

Whipping the bitter end of a fiber rope _____.

A. increases the circumference of the rope
B. makes for easier handling
⚓ C. prevents fraying of the bitter end
D. prevents moisture from entering the bitter end

SERVING

010250/DG00197   **WRIGHT**

Serving is _____.

A. marline or ratline wound along the grooves of a rope
B. narrow strips of light canvas or cotton cloth spiral-wrapped along the rope
⚓ C. marline tightly wound on the rope by means of a board or mallet
D. a splice made by laying the strand of one rope into the vacated grooves of another rope

DIAGRAM D030DG

010251/DG02075   **AMSM**

The knot lettered E is a _____. See Diagram D030DG

A. stopper hitch
B. blackwall hitch
⚓ C. timber and half hitch
D. bowline on a bight

010252/DG01517   **AMSM**

Which picture represents a timber hitch? See Diagram D030DG

⚓ A. E
B. F
C. N
D. U

010253/DG02225   **AMSM**

Which knot should be used to secure a line to a spar when the pull is perpendicular to the spar? See Diagram D030DG

A. E
⚓ B. F
C. N
D. P

010254/DG01960   **AMSM**

The knot lettered G in the illustration is a _____. See Diagram D030DG

A. round turn and two half hitches
⚓ B. fisherman's bend
C. timber hitch
D. barrel hitch

010255/DG01472   **AMSM**

Which knot represents a single becket bend? See Diagram D030DG

A. E
B. F
C. G
⚓ D. H

010256/DG01924   **AMSM**

The knot lettered I as shown is a _____. See Diagram D030DG

A. square knot
B. round knot
⚓ C. bowline on a bight
D. timber hitch

010257/DG01455   **AMSM**

Which letter represents a bowline on a bight? See Diagram D030DG

A. H
⚓ B. I
C. M
D. W

010258/DG01910   **AMSM**
The knot lettered J is a _____. See Diagram
D030DG
⚓ A. plain whipping
B. bowline
C. marline hitch
D. becket bend

010259/DG01427   **AMSM**
Which letter in illustration D030DG represents a plain
whipping? See Diagram D030DG
A. E
B. F
⚓ C. J
D. V

010260/DG02272   **AMSM**
Which knot is secure only when there is a strain on the
line? See Diagram D030DG
A. H
B. I
⚓ C. L
D. P

010261/DG01655   **AMSM**
Which knot represents a double blackwall hitch? See
Diagram D030DG
A. F
B. G
⚓ C. L
D. R

010262/DG02232   **AMSM**
The MAIN use of the knot lettered M is to
_____. See Diagram D030DG
⚓ A. marry two hawsers
B. form a temporary eye in the end of a line
C. secure a heaving line to a hawser
D. provide a seat for a man to work over the side

010263/DG01642   **AMSM**
Which illustration represents a carrick bend? See
Diagram D030DG
A. H
B. J
C. L
⚓ D. M

010264/DG02233   **AMSM**
The knot lettered N as shown is a _____. See
Diagram D030DG
A. timber hitch
B. rolling bowline
⚓ C. stopper
D. heaving line hitch

010265/DG01552   **AMSM**
Which picture represents a stopper hitch? See Diagram
D030DG
A. M
⚓ B. N
C. R
D. L

010266/DG02226   **AMSM**
The knot lettered O is a _____. See Diagram
D030DG
A. timber hitch
⚓ B. barrel hitch
C. carrick bend
D. blackwall hitch

010267/DG01595   **AMSM**
Which picture represents a barrel hitch? See Diagram
D030DG
⚓ A. O
B. U
C. E
D. P

010268/DG02217   **AMSM**
The knot lettered P is a _____. See Diagram
D030DG
⚓ A. rolling hitch
B. clove hitch
C. round turn and two half hitches
D. marline hitch

010269/DG02249   **AMSM**
Which knot should be used to secure a line to a spar
when the pull is parallel to the spar? See Diagram
D030DG
A. G
B. F
⚓ C. P
D. Q

010270/DG01895   **AMSM**
The knot lettered Q as shown is a _____. See
Diagram D030DG
A. square knot
B. clove hitch
⚓ C. bowline
D. round knot

010271/DG01802   **AMSM**
Which picture represents a bowline? See Diagram
D030DG
A. G
B. H
C. L
⚓ D. Q

010272/DG01886　　　　　　　　　　　AMSM
The knot lettered R is a _____. See Diagram D030DG
⚓ A. double becket bend
B. bowline
C. fisherman's bend
D. round turn and two half hitches

010273/DG01795　　　　　　　　　　　AMSM
Which knot represents a double sheet bend? See Diagram D030DG
A. F
B. L
⚓ C. R
D. T

010274/DG01097　　　　　　　　　　　HOUSE
Which of the knots, bends, or hitches shown in the illustration would you use to properly secure a bosun's chair to a gantline? See Diagram D030DG
A. I
B. P
⚓ C. R
D. X

010275/DG01083　　　　　　　　　　　HOUSE
Which of the knots, bends, or hitches shown in the illustration would you use to properly secure a bosun's chair to a gantline? See Diagram D030DG
A. G
B. I
C. Q
⚓ D. R

010276/DG01870　　　　　　　　　　　AMSM
The knot lettered S is a _____. See Diagram D030DG
A. bowline
⚓ B. blackwall hitch
C. half hitch
D. hook hitch

010277/DG01787　　　　　　　　　　　AMSM
Which picture represents a blackwall hitch? See Diagram D030DG
A. F
B. H
C. P
⚓ D. S

010278/DG01755　　　　　　　　　　　AMSM
Which knot shown is a French bowline? See Diagram D030DG
A. L
⚓ B. T
C. Q
D. W

010279/DG01849　　　　　　　　　　　AMSM
The knot lettered U is a _____. See Diagram D030DG
⚓ A. half hitch
B. round knot
C. becket bend
D. plain whipping

010280/DG01732　　　　　　　　　　　AMSM
Which picture in illustration D030DG represents a half hitch? See Diagram D030DG
⚓ A. U
B. S
C. K
D. H

010281/DG01842　　　　　　　　　　　AMSM
The knot shown lettered W is a _____. See Diagram D030DG
A. clove hitch
⚓ B. square knot
C. barrel hitch
D. stopper knot

010282/DG02224　　　　　　　　　　　AMSM
When improperly tied, which knot shown is called a granny or thief's knot? See Diagram D030DG
A. F
B. M
C. R
⚓ D. W

010283/DG01816　　　　　　　　　　　AMSM
Which picture shown represents a square knot? See Diagram D030DG
⚓ A. W
B. R
C. P
D. H

010284/DG01435　　　　　　　　　　　AMSM
Which letter shown represents a clove hitch? See Diagram D030DG
⚓ A. X
B. U
C. T
D. R

SPLICING FIBER & WIRE ROPE

SPLICING EQUIPMENT

010285/DG00614　　　　　　　　　　　AMSM
A fid is a _____.
A. mallet used when splicing wire rope
B. sharp pointed crow bar used to unlay wire rope
C. tapered steel pin used to separate wire rope
⚓ D. tapered wooden pin used when splicing heavy rope

010286/DG02600   **CHAPMAN**

A smooth, tapered pin, usually of wood, used to open up the strands of a rope for splicing is called a(n) _____.

A. batten
B. bench hook
C. awl
⚓ D. fid

010287/DG01653   **AMSM**

Which tool is used to open the strands of fiber lines when making an eye splice?
A. Belaying spike
⚓ B. Fid
C. Heaver
D. Pricker

010288/DG00624   **AMSM**

A serving mallet is used in _____.
⚓ A. covering wire or fiber rope
B. forcing fids into a line
C. dogging hatches
D. splicing lines

010289/DG01543   **AMSM**

Which is normally used to hold wire rope for splicing?
A. Come along
B. Jigger
⚓ C. Rigger's screw
D. Sealing clamp

010290/DG01484   **AMSM**

A metal eye spliced into a wire is called a _____.
A. cyclops
B. fish eye
⚓ C. thimble
D. chip

010291/DG02355   **BRADY**

The metal, teardrop-shaped object sometimes used within an eye splice is a _____.
A. grommet
B. reinforcement
C. splice form
⚓ D. thimble

010292/DG02325   **KNIGHTS**

Which line cannot be spliced?
A. Braided line with a hollow core
B. Double-braided line
⚓ C. Braided line with a solid core
D. Any line can be spliced

010293/DG02360   **AMSM**

Splices made in nylon should _____.
A. be long splices only
⚓ B. have extra tucks taken
C. be short splices only
D. be around a thimble

010294/DG02335   **CHAPMAN**

When two lines are spliced together, _____.
A. the size of the lines at the splice decreases
⚓ B. they are stronger than if knotted together
C. the overall strength of each line is increased
D. the bitter ends will resist rotting

010295/DG01563   **CHAPMAN**

Which statement about two lines spliced together is TRUE?
A. Splicing is used to increase the circumference of each line.
⚓ B. Splicing two lines together is stronger than knotting two lines together.
C. Splicing is used to increase the overall strength of the line.
D. Splicing is used to prevent rotting of the lines bitter end.

SHORT SPLICE

010296/DG01533   **KNIGHTS**

What is the best splice for repairing a parted synthetic fiber mooring line?
A. Liverpool splice
B. Locking long splice
C. Long splice
⚓ D. Short splice

010297/DG01623   **CHAPMAN**

A short splice in a line _____.
A. decreases the size of the line
B. should be used if the line is going through a block
C. should only be used in wire rope
⚓ D. doubles the size of the line

010298/DG01633   **CHAPMAN**

The strongest way to join the ends of two ropes is with a _____.
A. back splice
⚓ B. short splice
C. square knot
D. carrick bend

010299/DG01583   **CHAPMAN**

Which statement concerning a short splice is TRUE?
A. It is used to temporarily join two lines together.
⚓ B. A short splice is stronger than two lines joined by a knot.
C. A short splice decreases the diameter of the line.
D. None of the above

010300/DG01603   CHAPMAN; HOUSE; DODGE
Which weakens a line the LEAST?
A. Clove hitch
B. Long splice
⚓ C. Short splice
D. Square knot

LONG SPLICE

010301/DG01593   CHAPMAN; KNIGHTS
A long splice in a line _____.
⚓ A. is used in running rigging
B. doubles the size of the line
C. is only used on fiber rope
D. is very weak

010302/DG02345   AMSM
A splice that can be used in running rigging, where the line will pass through blocks, is a _____.
A. short splice
⚓ B. long splice
C. back splice
D. spindle splice

010303/DG01643   CHAPMAN
The splice designed to pass easily through a block is called a(n) _____.
A. eye splice
B. short splice
⚓ C. long splice
D. block splice

010304/DG02315   AMSM
Which splice is used to connect two separate lines together?
A. Back splice
B. Chain splice
C. Eye splice
⚓ D. Long splice

010305/DG01573   CHAPMAN
Which statement about splices is TRUE?
A. A back splice is used to permanently connect two lines together.
⚓ B. A long splice is used to connect two lines that will pass through narrow openings.
C. A short splice is used to temporarily connect two lines.
D. In splicing fiber rope, you would splice with the lay of the line.

EYE SPLICE

010306/DG01613   CHAPMAN
Which splice should you use in order to make a permanent loop in a line?
A. Back splice
⚓ B. Eye splice
C. Long splice
D. Short splice

WIRE SPLICING

010307/DG01494   AMSM
After splicing an eye in a piece of wire rope, the splice should be parceled and served to _____.
A. strengthen the line
B. increase its efficiency
⚓ C. prevent hand injury by covering loose ends
D. make the line more flexible

010308/DG01474   KNIGHTS
To find the distance the strands should be unlaid for an eye splice, multiply the diameter of the wire in inches by _____.
A. 12
B. 24
⚓ C. 36
D. 48

010309/DG01523   AMSM
When making a short splice in wire rope _____.
⚓ A. all tucks go against the lay
B. all tucks go with the lay
C. the first three wires are tucked against the lay and the last three go with the lay
D. the first three wires are tucked with the lay and the last three go against the lay

WIRE CLIPS

010310/DG02350   AMSM
A temporary wire eye splice made with three wire rope clamps will hold approximately what percentage of the total rope strength?
A. 20%
B. 50%
⚓ C. 80%
D. 99%

010311/DG01553   AMSM
The correct way to make an eye in a wire rope with clips is to place the clips with the _____.
A. first and third U-bolts on the bitter end and the second U-bolt on the standing part
B. first and third U-bolts on the standing part and the second U-bolt on the bitter end
⚓ C. U-bolts of all clips on the bitter end
D. U-bolts of all clips on the standing part

010312/DG02343   **PETEX**

When securing a hook to the end of a wire rope you should _____.

A. a bowline knot
B. a long splice
C. an overhand knot with a wire rope clip
⚓ D. wire rope clips with a thimble eye

DIAGRAM D058DG

010313/DG04444   **AMSM**

According to the illustration, which of the figures is the preferred method of forming a temporary eye splice using wire rope clips? See Diagram D058DG

A, A.
B. B.
⚓ C. C.
D. D.

010314/DG01352   **AMSM**

According to the illustration, which of the figures protects the stress bearing end of a wire rope from being crushed while forming a temporary eye splice using wire rope clips? (Diagram DG-0058) See Diagram D058DG

A. A.
B. B.
⚓ C. C.
D. All the above.

010315/DG01353   **AMSM**

When using wire rope clips to form a temporary eye in wire rope, you should _____. See Diagram D058DG

⚓ A. place the U-bolt of the wire rope clips on the dead end of the rope
B. check the clips after an hour of operation to determine if the clips loosened due to wire rope expansion
C. replace the entire wire rope if broken wires are detected around the clips
D. wire rope clips should never be used to form a temporary eye splice

WIRE ROPE SOCKETS

010316/DG03476   **BRADY**

The strongest method of forming an eye in wire rope is using _____.

A. three wire rope clamps
B. an eye splice with four or five tucks
C. a thimble fastened with four or five tucks
⚓ D. a wire rope socket attached with zinc

010317/DG02980   **NVIC**

What is a step in attaching a poured metal socket to a wire rope?

⚓ A. Etch the wire with acid.
B. Install a wire seizing on the wire that will be inside the socket.
C. Ensure the fiber core is well lubricated.
D. Pour molten babbitt metal into the socket.

010318/DG02970   **NVIC 2-80**

What material may be substituted for zinc when making a poured metal socket ending to a wire rope?

A. Lead
B. Babbitt
C. Solder
⚓ D. Nothing

010319/DG01364   **AMSM**

Which molten substance is poured into the basket of a wire rope socket being fitted to the end of a wire rope?

A. Babbitt
B. Bronze
C. Lead
⚓ D. Zinc

BLOCKS & TACKLE

WHIP (DISADVANTAGE)

010320/DG02230   **AMSM**

What is the name of tackle number 1? See Diagram D029DG

⚓ A. Whip
B. One-fold purchase
C. Gun tackle
D. Runner

GUN TACKLE (DISADVANTAGE)

010321/DG02199   **AMSM**

What is the name of tackle number 2? See Diagram D029DG

A. Whip
B. Onefold purchase
C. Single purchase
⚓ D. Gun tackle

SINGLE LUFF/HANDY-BILLY/WATCH TACKLE (DISADVANTAGE)

010322/DG01887   **AMSM**

A small light tackle with blocks of steel or wood that is used for miscellaneous small jobs is called a _____.

A. snatch block
B. threefold purchase
⚓ C. handy-billy
D. chockablock

010323/DG02190   **AMSM**

What is the name of tackle number 3? See Diagram D029DG

A. 1-2 purchase
B. Gun tackle
⚓ C. Single luff tackle
D. Double whip

TWO FOLD TACKLE (DISADVANTAGE)

010324/DG02182   **AMSM**

What is the name of tackle number 4? See Diagram D029DG

A. Double whip
B. Luff tackle
⚓ C. Two-fold purchase
D. 2-2 tackle

DOUBLE LUFF TACKLE (DISADVANTAGE)

010325/DG02173   **AMSM**

What is the name of tackle number 5? See Diagram D029DG

A. 3-2 purchase
⚓ B. Double luff tackle
C. Two-fold purchase
D. Four-fold whip

THREE FOLD TACKLE (DISADVANTAGE)

010326/DG02168   **AMSM**

What is the name of tackle number 6? See Diagram D029DG

A. Triple purchase
B. Clew garnet tackle
C. Boat falls
⚓ D. Threefold purchase

RUNNER (ADVANTAGE)

010327/DG02163   **AMSM**

What is the name of tackle number 7? See Diagram D029DG

⚓ A. Runner
B. Inverted whip
C. Whip
D. Single purchase

GUN TACKLE (ADVANTAGE)

010328/DG02147   **AMSM**

What is the name of tackle number 8? See Diagram D029DG

A. Parbuckle
⚓ B. Gun tackle
C. Single purchase
D. Single luff tackle

SINGLE LUFF/HANDY-BILLY/WATCH TACKLE (ADVANTAGE)

010329/DG02122   **AMSM**

What is the name of tackle number 9? See Diagram D029DG

A. Single purchase
B. One-two tackle
C. Double whip
⚓ D. Luff tackle

DOUBLE LUFF TACKLE (ADVANTAGE)

010330/DG02097   **AMSM**

What is the name of tackle number 11? See Diagram D029DG

A. Three-two purchase
⚓ B. Double luff tackle
C. Gun tackle
D. Topping lift

THREE FOLD TACKLE (ADVANTAGE)

010331/DG01997   **AMSM**

What is the name of tackle number 12? See Diagram D029DG

⚓ A. Threefold purchase
B. Davit tackle
C. Deck tackle
D. Gin tackle

SNATCH BLOCK

010332/DG02005   **MMOH**

A block that can be opened at the hook or shackle end to receive a bight of the line is a _____.

A. bight block
B. gin block
C. heel block
⚓ D. snatch block

010333/DG01803   **ENCY. NAUT. KNOW.**

A snatch block is a _____.

A. block used only with manila rope
B. chock roller
⚓ C. hinged block
D. strong block used for short, sharp pulls

010334/DG01813   **ENCY. NAUT. KNOW.**

A snatch block would most likely be used as a _____.

A. boat fall
⚓ B. fairlead
C. riding pawl
D. topping lift

BLOCK COMPONENTS

010335/DG02959   **SEATECH**
A metal ring on the bottom of a block, to which the standing part of a tackle is spliced, is known as a(n) _____.

⚓ A. becket
   B. loop
   C. swivel
   D. eye

010336/DG02061   **AMSM**
A sheave is a _____.
⚓ A. grooved wheel in a block
   B. line to hold a lifeboat next to the embarkation deck
   C. partial load of grain
   D. seaman's knife

010337/DG02341   **KNIGHTS**
The grooved wheel inside a block is called a _____.

   A. cheek
   B. gypsy
⚓ C. sheave
   D. drum

010338/DG01833   **AMSM**
The standing part of a tackle is _____.
   A. all the fall except the hauling part
   B. the hook that engages the weight to be moved
   C. that part to which power is applied
⚓ D. that part of the falls made fast to one of the blocks

BLOCK SIZE

010339/DG01713   **MMOH**
The cheek length of a block in inches should be about _____.

⚓ A. three times the circumference of a manila line
   B. five times the diameter of a manila line
   C. twice the diameter of its sheaves for manila line
   D. twenty times the diameter of a manila line

010340/DG01773   **MMOH**
What size block shell should be used with a 4-inch manila line?
   A. 8"
⚓ B. 12"
   C. 16"
   D. 24"

010341/DG01843   **MMOH**
The sheave diameter to be used with a 3-inch manila rope is _____.
   A. 3 inches
⚓ B. 6 inches
   C. 9 inches
   D. 12 inches

010342/DG03662   **PETEX**
Unless extremely flexible wire rope is used, the sheave diameter should always be as large as possible, but should never be less than _____.
⚓ A. 20 times the rope diameter
   B. 10 times the rope diameter
   C. 2 times the rope diameter
   D. the rope diameter

010343/DG01979   **AMSM**
What is a proper size block to use with a 3-inch circumference Manila line?
   A. At least a 12-inch sheave
⚓ B. 9-inch cheek, 6-inch sheave
   C. 8-inch cheek, any size sheave
   D. 6-inch cheek, 4-inch sheave

010344/DG02034   **AMSM; MMOH**
You are ordering a new block to use with a 3-inch circumference manila line. Which represents a proper size block for this line?
   A. 6-inch cheek, 4-inch sheave
   B. 8-inch cheek, any size sheave
⚓ C. 9-inch cheek, 6-inch sheave
   D. At least a 12-inch sheave

BLOCK & TACKLE OPERATIONS

010345/DG01733   **AMSM**
Separating both blocks of a tackle to prepare it for reuse is called _____.
   A. chockablocking
   B. out-hauling
⚓ C. over-hauling
   D. two-blocking

010346/DG01729   **MARINE CARGO OPS.**
The greatest strain, when lifting a load with the jumbo purchase, is on _____.
   A. all of the parts, dividing the load equally
⚓ B. the hauling part because it must absorb the frictional losses of all the sheaves
   C. the parts in the movable block
   D. the standing part because it is directly connected to the weight

010347/DG02020   **AMSM**
To facilitate passing the end of a large rope through a block, you could use a _____.
   A. gantline
   B. head line
⚓ C. reeving line
   D. sail line

010348/DG01753 AMSM
To reeve a right-angle threefold purchase start with the _____.
A. left sheave bottom block
B. left sheave top block
C. middle sheave top block
D. right sheave bottom block

010349/DG01893 MMOH
A block and tackle is "rove to advantage". This means that the _____.
A. blocks have been overhauled
B. hauling parts of two tackles are attached
C. hauling part leads through the movable block
D. hauling part leads through the standing block

010350/DG01568 AMSM
A tackle is "two blocked" when the blocks are _____.
A. equally sharing the load
B. jammed together
C. as far apart as possible
D. rove to the highest mechanical advantage

010351/DG01723 AMSM
What is meant by the term "two-blocked"?
A. The bottom block touches the top block.
B. The line has jumped the sheaves.
C. There are turns in the fall.
D. You have two blocks.

010352/DG01853 MMOH
A breeches buoy is being rigged from the shore to a stranded vessel. The initial shot line passed to the vessel is normally made fast to a _____.
A. hawser which is used to pass a tail-block and whip to the vessel
B. hawser with breeches buoy and harness attached
C. hawser which should be made fast to the vessel below the intended location of the tail-block
D. tail-block and whip which may be used to pass a hawser to the vessel

BLOCK & TACKLE MECHANICAL ADVANTAGE

010353/DG02041 AMSM (MA = 1); MMOH
Which tackle arrangement has the LEAST mechanical advantage?
A. Single whip
B. Gun tackle
C. Luff tackle
D. Twofold purchase

010354/DG02240 AMSM (MA = 1)
What is the mechanical advantage of tackle number 1? See Diagram D029DG
A. 0.5
B. 1.0
C. 1.5
D. 2.0

010355/DG02231 AMSM (MA = 2)
What is the mechanical advantage of tackle number 2? See Diagram D029DG
A. 0.5
B. 1.0
C. 2.0
D. 3.0

010356/DG02223 AMSM (MA =3)
What is the mechanical advantage of tackle number 3? See Diagram D029DG
A. 1
B. 2
C. 3
D. 4

010357/DG01923 AMSM (MA = 4)
Disregarding friction, a twofold purchase when rove to disadvantage has a mechanical advantage of _____.
A. 2
B. 3
C. 4
D. 5

010358/DG02216 AMSM (MA = 4)
What is the mechanical advantage, neglecting friction, of tackle number 4? See Diagram D029DG
A. 1
B. 2
C. 3
D. 4

010359/DG02211 AMSM (MA = 5)
What is the mechanical advantage, neglecting friction, of tackle number 5? See Diagram D029DG
A. 2.0
B. 4.0
C. 5.0
D. 5.5

010360/DG01879 AMSM (MA = 6)
What is the mechanical advantage of a threefold purchase when rove to disadvantage and neglecting friction?
A. 3
B. 4
C. 5
D. 6

010361/DG02194   **AMSM (MA = 6)**
What is the mechanical advantage of tackle number 6?
See Diagram D029DG
⚓ A. 6.0
  B. 5.5
  C. 5.0
  D. 3.0

010362/DG02186   **AMSM (MA = 2)**
What is the mechanical advantage of tackle number 7?
See Diagram D029DG
  A. 0.0
  B. 0.5
  C. 1.0
⚓ D. 2.0

010363/DG02169   **AMSM (MA = 3)**
What is the mechanical advantage of tackle number 8?
See Diagram D029DG
⚓ A. 3.0
  B. 1.5
  C. 1.0
  D. 0.5

010364/DG02159   **AMSM (MA =4)**
What is the mechanical advantage of tackle number 9?
See Diagram D029DG
  A. 1
  B. 2
  C. 3
⚓ D. 4

010365/DG02093   **AMSM (MA = 5)**
What is the mechanical advantage of tackle number 10?
See Diagram D029DG
  A. 4.0
  B. 4.5
⚓ C. 5.0
  D. 5.5

010366/DG02086   **AMSM (MA = 6)**
What is the mechanical advantage of tackle number 11?
See Diagram D029DG
  A. 7.0
⚓ B. 6.0
  C. 5.5
  D. 5.0

010367/DG02067   **AMSM (MA = 7)**
What is the mechanical advantage, neglecting friction,
of tackle number 12? See Diagram D029DG
  A. 3.0
  B. 5.5
  C. 6.0
⚓ D. 7.0

MULTI-PARTS BLOCK & TACKLE
MECHANICAL ADVANTAGE

010368/DG02254   **AMSM (MA = 4 x 5 = 20)**
You are using tackle number 4 to lift a weight. The
hauling part of this tackle is bent to the weight hook
(w) of tackle number 10. What is the mechanical
advantage of this rig? See Diagram D029DG
  A. 4
  B. 5
  C. 9
⚓ D. 20

010369/DG02243   **AMSM (MA = 4 x 6 = 24)**
You are using tackle number 4, as shown, to lift a
weight. The hauling part of this tackle is bent to the
weight hook of tackle number 11. What is the
mechanical advantage of this rig? See Diagram
D029DG
  A. 4
  B. 6
  C. 10
⚓ D. 24

010370/DG02221   **AMSM (MA = 5 x 3 = 15)**
You are using tackle number 5 to lift a weight. The
hauling part of this tackle is bent to the weight hook
(w) of tackle number 8. What is the mechanical
advantage of this rig? See Diagram D029DG
  A. 20
⚓ B. 15
  C. 10
  D. 5

010371/DG02229   **AMSM (MA = 5 x 4 = 20)**
You are using tackle number 5 to lift a weight. The
hauling part of this tackle is bent to the weight hook of
tackle number 9. What is the mechanical advantage of
this rig? See Diagram D029DG
⚓ A. 20
  B. 9
  C. 5
  D. 4

010372/DG02213   **AMSM (MA = 6 x 3 = 18)**
You are using tackle number 6 to lift a weight. The
hauling part of this tackle is bent to the weight hook
(w) of tackle number 8. Disregarding friction, what is
the mechanical advantage of this rig? See Diagram
D029DG
  A. 11
  B. 16
⚓ C. 18
  D. 24

010373/DG02196 **AMSM (MA = 5 x 4 = 20)**

You are using tackle number 10 to lift a weight. The hauling part of this tackle is bent to the weight hook (w) of tackle number 4. What is the mechanical advantage of this rig? See Diagram D029DG

  A. 24
⚓ B. 20
  C. 13
  D. 9

010374/DG02014 **AMSM (MA = 7 x 2 = 14)**

You are using tackle number 12, as shown, to lift a weight. The hauling part of this tackle is bent to the weight hook (w) of tackle number 2. What is the mechanical advantage of this rig? See Diagram D029DG

  A. 9
  B. 10
⚓ C. 14
  D. 21

SEAMANSHIP COMPUTATIONS

STRESS ON THE HAULING PART (NO FRICTION)

010375/DG01862 **AMSM**

How much force would be required to lift a weight of 200 lbs. using a gun tackle rigged to disadvantage (do not consider friction)?

  A. 50 lbs.
⚓ B. 100 lbs.
  C. 150 lbs.
  D. 200 lbs.

010376/DG01873 **AMSM**

How much weight can you lift by applying 100 lbs. of force to a twofold purchase rigged to disadvantage (do not consider friction)?

  A. 200 lbs.
  B. 300 lbs.
⚓ C. 400 lbs.
  D. 500 lbs.

STRESS ON THE HAULING PART (INCLUDING FRICTION)

010377/DG02255 **AMSM**

You are using tackle number 2 to lift a weight of 100 lbs. If you include 10 percent of the weight for each sheave for friction, what is the pull on the hauling part required to lift the weight? See Diagram D029DG

  A. 50 lbs.
  B. 55 lbs.
⚓ C. 60 lbs.
  D. 110 lbs.

010378/DG02239 **AMSM**

You are using tackle number 3 to lift a weight of 120 lbs. If you include 10 percent of the weight for each sheave for friction, what is the pull on the hauling part required to lift the weight? See Diagram D029DG

⚓ A. 52 lbs.
  B. 49 lbs.
  C. 40 lbs.
  D. 27 lbs.

010379/DG01693 **MMOH**

What is the stress on the hauling part when lifting a 4900 lbs. weight using a twofold purchase rove to least advantage? (Allow 10 percent of the weight per sheave for friction.)

  A. 980 lbs.
  B. 1225 lbs.
⚓ C. 1715 lbs.
  D. 1837 lbs.

010380/DG02219 **AMSM**

You are using tackle number 5 to lift a weight of 300 lbs. If you include 10 percent of the weight for each sheave for friction, what is the pull on the hauling part required to lift the weight? See Diagram D029DG

  A. 50 lbs.
  B. 75 lbs.
⚓ C. 90 lbs.
  D. 112 lbs.

010381/DG02185 **AMSM**

You are using tackle number 7 to lift a weight of 100 lbs. If you include 10 percent of the weight for each sheave for friction, what is the pull on the hauling part required to lift the weight? See Diagram D029DG

  A. 200 lbs.
  B. 150 lbs.
  C. 110 lbs.
⚓ D. 55 lbs.

010382/DG01982 **AMSM**

You are using tackle number 8 to lift a weight of 100 lbs. If you include 10 percent of the weight for each sheave for friction, what is the pull on the hauling part required to lift the weight? See Diagram D029DG

  A. 120 lbs.
  B. 55 lbs.
⚓ C. 40 lbs.
  D. 37 lbs.

010383/DG01703   **AMSM; KNIGHTS**
What is the stress on the hauling part when lifting a 4,200 lbs. weight using a threefold purchase rove to advantage? (Allow 10 percent of the weight per sheave for friction.)
A. 571.4
B. 715.2
⚓ C. 960.0
D. 1066.7

010384/DG01931   **AMSM**
You are using tackle number 12 to lift a weight of 300 lbs. If you include 10 percent of the weight for each sheave for friction, what is the pull on the hauling part required to lift the weight? See Diagram D029DG
A. 80 lbs.
⚓ B. 69 lbs.
C. 55 lbs.
D. 50 lbs.

BREAKING STRENGTH

010385/DG00734   **MMOH**
What is the computed breaking strength of a 4-inch manila line?
A. 5,280 lbs.
B. 7,700 lbs.
C. 12,200 lbs.
⚓ D. 14,400 lbs.

010386/DG01594   **AMSM**
What is the breaking strain of steel wire rope with a 5/8" diameter?
A. 1.0 tons
B. 6.6 tons
⚓ C. 9.6 tons
D. 15.6 tons

SAFETY FACTOR & SAFE WORKING LOAD

010387/DG01304   **AMSM**
A nylon line is rated at 12,000 lbs. breaking strain. Using a safety factor of 5, what is the safe working load (SWL)?
A. 2,000 lbs.
⚓ B. 2,400 lbs.
C. 12,000 lbs.
D. 60,000 lbs.

010388/DG00865   **AMSM**
A nylon line is rated at 15,000 lbs. breaking strain. Using a safety factor of 5, what is the safe working load (SWL)?
⚓ A. 3,000 lbs
B. 5,000 lbs
C. 15,000 lbs
D. 65,000 lbs

010389/DG00844   **AMSM**
Using a safety factor of five, determine the safe working load of a line with a breaking strain of 20,000 pounds.
⚓ A. 4,000
B. 5,000
C. 20,000
D. 100,000

010390/DG01213   **KNIGHTS**
What minimum size manila line is required to hold a weight of 932 pounds, if you use a safety factor of six?
A. 2.0"
⚓ B. 2.5"
C. 3.0"
D. 3.5"

010391/DG00724   **AMSM**
Using a safety factor of five, determine what is the safe working load for 3-1/2 inch manila line with a breaking stress of 4.9 tons.
A. 0.82 ton
⚓ B. 0.98 ton
C. 2.45 tons
D. 12.25 tons

010392/DG01044   **AMSM**
Using a safety factor of 6, determine the safe working load of a line with a breaking strain of 30,000 pounds.
A. 4,000 lbs.
⚓ B. 5,000 lbs.
C. 20,000 lbs.
D. 100,000 lbs.

010393/DG00714   **MARINE CARGO OPS.**
Using a safety factor of 6, determine the safe working load of manila line with a breaking stress of 8 tons.
A. 0.75 tons
B. 1.25 tons
⚓ C. 1.33 tons
D. 8.00 tons

010394/DG01314   **MMOH**
A wire rope rove through two single blocks with two parts at the moving block is used for a boat fall. The weight of the 100-person boat is 5 tons. Compute the required breaking strain. Safety Factor - 6, weight per person - 165 lbs., 10% friction per sheave (2 sheaves).
A. 18.30 tons B.S.
B. 20.29 tons B.S.
⚓ C. 22.27 tons B.S.
D. 24.31 tons B.S.

BREAKING STRENGTH/SAFETY FACTOR & REQIURED CHAIN SIZE

010395/DG01334   **MMOH**
Close link chain of not less the 3/4" (or the wire rope equivalent) is required for lashing deck cargoes of timber. What size flexible wire rope would provide the strength equivalent to 3/4" chain, using a safety factor of 5?
A. 9/16"
⚓ B. 1"
C. 1-1/4"
D. 1-3/8"

SAFE WORKING LOAD & REQUIRED SHACKLE SIZE

010396/DG03414   **SEATECH**
You are lifting a 3-ton weight with a single whip rove on a swinging boom set at an angle 20° to the horizontal. Use the formula for the size of a shackle with a safe working load and determine the minimum size shackle that should be used to secure the head block to the boom.
⚓ A. 1-3/8 inch
B. 1-1/2 inch
C. 1-5/8 inch
D. 1-3/4 inch

010397/DG03014   **SEATECH**
You are lifting a 3 ton weight with a single whip rove on a swinging boom set at an angle of 60° to the horizontal. Use the formula for the size of a shackle with a safe working load and determine the minimum size shackle that should be used to secure the head block to the boom.
A. 1-1/8 inch
⚓ B. 1-1/2 inch
C. 1-3/4 inch
D. 2 inch

010398/DG03116   **SEATECH**
You are lifting a 5-ton weight with a single whip rove on a swinging boom set at an angle of 20° to the horizontal. Use the formula for the size of a shackle with a safe working load and determine the minimum size shackle that should be used to secure the head block to the boom.
A. 1-3/8 inch
B. 1-1/2 inch
⚓ C. 1-3/4 inch
D. 1-7/8 inch

010399/DG03489   **SEATECH**
You are lifting a 5-ton weight with a single whip rove on a swinging boom set at an angle of 60° to the horizontal. Use the formula for the size of a shackle with a safe working load and determine the minimum size shackle that should be used to secure the head block to the boom?
A. 1 inch
B. 1-3/8 inch
C. 1-1/2 inch
⚓ D. 1-7/8 inch

SLING STRESS

010400/DG01749   **MARINE CARGO OPS.**
A sling is rigged on a piece of pipe weighing 1000 lbs. The angle between the sling legs is 140° and the legs are of equal length. What stress is exerted on each sling leg when the pipe is lifted?
A. 1318 lbs.
B. 1366 lbs.
C. 1414 lbs.
⚓ D. 1462 lbs.

FALL STRESS

010401/DG01739   **MARINE CARGO OPS.**
If two falls are attached to lift a one-ton load, what angle between the falls will result in the stress on each fall being equal to the load being lifted?
A. 60°
B. 75°
⚓ C. 120°
D. 150°

010402/DG01759   **MARINE CARGO OPS.**
The amount of strain on each runner of a married fall system lifting 2000 lbs. when the angle made by the legs is 90° would be _____.
A. 1000 lbs.
B. 1154 lbs.
⚓ C. 1414 lbs.
D. 2000 lbs.

010403/DG01769   **MARINE CARGO OPS.**
Two falls are supporting a 1.5 ton load. The port fall is at an angle of 40° from the vertical. The starboard fall is at an angle of 70° from the vertical. What is the stress on each fall?
⚓ A. Port 1.5 tons, starboard 1.0 tons
B. Port 1.5 tons, starboard 1.5 tons
C. Port 1.7 tons, starboard 1.3 tons
D. Port 1.7 tons, starboard 2.0 tons

DRY CARGO VESSEL OPERATIONS

DRY CARGO TERMINOLOGY & MEASURES

010404/DG00648　　　　　**ENCY. NAUT. KNOW.**
Bulk cargo refers to _____.
A. cargo which occupies a large volume of space
B. cargo which requires refrigeration
C. cargo which is very dense
⚓ D. homogeneous cargo not enclosed in a container

010405/DG02201　　　　　**CARGO HANDLING**
When referring to dry bulk cargoes, the term "flow state" _____.
A. designates the state of a commodity when the ship is heeled past the angle of repose
B. relates to the suitability of loading a cargo by flowing down inclined chutes
⚓ C. refers to the saturation of a dry bulk product with water to the point where it acts as a liquid
D. relates to the minimum granule size of a particular product where it will flow like a liquid at an angle of 30°

010406/DG02286　　　　　**MARINE CARGO OPS.**
Cargo that is highly susceptible to damage by tainting from odorous cargo is called _____.
A. clean cargo
⚓ B. delicate cargo
C. dry cargo
D. immune cargo

010407/DG00098　　　　　**MARINE CARGO OPS.**
A hygroscopic cargo is defined as a cargo _____.
⚓ A. capable of absorbing moisture in the form of a gas
B. capable of giving off moisture in the form of a liquid
C. that is shipped in a liquid state
D. that will ignite in contact with water

010408/DG02260　　　　　**MARINE CARGO OPS.**
Cargo that gives off fumes that may contaminate other cargo is known as a(n) _____.
A. delicate cargo
B. dirty cargo
C. toxic cargo
⚓ D. odorous cargo

010409/DG00058　　　　　**MARINE CARGO OPS.**
Odorous cargoes are those that _____.
A. are exceptionally dusty and leave a residue
B. are liquid but are in containers
C. are susceptible to damage by tainting
⚓ D. give off fumes that may damage other cargoes

010410/DG00068　　　　　**MARINE CARGO OPS.**
Odorous cargoes are those that _____.
A. are susceptible to damage by tainting
B. are exceptionally dusty and leave a residue
C. are liquid, but in containers
⚓ D. give off fumes that may damage other cargoes

010411/DG00128　　　　　**THOMAS**
Which is characteristic of a "special cargo"?
A. The cargo gives off toxic gases when heated.
B. Periodic inspection is required while in transit to prevent spoilage.
⚓ C. It is of high value or easily pilferable.
D. It must be stowed on deck.

010412/DG02248　　　　　**MARINE CARGO OPS.**
A "wet cargo" refers to _____.
A. a cargo that will be damaged if it gets wet
B. bulk liquids
C. cargoes that will cause condensation
⚓ D. liquids in containers

010413/DG02246　　　　　**MARINE CARGO OPS.**
Cargoes that might leak from containers are known as _____.
A. dirty cargoes
B. caustic cargoes
⚓ C. wet cargoes
D. bulk cargoes

010414/DG02782　　　　　**MARINE CARGO OPS.**
What is a wet cargo?
A. A liquid cargo carried in the deep tanks
⚓ B. A canned or bottled liquid such as beer
C. A cargo that contains hygroscopic moisture
D. A cargo particularly susceptible to damage by moisture

010415/DG02592　　　　　**SEATECH**
The internal volume of a cargo hold measured from the inside faces of the cargo battens, the lower side of the deck beams, and the top of the tank top ceiling is known as the _____.
A. gross tonnage
B. deadweight space
⚓ C. bale cubic
D. stowage area

010416/DG02742　　　　　**SEATECH**
The internal volume of a cargo hold measured from the inside of the side shell, the underside of the deck, and the tank top is known as the _____.
A. gross tonnage
B. deadweight space
C. measurement space
⚓ D. grain cubic

010417/DG00028 MARINE CARGO OPS.

The stowage factor for a cargo is based upon _____.

- A. one short ton
- B. one short metric ton
- ⚓ C. one long ton
- D. one long metric ton

010418/DG00048 MMOH

Which term describes goods having a stowage factor below 40?

- ⚓ A. Deadweight cargo
- B. Full-and-down cargo
- C. Heavy-lift cargo
- D. Measurement cargo

010419/DG00038 MARINE CARGO OPS.

A cargo that has a stowage factor over 40 is known as a _____.

- A. hygroscopic cargo
- ⚓ B. measurement cargo
- C. stowage cargo
- D. weight cargo

010420/DG00364 ENCY. NAUT. KNOW.

A long ton is _____.

- A. 1,000 pounds
- B. 2,000 pounds
- ⚓ C. 2,240 pounds
- D. 2,400 pounds

010421/DG03691 CHS

On the cargo manifest, the gross weight of a box containing cargo is the weight of the _____.

- A. cargo
- B. box
- ⚓ C. cargo and box
- D. rate weight

010422/DG02010 CHS

On the cargo manifest, the total weight of a box containing cargo is the _____.

- A. tare weight
- B. net weight
- ⚓ C. gross weight
- D. cargo weight

010423/DG00287 CHS

On the cargo manifest, the weight of the cargo inside a box is called _____.

- A. gross weight
- ⚓ B. net weight
- C. light weight
- D. rate weight

010424/DG00767 CHS

On the cargo manifest, the total weight of an empty cargo box is the _____.

- ⚓ A. tare weight
- B. net weight
- C. gross weight
- D. cargo weight

010425/DG00408 TABAK

What is the meaning of the term tare weight?

- A. Pounds of force necessary to damage a container
- B. Total weight of a container and contents
- ⚓ C. Weight of a container
- D. Weight of the contents of a container

010426/DG00222 THOMAS

A lot of special cargo of similar cartons, as shown, is to be loaded. What is the weight of the consignment? See Diagram D042DG

- A. 50 pounds
- B. 1100 pounds
- C. 1200 pounds
- ⚓ D. 1250 pounds

010427/DG01951 THOMAS

A case received for shipment is marked as shown. The portion of the symbol indicated by the letter A is _____. See Diagram D043DG

- ⚓ A. a stowage sequence marking
- B. the consignee's marking
- C. a stowage mark, showing the top of the case
- D. the symbol for toxic contents

TYPES OF STOWAGE

010428/DG00168 MARINE CARGO OPS.

Block stowage means _____.

- A. having the cargo on pallets
- ⚓ B. stowing all the cargo for a port in the same area
- C. using port marks on the cargo
- D. using separation cloths to separate different kinds of cargo

TYPES OF CARGO DAMAGE

010429/DG00108 MARINE CARGO OPS.

Damage to cargo caused by dust is known as _____.

- ⚓ A. contamination
- B. oxidation
- C. tainting
- D. vaporization

010430/DG00178   MMOH

Which can be prevented only by segregating two lots of cargo into separate holds?

A. Contamination of dry cargo by a wet cargo
B. Contamination of a clean cargo by a dirty cargo
C. Contamination of a food cargo by an odorous cargo
D. Overcarriage, overstowage, and short landing

010431/DG02234   MARINE CARGO OPS.

Keeping certain cargoes separated because of their inherent characteristics is known as _____.

A. overstowage
B. segregation
C. spot loading
D. cargo typing

010432/DG02178   MARINE CARGO OPS.

Segregation of cargoes refers to _____.

A. separating cargoes so that the inherent characteristics of one cannot damage the other
B. separating cargoes by destination
C. classifying cargoes according to their toxicity
D. listing the cargoes in order of their flammability

010433/DG00118   MARINE CARGO OPS.

Damage to cargo caused by fumes or vapors from liquids, gases, or solids is known as _____.

A. contamination
B. oxidation
C. tainting
D. vaporization

010434/DG02209   MARINE CARGO OPS.

Certain cargoes must be segregated because of their _____.

A. inherent characteristics
B. weight
C. destination
D. danger to humans

010435/DG00078   MMOH

Which is an example of cargo damage caused by inherent vice?

A. Sublimation of chemicals
B. Heating of grain
C. Stevedore damage
D. Wear and tear

010436/DG00088   MMOH

Which is an example of cargo damage caused by inherent vice?

A. Tainting
B. Wear and tear
C. Stevedore damage
D. Heating of grain

CARGO HANDLING EQUIPMENT

010437/DG03606   PETEX

A spreader bar is used to _____.

A. increase the lifting capacity
B. increase the lifting radius
C. protect the slings
D. protect the upper part of a load

010438/DG00240   AMSM

The best way to lift many small articles aboard your vessel is with a _____.

A. pallet
B. barrel hook
C. spreader
D. snotter

010439/DG02558   AMSM

A sling is a device used in _____.

A. hoisting cargo aboard a vessel
B. hoisting personnel aboard a vessel
C. securing a small boat to a large vessel
D. hoisting the anchor

010440/DG03486   PETEX

When a two-leg sling is used to lift a load, a sling 40 feet long is better than one of 30 feet because the _____.

A. tension in the sling legs is less
B. load can be lifted higher
C. sling will be easier to attach
D. sling will be easier to remove

CARGO GEAR INSPECTIONS

010441/DG01424   *46 CFR 91.25; MMOH; MARINE CARGO OPS.

A wire rope for a 10-ton boom on a vessel shows signs of excessive wear and must be replaced. What safety factor should be used when ordering a new wire?

A. 4
B. 5
C. 6
D. 7

010442/DG01549   *46 CFR 91.25; MMOH; MARINE CARGO OPS.

On your vessel, a wire rope for the cargo gear shows signs of excessive wear and must be replaced. In ordering a new wire for this 10-ton boom, what safety factor should you use?

A. Three
B. Five
C. Six
D. Seven

010443/DG00349   ***46 CFR 91.25-25**
The periodic weight testing of a vessel's cargo booms may be performed by the _____.
A. U.S. Coast Guard
B. American Bureau of Shipping
C. National Cargo Bureau
D. Society of Naval Architects and Marine Engineers

010444/DG00321   ***46 CFR 91.25-25**
Which is a TRUE statement concerning the examining of cargo equipment at the time of a vessels Inspection for Certification?
A. Cargo booms must be weight tested at this time by the U.S. Coast Guard.
B. Cargo booms must be weight tested at this time by the American Bureau of Shipping.
C. Cargo booms must be weight tested at this time by the National Cargo Bureau.
D. No test at this time is required.

010445/DG01609   ***46 CFR 91.37-1 (d); MMOH**
For vessels fitted with cargo gear, an initial test of the units under a proof load shall be conducted. Subsequent tests and exams of the same nature shall be carried out at what time interval?
A. 1 year
B. 3 years
C. 4 years
D. 5 years

010446/DG01319   ***46 CFR 91.37-3 (e); AMSM; MMOH**
In relation to cargo gear, what does "SWL" mean?
A. Safe working load
B. Ship's working lift
C. Starboard wing lift
D. Stress, weight, load

010447/DG01619   ***46 CFR 91.37-5; MMOH**
A periodic thorough examination of the cargo gear proves satisfactory. What percentage of the total gear must be dismantled to determine actual internal condition?
A. None
B. 10%
C. 25%
D. 100%

010448/DG01639   ***46 CFR 91.37-35**
All wire rope used in shipboard cargo gear must be identified and described in a certificate. The certificate shall certify all of the following EXCEPT the _____.
A. date of the test
B. load at which a test sample broke
C. name of the vessel
D. number of strands and of wires in each strand

010449/DG01384   ***46 CFR 91.37-35 (a)**
The wire rope used for cargo handling on board your vessel has a safe working load of eight tons. It shall be able to withstand a breaking test load of _____.
A. 32 tons
B. 40 tons
C. 48 tons
D. 64 tons

010450/DG01659   ***46 CFR 91.37-45;**
MARINE CARGO OPS.
The safe working load for the assembled cargo gear and the minimum angle to the horizontal for which the gear is designed shall be marked on the _____.
A. deck
B. head of the boom
C. heel of the boom
D. mast or king post

010451/DG01649   ***46 CFR 91.37-45;**
MARINE CARGO OPS.
What is required to be stenciled at the heel of a cargo boom?
A. Maximum angle of elevation permitted
B. Date of the last quadrennial test
C. Safe working load
D. Maximum load when doubled up

DRY CARGO GEAR

CARGO BOOMS

010452/DG04071   **INT. MARITIME DICTIONARY**
The head block is located _____.
A, at the base of the boom
B. at the head of the boom
C. at the head of the mast
D. on top of the jack staff

010453/DG01379   **ENCY. NAUT. KNOW.**
The heel block is located _____.
A. at the base of the boom
B. at the cargo hook
C. near the midships guy
D. near the spider band

010454/DG01389   **ENCY. NAUT. KNOW.**
A band or collar on the top end of a boom to which the topping lift, midships guy, and outboard guys are secured, is called the _____.
A. collar band
B. guy band
C. pad eye collar
D. spider band

010455/DG01399   MARINE CARGO OPS.
Which part of a cargo boom has the greatest diameter?
A. Head
B. Middle
C. Heel
D. It has the same diameter along its complete length.

010456/DG00245   MARINE CARGO OPS.
The fitting that allows a boom to move freely both vertically and laterally is called the _____.
A. swivel
B. lizard
C. spider band
D. gooseneck

010457/DG01369   AMSM
What is meant by "spotting the boom"?
A. Lowering it into a cradle
B. Placing it in a desired position
C. Spotting it with wash primer and red lead
D. Two-blocking it

010458/DG02921   AMSM
The process of lowering a boom to a horizontal position and onto its deck support is called _____.
A. spotting a boom
B. collaring a boom
C. cradling a boom
D. toppling a boom

010459/DG02532   SEATECH
For a given weight of cargo, the stress on the heel block of a cargo boom _____.
A. increases as the cargo closes the head while hoisting
B. increases if the cargo runner is doubled up
C. decreases as the boom is topped to a greater angle
D. is determined by the thrust stresses on the boom

010460/DG01809   MARINE CARGO OPS.
The greatest horizontal stress between the heads of the booms in the yard and stay rig occurs when the load is in such a position that the _____.
A. falls are at an equal angle to the horizontal
B. stay fall is vertical
C. stay fall is at a greater angle to the horizontal than the yard fall
D. yard fall is at a greater angle to the horizontal than the stay fall

010461/DG04088   SEATECH
With a given load on the cargo hook, the thrust on a cargo boom _____.
A, increases as the angle to the horizontal increases
B. increases as the angle to the horizontal decreases
C. is greatest at an angle of 45° and decreases as the boom is raised or lowered
D. is least at an angle of 45° and increases as the boom is raised or lowered

010462/DG03632   SEATECH
You are lifting a one-ton weight with a swinging boom. When comparing the stresses on the rig with the boom at 20° to the horizontal to the stresses when the boom is at 60° to the horizontal, which statement is TRUE?
A. The thrust on the boom is greater at 60°.
B. The stress on the topping lift is greater at 60°.
C. The stress on the heel block is less at 20°.
D. The stress on the head block is less at 60°.

010463/DG03726   SEATECH
You are lifting a one-ton weight with a swinging boom. When comparing the stresses on the rig with the boom at 20° to the horizontal to the stresses when the boom is at 60° to the horizontal, which statement is TRUE?
A. The angle of elevation does not change the stresses in the masthead fairlead for the topping lift.
B. The stress on the head block is greater at 60°.
C. The stress on the heel block is greater at 60°.
D. The thrust on the boom is greater at 20°.

010464/DG03840   SEATECH
You are lifting a one-ton weight with a swinging boom. When comparing the stresses on the rig with the boom at 20° to the horizontal to the stresses when the boom is at 60° to the horizontal, which statement is true?
A. The thrust on the boom is greater at 20°.
B. The stress on the topping lift is greater at 60°.
C. The stress on the heel block is less at 60°.
D. The change in angle of elevation has no effect on the stresses in the head block.

010465/DG03652   SEATECH
You are lifting a one-ton weight with a swinging boom. When comparing the stresses in the rig with the boom at 20° to the horizontal to the stresses when the boom is at 60° to the horizontal, which statement is TRUE?
A. The stress on the topping lift is greater at 60°.
B. The thrust on the boom is greater at 20°.
C. The stress on the heel block is less at 20°.
D. The stress on the masthead fairlead for the topping lift is greater at 20°.

GUYS & VANGS

010466/DG01209   **MARINE CARGO OPS.**
When cargo is being worked using a Burton or married fall system, which part of the cargo gear is most likely to fail?
A. Boom
B. Gooseneck
⚓ C. Guy tackle
D. Topping lift

010467/DG01459   **MARINE CARGO OPS.**
When handling cargo, the majority of cargo gear breakdowns is due to _____.
A. compression bending of the boom
B. extension failure of the boom
⚓ C. guy failures
D. topping lift failures

010468/DG01799   **MARINE CARGO OPS.**
The maximum theoretical stress that can be developed on a guy in a yard and stay rig is limited by the _____.
⚓ A. lifting capacity of the winch
B. location of the boom
C. position of the guy
D. weight of the load

TOPPING LIFT

010469/DG01289   **MARINE CARGO OPS.**
What would you use to adjust the height of a cargo boom?
A. Lizard
B. Spanner guy
⚓ C. Topping lift
D. Working guy

010470/DG00292   **MARINE CARGO OPS.**
Stress on the topping lift of a swinging boom can be reduced by _____.
A. rigging a back stay
⚓ B. raising the boom
C. increasing the mechanical advantage of the cargo purchase
D. taking all slack out of the preventer

010471/DG03938   **SEATECH**
With a given load on the cargo hook, tension in a single span topping lift _____.
A. increases as the boom's angle to the horizontal increases
B. is at a maximum when the boom is at a 45° angle to the horizontal
⚓ C. increases as the boom's angle to the horizontal decreases
D. decreases as the boom's angle to the horizontal decreases

010472/DG01299   **MARINE CARGO OPS.**
Which part of a conventional cargo gear rig provides for vertical control and positioning of a boom?
A. Cargo whip
B. Gooseneck fitting
C. Spider band
⚓ D. Topping lift

010473/DG01269   **ENCY. NAUT. KNOW.**
What is meant by the term "topping the boom"?
A. Lowering the boom
⚓ B. Raising the boom
C. Spotting the boom over the deck
D. Swinging the boom athwartships

CARGO FALLS & RUNNERS

010474/DG01559   ***46 CFR 41.37-50 (a); MMOH**
It is permissible to place an eye splice in wire rope used as cargo gear providing the splice is made using _____.
A. two tucks with whole strands and one tuck with one-half strand
⚓ B. three tucks with whole strands and two tucks with 1/2 the wire cut from the tucking strand
C. three tucks with whole strands
D. two tucks with whole strands and three tucks with half strands

010475/DG01579   ***46 CFR 41.37-50 (a); MMOH**
What is the minimum standard for making an eye splice in a wire to be used as cargo gear?
⚓ A. Make three tucks with full strands, remove half the wires from each strand, and make two more tucks.
B. Make four tucks in each strand, cut away every other strand, and make two more tucks with each remaining strand.
C. Make four tucks with each full strand.
D. Make six tucks with each strand, removing a few wires from each strand as each additional tuck is made.

010476/DG00235   **KNIGHTS**
Which ending is NOT acceptable in a wire rope that is free to rotate when hoisting?
A. Poured socket
⚓ B. Liverpool eye splice
C. Eye formed with a pressure clamped sleeve
D. Eye formed by clips

010477/DG01709   **MMOH**
The force acting on a single cargo runner which is vertically lifting or lowering a load is greatest when _____.
⚓ A. decelerating when lowering the load
B. decelerating when raising the load
C. lowering the load at constant speed
D. raising the load at constant speed

CARGO WINCHES

010478/DG01509   **MARINE CARGO OPS.**

If an electric cargo winch is being used to lift a draft of cargo and the engine room loses all power, which will occur?

A. A pawl, forced by a spring mechanism, will engage the teeth of the bull gear and hold the load.

B. An electromagnetic brake will hold the load where it is suspended.

C. The load will fall rapidly to the deck unless the foot brake is engaged.

D. The load will slowly lower to the deck under control of the drag of the winch motor.

010479/DG01005   **MARINE CARGO OPS.**

Which device is designed to automatically hold the load if power should fail to an electric winch?

A. Pneumatic brake

B. Electromagnetic brake

C. Hand brake

D. Motor controller

010480/DG01539   **MARINE CARGO OPS.**

Electric cargo winches have an overload safety device which normally cuts the current to the winch motor _____.

A. after torque causes line pull to exceed the rated capacity of the winch

B. before the line pull reaches the rated capacity of the winch

C. when the line pull reaches the breaking strength of the fall

D. before the safe working load of the fall is reached

010481/DG01030   **MARINE CARGO OPS.**

If an attempt is made to hoist a load that exceeds the capacity of an electric winch, an overload safety device causes a circuit breaker to cut off the current to the winch motor _____.

A. when the line pull reaches the rated winch capacity

B. after the line pull exceeds the rated winch capacity

C. after a short build-up of torque

D. immediately

010482/DG01045   **MARINE CARGO OPS.**

If a hydraulic pump on a winch accidentally stops while hoisting, the load will stay suspended because _____.

A. a check valve will close and prevent reverse circulation

B. a centrifugal counterweight counteracts the force of gravity.

C. the electric pump motor will cut out

D. the control lever will move to the stop position

SHIPBOARD CRANES

010483/DG02453   **PETEX**

On a ship's crane, the load chart relates the allowable load to the combination of the boom length and _____.

A. winch speed

B. boom strength

C. load radius

D. cable strength

010484/DG02463   **PETEX**

The crane manufacturer's load chart should be posted at or near the _____.

A. crane pedestal

B. wire rope locker

C. main deck

D. crane control console

010485/DG04875   ***46 CFR 91.37-45**

The crane manufacturer's operating tables are posted near the _____.

A, crane pedestal

B. wire-rope locker

C. main deck

D. crane controls

010486/DG02220   **PETEX**

The load chart of a crane enables the operator to combine the load radius with boom length to determine the _____.

A. maximum counter weight required

B. minimum horsepower required

C. hoist rope strength

D. allowable load

010487/DG04036   ***46 CFR 91.37-45 (b)**

When a cargo boom or crane is rated at varying capacities, there will be a table at the controls which relates safe working load to _____.

A, winch speed

B. boom strength

C. load radius

D. cable strength

010488/DG01977   **PETEX**

On a crane, the boom indicator tells the operator what angle the boom angle is compared to the _____.

A. vertical position

B. horizontal position

C. boom stop angle

D. minimum radius angle

010489/DG03446   **PETEX**

The best way to determine if a load is within maximum lift limits is to use _____.

- A. a boom angle indicator
- B. a load weight indicator
- C. material invoices for shipping weights
- D. prior experience with similar lifts

010490/DG02455   **PETEX**

The boom indicator on a crane will indicate the _____.

- A. length of the boom
- B. angle of the boom
- C. lifting capacity of the boom
- D. direction of the boom

010491/DG03682   **PETEX**

The boom indicator tells the operator at what angle the boom is compared to the _____.

- A. horizontal position of the boom
- B. vertical position of the boom
- C. horizontal position of the load being lifted
- D. vertical position of the load being lifted

010492/DG04212   **NAVSEA OPS. HDBK.**

What is another name for the boom of a crane?

- A, Lift
- B. Rider
- C. Jib
- D. All of the above

010493/DG04258   **NAVSEA OPS. HDBK.**

Which statement is TRUE regarding the operation of a crane?

- A, The crane jib is raised and lowered by the luffing winch.
- B. The crane jib is raised and lowered by the hoisting winch.
- C. The cargo block is raised and lowered by the luffing winch.
- D. The crane jib is raised and lowered by a jibing winch.

010494/DG03454   **PETEX**

For any given pedestal crane, when the boom is lengthened, the lifting capacity is _____.

- A. unchanged
- B. increased
- C. eliminated
- D. decreased

010495/DG01981   **PETEX**

The boom stops on a pedestal crane prevent the boom from _____.

- A. being raised too high
- B. swinging at sea
- C. overloading when not in use
- D. being lowered too low

010496/DG03712   **PETEX**

When should a crane boom-up so high that the boom hits the stops?

- A. Only if the load has not exceeded the limit at that angle
- B. Only if the load contains non-hazardous materials
- C. Only if necessary to perform a given lift
- D. Never

010497/DG04273   **NAVSEA OPS. HDBK.**

During which condition should the operator of a pedestal crane shutdown operations?

- A, Bunkering
- B. High winds
- C. Potable water spill on deck
- D. More than 3° list

010498/DG04240   **NAVSEA OPS. HDBK.**

It is the responsibility of the crane operator to, at all times, be aware of the location of the _____.

- A, load
- B. hook
- C. boom
- D. All of the above

010499/DG04238   **MARINE CARGO OPS.**

Most pedestal crane power is provided by _____.

- A, Electro-hydraulic units
- B. Steam units
- C. Independent internal combustion power units
- D. All of the above

010500/DG04211   **NAVSEA OPS. HDBK.**

Pedestal cranes have limit switches to restrict movement of which function(s)?

- A, Hoist upper & lower limits
- B. Luff travel limits
- C. Rider block hoist upper & lower limits
- D. All of the above

010501/DG04210   **NAVSEA OPS. HDBK.**

Pedestal cranes have limit switches to restrict the movement of which function?

- A, Luff rate limits
- B. Slew travel limits
- C. Swivel power limits
- D. Slew rate limits

010502/DG04209   **NAVSEA OPS. HDBK.**

Pedestal cranes have limit switches to restrict the movement of which function?

- A, Slew travel limits
- B. Turntable limits
- C. Luff travel limits
- D. All of the above

010503/DG04246   **MARINE CARGO OPS.**

What does "level-luffing" accomplish during crane operations?

A, It prevents the load from swinging when the boom level is adjusted.

B. Less power is needed when topping the boom with a load on the hook.

C. It maintains the height of the load above the deck.

⚓ D. All of the above

010504/DG04213   **NAVSEA OPS. HDBK.**

What does a jib refer to on a crane?

⚓ A, Boom

B. Topping lift

C. Control cab

D. Liftline

010505/DG04214   **NAVSEA OPS. HDBK.**

What does a jib refer to on a crane?

⚓ A, Boom

B. Topping lift

C. Control cab

D. Slewing control

010506/DG04245   **MARINE CARGO OPS.**

What is meant by the term "level-luffing" a crane?

⚓ A, Luffing while the load remains at a constant height

B. Maintaining the boom at a constant height

C. Slewing the boom left or right in a level planet

D. None of the above

010507/DG04244   **MARINE CARGO OPS.**

What is meant by the term "luffing the boom" of a crane?

A, Stopping the boom

⚓ B. Topping or lowering the boom

C. Moving the boom left or right

D. All of the above

010508/DG04237   **MARINE CARGO OPS.**

What is used to power modern pedestal cranes?

A, Steam

B. Water

⚓ C. Hydraulics

D. All of the above

010509/DG04243   **MARINE CARGO OPS.**

What is/are the advantage(s) of cranes over conventional cargo booms?

A, Cranes are able to pick up and drop loads over a greater spotting area

B. Increased safety because the deck is clear of running and standing rigging

C. Simplicity of operation of the crane by its operator

⚓ D. All of the above

010510/DG04241   **NAVSEA OPS. HDBK.**

What should be given, as a minimum, to personnel who are involved in crane cargo handling?

⚓ A. Protective head gear, gloves, and steel-toed safety shoes

B. A survival suit for work on the stern or side port

C. A life preserver for going aloft to work on the crane

D. All of the above

010511/DG04272   **NAVSEA OPS. HDBK.**

Which action should be taken immediately by the operator of a pedestal crane, if crane control is lost?

A, Increase power to the crane to regain control.

B. Place control levers in opposite positions.

⚓ C. Let go of both control levers and return to the neutral positions.

D. Check the circuit breakers.

010512/DG04249   **NAVSEA OPS. HDBK.**

Which action(s) are included in crane operations?

A, Pre-operation of the anchor windlass

B. Preparing steam on deck

⚓ C. Luff, slew, and hoist operations

D. All of the above

010513/DG04250   **NAVSEA OPS. HDBK.**

Which action(s) is/are included in crane operations?

A, Pre-operation checks and start-up

B. Removing booms from stowage

C. Luff, slew, and hoist operations

⚓ D. All of the above

010514/DG04251   **NAVSEA OPS. HDBK.**

Which action(s) is/are included in crane operations?

A, Single-mode set-up & operation

B. Twin-mode set-up & operation

C. Normal boom stowage and shutdown operation

⚓ D. All of the above

010515/DG04252   **NAVSEA OPS. HDBK.**

Which action(s) is/are included in crane operations?

A, Normal boom stowage and shutdown operations

B. Emergency shutdown operation

C. Removing booms from stowage

⚓ D. All of the above

010516/DG04269   **NAVSEA OPS. HDBK.**

Which action(s) should the operator of a pedestal crane take if crane control is lost?

A, Let go of both control levers and return to neutral position.

B. Press the emergency stop.

C. Notify the mate on watch.

⚓ D. All of the above

010517/DG04270   **NAVSEA OPS. HDBK.**

Which immediate action should the operator of a pedestal crane take if crane control is lost?

⚓ A, Let go of both control levers and return to neutral position.

B. Call the engine room.

C. Disconnect the power to the pedestal.

D. Call the electrician.

010518/DG04271   **NAVSEA OPS. HDBK.**

Which immediate action should the operator of a pedestal crane take if crane control is lost?

A, Sound the general alarm.

⚓ B. Return the control levers to the neutral positions.

C. Notify port security.

D. Hold the control levers all the way down.

010519/DG04204   **MARINE CARGO OPS.**

Which of the following statements is FALSE concerning cranes being installed on the centerline of vessels?

⚓ A, A centerline crane can never be operated in tandem.

B. One crane is able to work one end of two adjacent hatches.

C. These cranes are more economical and weigh less than outboard-mounted cranes.

D. One crane is able to work both sides of the ship.

010520/DG04247   **NAVSEA OPS. HDBK.**

Which of the following statements is TRUE regarding crane operations?

A, Radio communications allow the crane operator to disregard the use of hand signals.

⚓ B. The crane operators and signalman must be familiar with the correct hand signals.

C. The forward cranes can be operated from the bridge.

D. The aft cranes can be operated from the aft steering station.

010521/DG04203   **MARINE CARGO OPS.**

Which of the following statements is/are FALSE concerning cranes being installed on the centerline of vessels?

A, One crane is able to work both sides of the ship.

B. One crane is able to work one end of two adjacent hatches.

⚓ C. A centerline crane can never work more than one hatch.

D. All of the above

010522/DG04202   **MARINE CARGO OPS.**

Which of the following statements is/are TRUE concerning cranes being installed on the centerline of vessels?

A, One crane is able to work both sides of the ship.

B. One crane is able to work one end of two adjacent hatches.

C. They are more economical and weigh less.

⚓ D. All of the above

010523/DG04248   **NAVSEA OPS. HDBK.**

Which of the following statements is/are TRUE regarding crane operations?

⚓ A, The crane operator and signalman must be familiar with hand signals.

B. The cranes can be operated from shoreside.

C. The cranes can be operated from the bridge.

D. All of the above

010524/DG04259   **NAVSEA OPS. HDBK.**

Which statement is FALSE regarding the operation of a crane?

A, The crane jib is raised and lowered by the luffing winch.

B. The cargo block is raised and lowered by the hoisting winch.

⚓ C. The cargo block is raised and lowered by the luffing winch.

D. None of the above

010525/DG04265   **NAVSEA OPS. HDBK.**

Which statement(s) is/are FALSE concerning crane cargo operations?

A, Lifting points on all equipment must be safely checked prior to commencing a lift.

⚓ B. Cargo loaded into vehicles and/or containers prior to lifting need not be secured.

C. Never exceed crane manufacturer's limits concerning the safe working loads of cargo jibs.

D. All the above

010526/DG04264   **NAVSEA OPS. HDBK.**

Which statement(s) is/are TRUE concerning crane cargo operations?

A, Lifting points on all equipment need not be checked prior to commencing a lift.

B. Cargo loaded into vehicles and/or containers prior to lifting need not be secured.

⚓ C. Never exceed crane manufacturer's limits concerning the safe working loads of cargo jibs.

D. All the above

010527/DG04262   **NAVSEA OPS. HDBK.**

Which statement(s) is/are TRUE concerning crane cargo operations?

A, Do not exceed rated load capacity of crane and container spreader or slings.

B. During any cargo handling operation, the safety of personnel is paramount.

C. Cargo handlers must be outfitted with adequate protection from personal injury.

⚓ D. All the above

010528/DG04263   **NAVSEA OPS. HDBK.**

Which statement(s) is/are TRUE concerning crane cargo operations?

A, Lifting points on all equipment must be safely checked prior to commencing a lift.

B. Cargo loaded into vehicles and/or containers prior to lifting needs to be properly secured so as to prevent shifting during transport.

C. Never exceed crane manufacturer's limits concerning the safe working loads of cargo jibs.

⚓ D. All the above

010529/DG04260   **NAVSEA OPS. HDBK.**

Which statement(s) is/are TRUE regarding the operation of a crane?

⚓ A, The load is handled by the hoisting winch and cargo block.

B. The crane jib is raised and lowered by the hoisting winch.

C. The cargo block is raised and lowered by the luffing winch.

D. All the above

010530/DG04278   **NAVSEA OPS. HDBK.**

Which wire rope purchase(s) is/are optional with a 30-Ton pedestal crane?

A, Hoist

B. Luff

⚓ C. Rider block

D. All of the above

010531/DG04261   **NAVSEA OPS. HDBK.**

Who should be notified prior to starting up a crane?

A, The pumpman

B. The stevedore foreman

⚓ C. The engine room

D. All the above

010532/DG04280   **NAVSEA OPS. HDBK.**

Which statement is FALSE concerning a tagline as used with a 30-ton pedestal crane?

⚓ A. Taglines are wire rope purchases that raise and lower the jib.

B. Taglines are wire ropes for horizontal positioning of the rider block.

C. Taglines can be fastened to corners of vehicles or containers.

D. The crane might not have taglines installed in its rigging system.

010533/DG04279   **NAVSEA OPS. HDBK.**

Which statement is TRUE concerning a tagline as used with a 30-ton pedestal crane?

A, Taglines are wire rope purchases that raise and lower the jib.

⚓ B. Taglines are wire ropes payed-out or taken-in for horizontal positioning of the rider block.

C. Taglines can be can be fastened to the corners of the jib when lifting containers.

D. The taglines are wire rope purchases that raise and lower the topping lift.

010534/DG04281   **NAVSEA OPS. HDBK.**

Which statement is TRUE concerning a tagline as used with a 30-ton pedestal crane?

A, Taglines are wire rope purchases that raise and lower the jib.

B. Taglines are wire ropes payed-out or taken-in for positioning the crane pedestal.

⚓ C. Taglines can be fastened to the corners of vehicles or containers during cargo operations.

D. Taglines are wire rope purchases that raise and lower the topping lift.

010535/DG04282   **NAVSEA OPS. HDBK.**

Which statement is TRUE concerning a tagline as used with a 30-ton pedestal crane?

A, Taglines are wire rope purchases that raise and lower the jib.

B. Taglines can be fastened to the corners of the jib when lifting containers.

⚓ C. The crane might not have taglines installed in its rigging system.

D. The taglines are wire rope purchases that raise and lower the topping lift.

010536/DG04277   **NAVSEA OPS. HDBK.**

Which wire rope purchases may be used with a 30-ton pedestal crane?

A, Hoist

B. Luff

C. Rider block

⚓ D. All of the above

DIAGRAM D045DG

010537/DG04223   **NAVSEA OPS. HDBK.**
What does item "A" refer to in this illustration of a 30-ton pedestal crane? See Diagram D045DG
A, Boom luffing falls
B. Cargo hoist falls
C. Remote block tagline system
D. Slewing cable

010538/DG04383   **NAVSEA OPS. HDBK.**
What does item "A" refer to in this illustration of a 30-ton pedestal crane? See Diagram D045DG
A, Boom luffing falls
B. Cargo hoist falls
C. Remote block tagline system
D. Slewing cable

010539/DG04222   **NAVSEA OPS. HDBK.**
What does item "C" refer to in this illustration of a 30-ton pedestal crane? See Diagram D045DG
A, Equalizing beam
B. Hoist fall spreader
C. Rider block
D. Block/hook assembly

010540/DG04382   **NAVSEA OPS. HDBK.**
What does item "C" refer to in this illustration of a 30-ton pedestal crane? See Diagram D045DG
A, Equalizing beam
B. Hoist fall spreader
C. Rider block
D. Block/hook assembly

010541/DG04221   **NAVSEA OPS. HDBK.**
What does item "D" refer to in this illustration of a 30-ton pedestal crane? See Diagram D045DG
A, Heel block
B. Gin block
C. Rider block
D. Hook block

010542/DG04381   **NAVSEA OPS. HDBK.**
What does item "D" refer to in this illustration of a 30-ton pedestal crane? See Diagram D045DG
A, Heel block
B. Gin block
C. Rider block
D. Hook block

010543/DG04226   **NAVSEA OPS. HDBK.**
What does item "E" refer to in this illustration of a 30-ton pedestal crane? See Diagram D045DG
A, Tagline
B. Electric cable
C. Cargo snaking wire
D. Hook release cable

010544/DG04225   **NAVSEA OPS. HDBK.**
What does item "G" refer to in this illustration of a 30-ton pedestal crane? See Diagram D045DG
A, Mast
B. Pillar
C. Turntable
D. Pedestal

010545/DG04224   **NAVSEA OPS. HDBK.**
What does item "K" refer to in this illustration of a 30-ton pedestal crane? See Diagram D045DG
A, Manual slewing cables
B. Rider block taglines
C. Jib luffing cables
D. Cargo snaking cables

DIAGRAM D047DG

010546/DG04231   **MARINE CARGO OPS.**
The 30 ton capacity pedestal cranes shown in the illustration can lift a maximum weight of how many tons in the single mode? See Diagram D047DG
A, 15 tons
B. 30 tons
C. 60 tons
D. 120 tons

DIAGRAM D049DG

010547/DG04232   **MARINE CARGO OPS.**
The 30 ton capacity pedestal cranes shown in the illustration can lift a maximum weight of how many tons in the twin mode? See Diagram D049DG
A, 15 tons
B. 30 tons
C. 60 tons
D. 120 tons

DIAGRAM D051DG

010548/DG04233   **MARINE CARGO OPS.**
The 30 ton capacity pedestal cranes shown in the illustration can lift a maximum weight of how many tons when two cranes are married together in twin with the other pair of cranes at the opposite end of the hatch? See Diagram D051DG
A, 30 tons
B. 60 tons
C. 90 tons
D. 120 tons

010549/DG04274   **NAVSEA OPS. HDBK.**
During which condition should the operator of a pedestal crane shutdown operations?
A, Bunkering barge alongside
B. Potable water spill on deck
C. Crane hydraulic hose bursts
D. Trim greater than 4 feet

010550/DG04275 **NAVSEA OPS. HDBK.**

During which condition should the operator of a pedestal crane shutdown operations?

A, Lightning
B. High winds
C. Fire aboard
⚓ D. All of the above

010551/DG04276 **NAVSEA OPS. HDBK.**

During which condition should the operator of a pedestal crane shutdown operations?

A, Lightning in the vicinity
B. An approaching squall line
C. A fire on the pier
⚓ D. All of the above

010552/DG04239 **MARINE CARGO OPS.**

Which safety precaution(s) should be observed during crane operations?

A, Checking for proper lifting from beneath the load during cargo operations
⚓ B. Using the proper slings or other lifting devices during cargo operations
C. Relaying communications to port agents on the pier during cargo hoists
D. All of the above

010553/DG04215 **NAVSEA OPS. HDBK.**

The electrical components for each single crane are installed in its _____.

A, crane house
B. machinery base
C. turntable
⚓ D. All of the above

010554/DG04234 **NAVSEA OPS. HDBK.**

What describes a tandem crane lift?

A, Single crane hoisting 30 tons
B. Two cranes on a single pedestal hoisting 60 tons
⚓ C. Two sets of twin cranes hoisting 120 tons
D. All of the above

010555/DG04235 **NAVSEA OPS. HDBK.**

What describes a twin crane lift?

A, Single crane hoisting 30 tons
⚓ B. Two cranes on a single pedestal hoisting 60 tons
C. Two sets of twin cranes hoisting 120 tons
D. All of the above

010556/DG04236 **NAVSEA OPS. HDBK.**

What is another description for a tandem crane lift?

A, Single crane hoisting 30 tons
B. Twin cranes hoisting 60 tons
⚓ C. Quad lift hoisting 120 tons
D. All of the above

010557/DG04242 **MARINE CARGO OPS.**

What is the advantage of the tandem working arrangement of pedestal cranes when operating cargo?

A, The cranes enable the handling of heavy cargoes without shoreside assistance
B. The cargo discharge can be accomplished with controlled pendulation
C. The cargo discharge can be performed in port or at anchor
⚓ D. All of the above

010558/DG04208 **NAVSEA OPS. HDBK.**

What is the purpose of the equalizing beam aboard a crane vessel?

A, It allows for rotation of the hook in the single mode.
⚓ B. It is required to "twin-up" 30-ton pedestal cranes.
C. It is used to pick up light loads.
D. It is used to rigidly connect two cranes.

010559/DG04256 **NAVSEA OPS. HDBK.**

Which of the following statement(s) is/are FALSE regarding a twin pedestal crane set?

A, The cranes may be operated independently.
B. The cranes may be interconnected for twin operation.
⚓ C. The cranes are powered by independent internal combustion power units.
D. All of the above

010560/DG04255 **NAVSEA OPS. HDBK.**

Which of the following statement(s) is/are TRUE regarding a twin pedestal crane set?

A, The cranes may be operated independently.
B. The cranes may be interconnected for twin operation.
C. When twinned, the crane rotation on the foundation assembly is unlimited.
⚓ D. All of the above

010561/DG04253 **NAVSEA OPS. HDBK.**

Which of the following statement(s) is/are TRUE regarding twin pedestal cranes?

A, Each single boom is of the partial-level luffing type and is capable of limited rotation.
B. A slew drive system provides for rotation of each crane.
C. An independent slew drive system rotates the turntable.
⚓ D. All of the above

010562/DG04254   NAVSEA OPS. HDBK.
Which of the following statement(s) is/are TRUE regarding twin pedestal cranes?
A, Each single boom is of the partial-level luffing type and is capable of limited rotation.
B. A slew drive system provides for rotation of each crane.
C. Maintenance logs and records are to be kept for each crane.
⚓ D. All of the above

010563/DG04257   NAVSEA OPS. HDBK.
Which of the following statement(s) is/are TRUE regarding twin pedestal cranes?
A, A slew drive system provides for rotation of each crane.
B. An independent slew drive system rotates the turntable.
C. Each crane is supplied with luff, hoist, and slew functions for crane load handling.
⚓ D. All of the above

010564/DG04205   NAVSEA OPS. HDBK.
Which piece of equipment is required to "twin-up" 30-ton pedestal cranes aboard a crane vessel?
A, Portable power swivel
⚓ B. Equalizing beam
C. 20-foot container spreader
D. 40-foot container spreader

010565/DG04207   NAVSEA OPS. HDBK.
Which piece of equipment is required to "twin-up" 30-ton pedestal cranes aboard a crane vessel?
A, Portable power swivel
B. 20-foot container spreader
C. 40-foot container spreader
⚓ D. None of the above

010566/DG04206   NAVSEA OPS. HDBK.
Which piece(s) of equipment is/are required to "twin-up" 30-ton pedestal cranes aboard a crane vessel?
⚓ A, Equalizing beam
B. Portable power swivel
C. 20-foot container spreader
D. All of the above

010567/DG04267   MARINE CARGO OPS.
Which statement is TRUE concerning the tandem working arrangement of pedestal cranes when completing a quad lift?
⚓ A, The discharge is slow due to the size of the cargo and all the cranes working together.
B. The cargo discharge can be accomplished with controlled pendulation.
C. The cargo discharge can be performed in port or at anchor.
D. The cranes enable the handling of heavy cargoes without shoreside assistance.

010568/DG04268   MARINE CARGO OPS.
Which statement is TRUE concerning the tandem working arrangement of pedestal cranes when completing a quad lift?
A. The cargo discharge can be accomplished with controlled pendulation.
⚓ B. The discharge is slow due to the size of the cargo and all the cranes working together.
C. The cargo discharge can be performed in port or at anchor.
D. The cranes enable the handling of heavy cargoes without shoreside assistance.

010569/DG04266   MARINE CARGO OPS.
Which statement is TRUE concerning the tandem working arrangement of pedestal cranes when completing a quad lift?
A, The cranes require shoreside assistance to handle heavy cargoes.
B. The cargo discharge cannot be accomplished without pendulation.
C. The cargo discharge cannot be performed at anchor.
⚓ D. The discharge is slow due to the size of the cargo and all the cranes working together.

010570/DG04227   NAVSEA OPS. HDBK.
Which of the following is/are the component(s) of a twin crane set as shown? See Diagram D047DG
A, Foundation assembly
B. Turntable assembly
C. Crane house assembly
⚓ D. All of the above

010571/DG04228   NAVSEA OPS. HDBK.
Which of the following is/are the component(s) of a twin crane set as shown? See Diagram D047DG
A, Boom assembly
B. Hook block assembly
C. Operator's cab
⚓ D. All of the above

010572/DG04229   NAVSEA OPS. HDBK.
Which of the following is/are the optional component(s) of a twin crane set as shown? See Diagram D047DG
A, Boom assembly
B. Hook block assembly
⚓ C. Rider block tagline system
D. All of the above

010573/DG04230   **NAVSEA OPS. HDBK.**
Which of the following is/are the optional component(s) of a twin crane set as shown? See Diagram D047DG
A, Boom assembly
B. Hook block assembly
C. Crane house assembly
⚓ D. Rider block tagline system

CRANE HAND SIGNALS

010574/DG03192   **API RP 2D, *See Cargo Notes**
How should you signal the crane operator to hoist?
⚓ A. With forearm vertical and forefinger pointing up, move hand in small horizontal circles.
B. With arm extended downwards and forefinger pointing down, move hand in small horizontal circles.
C. Extend arm with fingers closed and thumb pointing upward.
D. Place both fists in front of body with the thumbs pointing upward.

010575/DG04062   **API RP 2D, *See Cargo Notes**
The signal man assisting the crane operator has his forearm vertical, forefinger pointing up, and moves his hand in a small horizontal circle. This is the signal to
_____.
A, swing
B. lower
⚓ C. hoist
D. extend

010576/DG02886   **API RP 2D, *See Cargo Notes**
How should you signal the crane operator to lower?
A. With forearm vertical and forefinger pointing up, move hand in small horizontal circles.
⚓ B. With arm extended downwards and forefinger pointing down, move hand in small horizontal circles.
C. Extend arm and point finger in the direction to move the boom.
D. Extend arm with thumb pointing downward, and flex fingers in and out.

010577/DG04034   **API RP 2D, *See Cargo Notes**
The signal man assisting the crane operator has his arm extended downwards, forefinger pointing down, and moves his hand in small horizontal circles. This is the signal to _____.
⚓ A, lower
B. swing
C. hoist
D. extend

010578/DG03146   **API RP 2D, *See Cargo Notes**
How should you signal the crane operator to use the main hoist?
A. Use one hand to give any motion signal, and place the other hand motionless in front of the hand giving the motion signal.
B. Extend arm with the thumb pointing up and flex the fingers in and out for as long as the load movement is desired.
C. First tap your elbow with one hand, and then proceed to use regular signals.
⚓ D. First tap the top of your head with your fist, and then proceed to use regular signals.

010579/DG03404   **API RP 2D, *See Cargo Notes**
The signal man assisting the crane operator first taps the top of his head with his fist and then proceeds to use regular signals. This is the signal to _____.
A. use the whip line
⚓ B. use the main hoist
C. use the auxiliary line
D. proceed slowly

010580/DG02908   **API RP 2D, *See Cargo Notes**
How should you signal the crane operator to use the whip line?
A. Extend arm with the thumb pointing up, and flex the fingers in and out for as long as the load movement is desired.
⚓ B. First tap your elbow with one hand, and then proceed to use regular signals.
C. First tap the top of your head with your fist, and then proceed to use regular signals.
D. Use one hand to give any motion signal, and place the other hand motionless in front of the hand giving the motion signal.

010581/DG03382   **API RP 2D, *See Cargo Notes**
The signal man assisting the crane operator first taps his elbow with one hand and then proceeds to use regular signals. This is the signal to _____.
A. use the main hoist
B. proceed slowly
C. increase speed
⚓ D. use the whip line

010582/DG03108   **API RP 2D, *See Cargo Notes**
How should you signal the crane operator to raise the boom?
A. Extend arm with the thumb pointing up and flex the fingers in and out.
B. Place both fists in front of the body with the thumbs pointing upward.
C. With forearm vertical and forefinger pointing up, move hand in small horizontal circles.
⚓ D. Extend arm with fingers closed and point thumb upward.

010583/DG03562   API RP 2D, *See Cargo Notes
The signal man assisting a crane operator has his arm extended with his fingers closed and thumb pointing upward. This is the signal to _____.
- A. raise the boom
- B. raise the hook
- C. raise the boom and hook
- D. check the boom stop

010584/DG03052   API RP 2D, *See Cargo Notes
How should you signal the crane operator to lower the boom?
- A. With arm extended and fingers closed, point thumb downward.
- B. With arm extended downwards and forefinger pointing down, move hand in small horizontal circles.
- C. Extend arm with the palm down, and hold this position rigidly.
- D. With hands clasped in front of your body.

010585/DG03352   API RP 2D, *See Cargo Notes
The signal man assisting the crane operator has his arm extended, his fingers closed, and his thumb pointing downward. This is the signal to _____.
- A. hoist the load
- B. raise the boom
- C. lower the boom
- D. lower the load

010586/DG02942   API RP 2D, *See Cargo Notes
How should you signal the crane operator to move slowly?
- A. Use one hand to give any motion signal, and place the other hand motionless in front of the hand giving the motion signal.
- B. Extend arm with the thumb pointing up, and flex the fingers in and out for as long as the load movement is desired.
- C. First tap your elbow with one hand and then proceed to use regular signals.
- D. First tap the top of your head with your fist and then proceed to use regular signals.

010587/DG03326   API RP 2D, *See Cargo Notes
The signal man assisting the crane operator uses one hand to give any motion signal and places the other hand motionless in front of the hand giving the motion signal. This is the signal to _____.
- A. move slowly
- B. increase speed
- C. proceed with caution
- D. stop

010588/DG02928   API RP 2D, *See Cargo Notes
How should you signal the crane operator to raise the boom and lower the load?
- A. Extend arm with the palm down and hold this position rigidly.
- B. Place both fists in front of your body with thumbs pointing toward each other.
- C. Clasp hands in front of your body.
- D. Extend arm with the thumb pointing up, and flex the fingers in and out for as long as the load movement is desired.

010589/DG03286   API RP 2D, *See Cargo Notes
The signal man assisting the crane operator has his arm extended, with the thumb pointing up, and is flexing his fingers in and out for as long as the load movement is desired. This is the signal to _____.
- A. lower the boom and raise the load
- B. raise the boom and lower the load
- C. lower the boom and lower the load
- D. raise the boom and raise the load

010590/DG03164   API RP 2D, *See Cargo Notes
How should you signal the crane operator to lower the boom and raise the load?
- A. Extend arm and point finger in the direction to move the boom.
- B. Extend arm with thumb pointing downward and flex fingers in and out.
- C. With forearm vertical and forefinger pointing up, move hand in small horizontal circles.
- D. With arm extended downwards and forefinger pointing down, move hand in small horizontal circles.

010591/DG03206   API RP 2D, *See Cargo Notes
The signal man assisting a crane operator has his arm extended, thumb pointing downwards, flexing fingers in and out. This is the signal to _____.
- A. lower the boom and raise the load
- B. lower the load and raise the boom
- C. raise the boom and lower the load
- D. raise the load and lower the boom

010592/DG03062   API RP 2D, *See Cargo Notes
How should you signal the crane operator to swing?
- A. With both arms extended out and palms down, move arms back and forth.
- B. With arm extended downwards and forefinger pointing down, move hand in small horizontal circles.
- C. Extend arm and point finger in the direction to move the boom.
- D. Place both fists in front of the body with the thumbs pointing outward.

010593/DG03252   API RP 2D, *See Cargo Notes

The signal man assisting the crane operator has his arm extended and is pointing his finger in the direction to move the boom. This is the signal to _____.

A. extend
B. lower
C. hoist
⚓ D. swing

010594/DG02982   API RP 2D, *See Cargo Notes

How should you signal the crane operator to stop?

A. Place both fists in front of your body with the thumbs pointing outward.
B. With both arms extended out and palms down, move arms back and forth.
⚓ C. Extend arm with the palm down and hold this position rigidly.
D. Clasp hands in front of your body.

010595/DG03232   API RP 2D, *See Cargo Notes

The signal man assisting the crane operator has his arm extended with the palm down and holds this position rigidly. This is the signal to _____.

A. hoist
B. swing
⚓ C. stop
D. lower

010596/DG04072   API RP 2D, *See Cargo Notes

How should you signal the crane operator to stop in an emergency?

A, Extend arm with the palm down and hold this position rigidly.
B. Place clasped hands in front of your body.
⚓ C. Extend arm and move hand rapidly right and left with the palm down.
D. Place both fists in front of the body with the thumbs pointing outward.

010597/DG03516   API RP 2D, *See Cargo Notes

The signal man has both arms extended out, palms down, and is moving his arms back and forth. This is the signal for _____.

A. keep lifting
B. swing right
C. swing left
⚓ D. emergency stop

010598/DG03436   API RP 2D, *See Cargo Notes

The signal man assisting the crane operator has one hand occupied and one fist in front of his chest with the thumb pointing outward and is tapping his chest with the heel of his fist. This is the signal to _____.

A. extend the boom
B. lower the boom
⚓ C. retract the boom
D. hoist the boom

010599/DG03024   API RP 2D, *See Cargo Notes

How should you signal the crane operator to dog everything?

A. Place both fists in front of your body with thumbs pointing toward each other.
⚓ B. Clasp hands in front of your body.
C. Extend arm with the palm down and hold this position rigidly.
D. Extend arm with the thumb pointing up, and flex the fingers in and out.

010600/DG03172   API RP 2D, *See Cargo Notes

The signal man assisting the crane operator has his hands clasped in front of his body. This is the signal to _____.

⚓ A. dog everything
B. stop
C. stand-by
D. prepare for signal

HEAVY LIFT BOOMS

010601/DG00247   KNIGHTS

The main advantage and chief characteristic of a Steulchen boom is that it can be _____.

A. operated by one winchman
B. cradled on deck
⚓ C. swung from one hatch to the adjacent hatch
D. collared to the mast

DRY CARGO STOWAGE

BREAK BULK CARGO

010602/DG00008   MARINE CARGO OPS.

What is NOT an advantage of filler cargo?

⚓ A. Overcarriage is reduced or eliminated.
B. Dunnage costs are reduced.
C. Voids in the cargo stow are filled.
D. The hold space has maximum utilization.

010603/DG02386   MARINE CARGO OPS.

A vessel has an amidships superstructure. Which location would be most suitable for main deck stowage of vehicles?

A. On top of #1 hatch
B. Beside the hatches, forward of the midships house
C. On top of the aftermost hatch on the vessel
⚓ D. On top of the hatch immediately aft of the midships house

010604/DG02376 MARINE CARGO OPS.

A vessel has an amidships superstructure. Which location would be most suitable for on-deck stowage of automobiles?

A. On top of #1 hatch

B. Beside the hatches, forward of the midships house

C. On top of the hatch immediately forward of the midships house

⚓ D. On top of the hatch immediately aft of the midships house

REFRIGERATED CARGO

010605/DG02218 MARINE CARGO OPS.

If reefer spaces are not properly cleaned prior to loading cargo, it will most likely cause _____.

⚓ A. mold to develop on commodities

B. malfunction of the refrigeration equipment

C. contamination of the insulation in the space

D. All of the above

010606/DG00256 MARINE CARGO OPS.

When fruit is carried as refrigerated cargo, the most frequent cause of its being infected at the discharge port is _____.

A. leaks in the ship's refrigeration system

⚓ B. improper cleaning of the cargo spaces

C. carriage at the wrong temperature

D. improper precooling of the cargo spaces

010607/DG02244 MARINE CARGO OPS.

If you are loading fruit in reefer spaces and you notice that the fruit is beginning to mold, you should _____.

A. carry the cargo at a cooler temperature than originally planned

⚓ B. write up exceptions on the cargo

C. refuse to carry the cargo

D. discharge CO2 into the compartment after loading

010608/DG00958 THOMAS

You are in a tropical port. The refrigeration machinery on a container loaded with air-cooled fruit fails. It cannot be repaired for 18 to 24 hours. Which step should you take to reduce the temperature rise and spoilage of the fruit?

A. Discharge a cylinder of nitrogen into the container

⚓ B. Shade the container and periodically hose it down

C. Seal any ventilation openings and add dry ice

D. Spread ice over the top layer and in any voids within the container

010609/DG00188 MARINE CARGO OPS.

Which cargoes require strips of common building lathe as dunnage in order to carry away heat generated by the cargo?

A. Canned soups packaged in crates

B. Cardboard cartons of shoes

C. Paper products packaged in rolls

⚓ D. Refrigerated fruit that is ripening

010610/DG00378 MMOH

In preparation for receiving chilled reefer cargo, the reefer space has been precooled for over twenty-four hours. Loading may begin when the space has been cooled to a temperature between _____.

A. -10° F (-23° C) and +10° F (-12° C)

B. 12° F (-11° C) and 20° F (-7° C)

⚓ C. 28° F (-2° C) and 40° F (4° C)

D. 42° F (6° C) and 55° F (13° C)

DRY BULK CARGO

010611/DG00138 MARINE CARGO OPS.

Which vessel is most likely to be loaded full but not down?

A. A bulk carrier loaded with heavy ore

B. A bulk carrier loaded with steel

⚓ C. A break bulk vessel loaded with palletized cargo

D. A tanker loaded with heavy grain

010612/DG00618 MARINE CARGO OPS.

When considering a vessel's stability, which spaces in a general cargo vessel are the best locations for the carriage of bulk grain?

⚓ A. Deep tanks

B. Lower holds

C. Lower holds at the ends of the vessel

D. 'Tween-decks

010613/DG00628 MARINE CARGO OPS.

Before loading bulk grain, bilge wells must be covered to _____.

A. add strength to the bilge well strainer

B. permit rapid flow of water to the bilge wells

⚓ C. prevent cargo sifting into the bilge wells

D. prevent oil, water, or other liquid from reaching the cargo

010614/DG02582 THOMAS

What is usually NOT required in preparing a hold for reception of a bulk grain cargo?

A. Remove residue of previous cargo.

B. Remove loose rust and scale.

⚓ C. Steam clean areas obstructed by structural members.

D. Spray or fumigate any insect colonies.

010615/DG00638   **MARINE CARGO OPS.**

Ship's officers should check every cargo compartment after it is filled with bulk grain to ensure _____.

A. all lighting circuits are energized

⚓ B. all void spaces are filled

C. the correct grade of cargo has been loaded

D. the heavier grade is in the lower hold

010616/DG00658   **MARINE CARGO OPS.**

When carrying a full or nearly full load of bulk ore in a general cargo type vessel which has engine spaces amidships, the cargo in each hold should be trimmed so that the bulk of the cargo lies _____.

A. along the centerline

B. toward the forward bulkhead of the forward holds and toward the after bulkhead of the after holds

⚓ C. toward the after bulkhead of the forward holds and the forward bulkhead of the after holds

D. toward the after bulkhead of all holds

010617/DG03069   **IKS**

Atmospheres laden with coal dust or grain dust caused by loading these cargoes _____.

A. require loading operations to be shut down until the atmosphere clears

B. are toxic to human life

C. are subject to spontaneous combustion

⚓ D. may be explosive in some concentrations

010618/DG02952   **KEMP CARGO; TAYLOR**

Spontaneous heating of coal rapidly accelerates at the approximate minimum temperature of _____.

A. 88° F

⚓ B. 100° F

C. 111° F

D. 119° F

010619/DG04028   **THOMAS**

Which statement about the carriage of coal is true?

A, Most problems with spontaneous combustion will occur within 72 hours of loading and after that the risk decreases.

B. Wet coal is more liable to spontaneous heating than dry coal.

C. Coal absorbs nitrogen from the air which reacts with methane and causes spontaneous heating.

⚓ D. Freshly worked coal is more dangerous than weathered coal.

010620/DG02979   **MMOH**

Which statement about shipping coal is TRUE?

A. Anthracite will generate more methane than bituminous coal.

B. Coal should not be shipped while wet.

⚓ C. Coal should be surface ventilated to remove methane gas.

D. The methane gas generated by coal will react with moisture on the ship's structure and accelerate corrosion.

010621/DG03012   **KEMP CARGO**

Which statement about the ventilation of bulk coal is TRUE?

A. Coal should not be ventilated; all oxygen should be excluded from the cargo.

B. Coal should be through-ventilated to remove methane and reduce the heat of spontaneous combustion.

C. Coal should be ventilated only if temperatures in the center of the cargo exceed 125° F.

⚓ D. Coal should be surface ventilated only.

010622/DG00668   **THOMAS**

Which statement is correct concerning the carriage of coal in bulk?

⚓ A. Coal should be vented with surface ventilation only.

B. Because of its inherent vice, coal should not be loaded wet.

C. Dunnage should be placed against ship's sides and around stanchions.

D. Through ventilation, as well as surface ventilation, should be provided whenever possible.

010623/DG03039   **THOMAS**

What is NOT a problem when carrying coal?

⚓ A. The requirement for through-ventilation

B. The corrosion some types of coal will cause to the ship

C. Spontaneous heating

D. Generation of methane gas

DUNNAGE

010624/DG00248   **THOMAS**

Dunnage may be used to protect a cargo from loss or damage by _____.

⚓ A. ship's sweat

B. inherent vice

C. tainting

D. hygroscopic absorption

010625/DG00218   **AMSM**
What is the main purpose of dunnage?
A. To act as ballast for light vessels
B. To provide ventilation and drainage for cargo
C. To secure the tarpaulins in place
D. To support weakened bulkheads

010626/DG02257   **MARINE CARGO OPS.**
Cribbing is _____.
A. wooden blocks or dunnage placed between a deck load and the deck
B. the chains and shackles used to secure a deck cargo
C. a crate in which a deck cargo is packaged
D. cardboard separation pieces placed between deck loads to prevent chafing

010627/DG02300   **MARINE CARGO OPS.**
In the stowage of deck cargo, "cribbing" is _____.
A. placed on deck to support the cargo
B. separation pieces used to keep cylinders upright and steady
C. shims for stowing baled cargo
D. nets placed across the hatch opening to keep the cargo from falling in the hatch

010628/DG00238   **MARINE CARGO OPS.**
A shore is a piece of securing dunnage that _____.
A. runs from a low supporting level up to the cargo at an angle
B. is also known as a "distance piece"
C. is placed on the deck under the cargo to distribute its weight evenly
D. is run horizontally from a support to the cargo

010629/DG00356   **MARINE CARGO OPS.**
It is possible, and sometimes necessary, to strengthen the deck of a vessel for carriage of deck cargo by _____.
A. placing bunker on the deck
B. building a stage on which to place the cargo
C. welding steel "feet" to the deck, on which the cargo is placed
D. erecting vertical pillars under the deck to support the cargo

010630/DG02366   **MARINE CARGO OPS.**
To "shore up" the main deck for the stowage of deck cargo means to _____.
A. weld pad eyes on deck in proper position to secure the cargo
B. strengthen the main deck by placing pillars underneath it in the tween-decks
C. distribute the weight of the cargo by placing fore-and-aft planks on the main deck
D. package the cargo in wooden crates so it will not damage the deck

010631/DG00208   **MARINE CARGO OPS.**
Your vessel has been damaged and you must shore a bulkhead. You should cut the shore _____.
A. approximately 1/2 inch longer than the measured length to allow for trimming
B. approximately 1/2 inch shorter than the measured length to allow for wedges
C. approximately 1/2 inch shorter per foot of shoring to allow for wet expansion
D. to the same length as the measured length

010632/DG00228   **MARINE CARGO OPS.**
Securing cargo by running timbers from an upper support down to the cargo, either vertically or at an angle, is called _____.
A. braces
B. dunnage
C. shores
D. toms

CARGO LASHINGS

010633/DG00278   ***46 CFR 42.11-15**
Regulations concerning the stowage, lashing, and securing of timber deck cargoes aboard general cargo vessels may be found in the _____.
A. International Cargo Bureau Regulations
B. Load Line Regulations
C. Rules and Regulations for Cargo and Miscellaneous Vessels
D. vessel's classification society rules and regulations

010634/DG00268   **MARINE CARGO OPS.**
When a deck cargo is secured with chain or wire lashings and grab (pear) links, which statement is FALSE?
A. The amount of take-up is limited by the length of the turnbuckle.
B. At the grab (pear) link, the slack end of chain should be led back and secured to the chain above the link.
C. The lashings should be inspected each day and any slack taken up.
D. The turnbuckle should be secured with a stick or lock nuts.

010635/DG00398   **MARINE CARGO OPS.**
Peck and Hale gear is used most commonly for securing _____.
A. automobiles
B. baled cargo
C. large wooden crates
D. palletized cargo

010636/DG01925 **MARINE CARGO OPS.**
Which material should NOT be used to secure cargo on deck for a voyage?
A. Steel chain
B. Wire rope
C. Steel strapping
⚓ D. Fiber rope

CONTAINERIZED CARGO

010637/DG02180 **THOMAS**
The weight of the container and its contents is supported on deck by what part(s)?
⚓ A. Four lower corner castings
B. Bottom, side, and end rails
C. Bottom flooring, side, and end rails
D. Bottom flooring only

010638/DG02164 **CARGO HANDLING**
What provides the majority of strength to an aluminum-sided container?
A. Corner fittings
⚓ B. Framework, primarily the corner posts
C. Framework and siding acting as a girder
D. Aluminum side and end panels

010639/DG02702 **KENDELL**
How long is the standard container used to measure equivalent units?
A. 10 feet (3 meters)
⚓ B. 20 feet (6 meters)
C. 35 feet (11 meters)
D. 40 feet (12 meters)

010640/DG03431 **MARINE CARGO OPS.**
A high cube container is designed specifically to _____.
⚓ A. carry low density cargoes
B. protect fragile cargoes
C. stow cargoes with concentrated weights such as machinery
D. carry cargoes of very low stowage factors

010641/DG03171 **MARINE CARGO OPS.**
A high cube container would most likely be used to stow _____.
A. dense bulk cargoes
⚓ B. household appliances
C. fragile cargoes
D. heavy industrial machinery

010642/DG03381 **MARINE CARGO OPS.**
A half-height container is used _____.
A. to carry cargoes of low density
B. when stowage space is limited
⚓ C. to carry cargoes such as steel products or drums
D. to double the stowage capacity of the vessel

010643/DG02085 **CARGO HANDLING**
What purpose does a bridge fitting serve when lashing containers?
A. Ties a container stack to the deck
B. Ties a container to the container below it
C. Restrains racking loads
⚓ D. Restrains the container against horizontal motion

010644/DG02208 **MARINE CARGO OPS.**
Under normal weather and sea conditions when securing a stack of containers with twist locks, lashings are required when the tier exceeds what height?
A. Lashings are always required
B. One container
⚓ C. Two containers
D. Three containers

010645/DG02184 **CARGO HANDLING**
The lashings on a stack of containers with interlocking fittings restrain the forces that cause _____.
A. toppling
⚓ B. racking
C. buckling
D. crushing

010646/DG02177 **CARGO HANDLING**
Under normal weather and sea conditions when securing a stack of containers with non-locking fittings, lashings are required when the tier exceeds what height?
⚓ A. Lashings are always required
B. One container
C. Two containers
D. Three containers

010647/DG02121 **CARGO HANDLING**
Which statement concerning the lashings of containers with solid bar or wire rope lashings is TRUE?
⚓ A. Stack weights should be less when using a solid bar lashing as compared to a wire lashing.
B. Stack heights may be increased when using a solid bar lashing.
C. Stack heights should be reduced when using a solid bar lashing.
D. Solid bars should be used for lashing the first tier only, with wire lashings on the higher tier(s).

010648/DG03211 **MARINE CARGO OPS.**
With the buttress securing system, containers of different heights must be stowed _____.
A. on the bottom tier on deck
B. in the hold
C. next to the buttress tower
⚓ D. on the top tier

010649/DG00588   **MARINE CARGO OPS.**

Because of the arrangement of the cell guides, the MOST important factor while loading containers is the _____.

    A. contents of the container
⚓ B. list of the vessel
    C. size of the shoreside crane
    D. weight of the container

010650/DG02542   **THOMAS**

When loading containers into the cell guides in the hold of a container ship, which statement is TRUE?

⚓ A. No further securing is usually required.
    B. Containers must have vertical lashings if they do not have twist lock securing.
    C. All containers must have vertical and horizontal lashings.
    D. The container must be locked into the cell guide.

010651/DG03141   **MARINE CARGO OPS.**

What is NOT a securing system used on a containership?

    A. Lashing system
⚓ B. Stacking system
    C. Locking system
    D. Buttress system

010652/DG00913   **THOMAS**

When commencing cargo operations on a container ship, one cell at a hatch is generally discharged completely (to the bottom of the ship) before removing any containers from the adjoining cells to _____.

    A. remove an existing list that would slow down cargo operations
⚓ B. initiate loading in conjunction with unloading at the hatch
    C. improve stability during cargo operations
    D. allow longshoremen easy access to the hatch

010653/DG00578   **MARINE CARGO OPS.**

When loading a container vessel, the operation is basically that of vertical loading. The important factors to be considered when loading containers are port of discharge, _____.

    A. available dunnage, and chocking
    B. crushability, and inherent vice
    C. sweat, and weight
⚓ D. weight, and refrigeration

010654/DG00568   **THOMAS**

Which statement concerning the carriage of containers is TRUE?

    A. The Chief Mate and Master of a container ship should have the proposed stowage plan ready for the stevedore upon arrival in port.
    B. When stowed on deck of a break bulk ship, the bottom of the container must be evenly supported throughout.
⚓ C. With tiered containers, a 40-foot container may be stowed on top of two 20-foot containers.
    D. Deck load calculations must take into account the square footage of the entire container bottom.

010655/DG02205   **CARGO HANDLING**

On the fully containerized ship, approximately one-third or more of the cargo is on deck above the rolling center. Top stowed containers are subject to _____.

⚓ A. accelerations greater than on conventional vessels
    B. accelerations less than on conventional vessels
    C. accelerations the same as on conventional vessels
    D. no accelerations

010656/DG02137   **CARGO HANDLING**

The securing systems for containers were developed to prevent container movement during which ship motion?

    A. Surge
⚓ B. Roll
    C. Sway
    D. Yaw

010657/DG02167   **CARGO HANDLING**

Which statement concerning sweat damage in containers is TRUE?

    A. Sweat damage in containers is unusual due to the small enclosed volume of air.
    B. In general, containerized hygroscopic cargoes are the only ones subject to sweat damage.
⚓ C. Containers should be ventilated, dehumidified, or the contents physically protected against sweat damage.
    D. Sweat damage is not a problem except in insulated and refrigerated containers.

010658/DG00598   **MARINE CARGO OPS.**

What is NOT an advantage of containership operations over conventional break-bulk operations?

⚓ A. Flexibility of operation
    B. Greater operational safety
    C. Lower stevedoring costs
    D. Reduction of cargo damage

RO-RO VESSEL FUNDAMENTAL CHARACTERISTICS

010659/DG04108   **CARGO STOWAGE IMO**

Any vehicle to be loaded aboard a Ro-Ro vessel must _____.

A, weigh less than 22 tons
⚓ B. be provided with an effective braking system
C. have securing points with each aperture capable of accepting more than one lashing
D. All of the above

010660/DG04105   **CARGO HANDLING**

Cargo that is suitable for carriage on Ro-Ro vessels includes _____.
A, trailers
B. rolling vehicles
C. containers
⚓ D. All of the above

010661/DG04107   **CARGO STOWAGE IMO**

Which of the following are considered to be "road vehicles" that can be carried on Ro-Ro vessels?
⚓ A, Semi-trailer
B. Train
C. Articulated train
D. All of the above

010662/DG04106   **CARGO STOWAGE IMO**

Which of the following are considered to be "road vehicles" that can be carried on Ro-Ro vessels?
A, Semi-trailer
B. Road train
C. Articulated road train
⚓ D. All of the above

010663/DG04103   **CARGO HANDLING**

Which of the following is not a loading or transfer feature aboard a Ro-Ro vessel?
A, Stern ramp and/or side ramp
B. Cargo lift
C. Hatch opening designed as a lift
⚓ D. Stuelcken boom

010664/DG04104   **CARGO HANDLING**

The primary objective of a Ro-Ro vessel is to _____.

A, transfer containers without chassis
B. load the vessel with palletized cargo
⚓ C. transport vehicles
D. be loaded full and down to her marks

010665/DG04102   **CARGO HANDLING**

What characterizes a Ro-Ro vessel?
A, May carry up to 24 passengers
⚓ B. High freeboard and sail area
C. Long port stays required for cargo securing
D. Lightweight securing equipment trailers

010666/DG04101   **CARGO HANDLING**

Which of the following is a characteristic of a Ro-Ro vessel?
A, Passenger tours available upon docking
B. Long port stays necessary to secure vehicles
⚓ C. Short in port turnaround times
D. Heavy vehicles only require lightweight securing equipment

RO-RO VESSEL CARGO OPERATIONS

010667/DG04156   **CARGO STOWAGE IMO**

Which element(s) should be taken into account in the preparation of the "Cargo Securing Manual"?
A, Weight of the vehicles
B. Geographical area of the voyage
C. Dynamic forces under adverse weather conditions
⚓ D. All of the above

010668/DG04157   **CARGO STOWAGE IMO**

Which of the following element(s) should be taken into account in the preparation of the "Cargo Securing Manual"?
A, Duration of the voyage
B. Types of cargo units and vehicles to be carried
C. Weight of cargo units and vehicles
⚓ D. All of the above

010669/DG04158   **CARGO STOWAGE IMO**

Which of the following element(s) should be taken into account in the preparation of the "Cargo Securing Manual"?
A, Weight of cargo units and vehicles
B. Types of cargo units and vehicles to be carried
C. Dynamic forces under adverse weather conditions
⚓ D. All of the above

010670/DG04159   **CARGO STOWAGE IMO**

According to the IMO Code, what are the minimum number of securing points that should be on each side of a "road vehicle", whose gross vehicle mass is between 3.5 Tons and 20 Tons, when carried on Ro-Ro vessels?
A, One
⚓ B. Two
C. Three
D. Four

010671/DG04162   **CARGO STOWAGE IMO**

According to the IMO Code, what are the minimum number of securing points that should be on each side of a "road vehicle", whose gross vehicle mass is between 3.5 tons and 20 tons, when carried on Ro-Ro vessels?
A, One
⚓ B. Two
C. Three
D. None of the above

010672/DG04160   **CARGO STOWAGE IMO**

According to the IMO Code, what are the minimum number of securing points that should be on each side of a "road vehicle", whose gross vehicle mass is between 20 tons and 30 tons, when carried on Ro-Ro vessels?

A, One
B. Two
⚓ C. Three
D. Four

010673/DG04163   **CARGO STOWAGE IMO**

According to the IMO Code, what are the minimum number of securing points that should be on each side of a "road vehicle", whose gross vehicle mass is between 20 tons and 30 tons, when carried on Ro-Ro vessels?

A, One
B. Two
⚓ C. Three
D. None of the above

010674/DG04161   **CARGO STOWAGE IMO**

According to the IMO Code, what are the minimum number of securing points that should be on each side of a "road vehicle", whose gross vehicle mass is between 30 tons and 40 tons, when carried on Ro-Ro vessels?

A, One
B. Two
C. Three
⚓ D. Four

010675/DG04164   **CARGO STOWAGE IMO**

According to the IMO Code, what are the minimum number of securing points that should be on each side of a "road vehicle", whose gross vehicle mass is between 30 tons and 40 tons, when carried on Ro-Ro vessels?

A, One
B. Two
C. Three
⚓ D. None of the above

010676/DG04127   **CARGO HANDLING**

Which lashing device(s) would be used in securing heavy vehicles aboard Ro-Ro vessels?

A, Buckle or ratchet tensioner
B. Webbing
⚓ C. Chain
D. All of the above

010677/DG04128   **CARGO HANDLING**

Which of the following lashing materials would be used in securing heavy vehicles aboard Ro-Ro vessels?

⚓ A, Chain lever or turnbuckle
B. Webbing
C. Buckle or ratchet tensioner
D. All of the above

010678/DG04144   **CARGO HANDLING**

Which tensioning device is used with chain to secure heavy vehicles aboard Ro-Ro vessels?

⚓ A, Chain lever
B. Buckle tensioner
C. Adjust-a-matic tensioner
D. Ratchet tensioner

010679/DG04148   **CARGO HANDLING**

Which tensioning device is used with chain to secure heavy vehicles aboard Ro-Ro vessels?

A, Ratchet tensioner
B. Buckle tensioner
C. Adjust-a-matic tensioner
⚓ D. Turnbuckle

010680/DG04135   **CARGO HANDLING**

An advantage of using chain lashing on heavy vehicles aboard Ro-Ro vessels is that it _____.

⚓ A, has long life
B. is light weight
C. absorbs shock
D. has fine adjustment

010681/DG04139   **CARGO HANDLING**

A disadvantage of using chain lashing on heavy vehicles aboard Ro-Ro vessels is that _____.

A, it is easily damaged
B. it is affected by temperature
⚓ C. the links lose strength if placed over corners
D. it has high initial cost

010682/DG04136   **CARGO HANDLING**

A disadvantage of using chain lashing on heavy vehicles aboard Ro-Ro vessels is that it _____.

A, can wrap around cargo
B. is easily damaged
C. is affected by temperature
⚓ D. does not absorb shock

010683/DG04137   **CARGO HANDLING**

A disadvantage of using chain lashing on heavy vehicles aboard Ro-Ro vessels is that it is _____.

⚓ A, heavy
B. easily damaged
C. affected by temperature
D. costly relative to the strength ratio

010684/DG04138   **CARGO HANDLING**
The disadvantage(s) of using chain lashing on heavy vehicles aboard Ro-Ro vessels is that _____.
A, it is heavy
B. the links lose strength if placed over corners
C. it does not absorb shock
D. All of the above

010685/DG04132   **CARGO HANDLING**
What is used when securing heavy vehicles aboard Ro-Ro vessels?
A, Buckle or ratchet tensioner
B. Webbing
C. Manila rope
D. None of these

010686/DG04121   **CARGO HANDLING**
The lashings used on Ro-Ro vessels should be capable of withstanding the forces of _____.
A, rolling
B. pitching
C. heaving
D. All of the above

010687/DG04122   **CARGO HANDLING**
The lashings used on Ro-Ro vessels should be capable of withstanding the forces of _____.
A, pitching and heaving
B. rolling
C. any force of gravity acting on the lashes
D. All of the above

010688/DG04123   **CARGO HANDLING**
The lashings used on Ro-Ro vessels should be capable of withstanding the forces of _____.
A, any force of gravity acting on the lashes
B. rolling
C. pitching
D. All of the above

010689/DG04118   **CARGO HANDLING**
Which factor(s) affect lashing requirements aboard Ro-Ro vessels?
A, Ship's characteristics and motion in a seaway
B. Trim of the vessel
C. Wide variations of air temperature
D. All of the above

010690/DG04133   **CARGO HANDLING**
What is used when securing light vehicles aboard Ro-Ro vessels?
A, Chain lever or turnbuckle
B. Chain
C. Wire
D. None of these

010691/DG04120   **CARGO HANDLING**
Which of the following is considered auxiliary securing equipment that provides extra reliability to lashing in Ro-Ro transport operations?
A, Trailer trestles
B. Pedestals
C. Wheel chocks
D. All of the above

010692/DG04113   **CARGO HANDLING**
What is (are) standard operating procedure(s) used on a Ro-Ro vessel?
A, Periodic inspection and retensioning of lashings as required during voyage
B. Lashings may be completed after the vessel leaves port
C. One QMED assigned to oversee the initial loading and lashing
D. All of the above

010693/DG04111   **CARGO HANDLING**
What is (are) standard operating procedure(s) used on a Ro-Ro vessel?
A, Two deck officers assigned to oversee the initial loading and lashing
B. Lashings may be completed after leaving port
C. Periodic inspection and retensioning of lashings as required during voyage
D. All of the above

010694/DG04112   **CARGO HANDLING**
What is (are) standard operating procedure(s) used on a Ro-Ro vessel?
A, One engineer officer assigned to oversee the initial loading and lashing
B. Cargo lashings may be removed at sea for maintenance
C. Periodic inspection and retensioning of lashings during the voyage
D. All of the above

010695/DG04110   **CARGO HANDLING**
Which standard operating procedure(s) should be adhered to on a Ro-Ro vessel?
A, Periodic inspection and retensioning of lashings as required during voyage
B. Battery cables must be disconnected to prevent fire hazard
C. One deck engine mechanic assigned to oversee the initial loading and lashing
D. All of the above

010696/DG04182   **CARGO HANDLING**
Which lashing gear used aboard Ro-Ro vessels should be painted or soaked in oil when not in use?
⚓ A. Chain
B. Wire rope
C. Webbing
D. All of the above

010697/DG04181   **CARGO HANDLING**
Which lashing gear used aboard Ro-Ro vessels should be painted or soaked in oil when not in use?
A. Wire rope.
⚓ B. Chain
C. Webbing
D. All of the above

010698/DG04183   **CARGO HANDLING**
Which of the following lashing gear used aboard Ro-Ro vessels should be maintained when not in use?
A. Chain
B. Wire rope
C. Webbing
⚓ D. All of the above

010699/DG04117   **CARGO HANDLING**
Cargo securing for Ro-Ro is based on the concept of _____.
A. solid packing
⚓ B. rapid loading and discharge
C. vessel loaded full and down to her marks
D. palletized cargo

010700/DG04154   **CARGO HANDLING**
What should you be concerned with when loading and securing vehicles aboard a Ro-Ro vessel?
A. That all fuel is drained from the vehicles' tanks to prevent fire hazard
⚓ B. The size, weight, and center of gravity of vehicle/cargo unit
C. The preferred stowage of vehicles is athwartships wherever possible
D. The vehicles' brakes should not be set to allow for adjusting the lashings

010701/DG04153   **CARGO HANDLING**
What should you be concerned with when loading and securing vehicles on a Ro-Ro?
⚓ A. Number, position and angle of lashes
B. Number of axles
C. Disconnecting the battery cables to prevent fire hazard
D. Minor air pressure changes in the tires

010702/DG04114   **CARGO STOWAGE IMO**
When accepting vehicles for shipment, the Master should ensure that _____.
A. all decks intended for the stowage of vehicles are, in so far as is practicable, free from oil and grease
B. the ship has on board an adequate supply of cargo securing gear, which is maintained in sound working condition
C. vehicles are in apparent good order and condition suitable for sea transport, particularly with regards to securing
⚓ D. All of the above

010703/DG04155   **CARGO HANDLING**
Which factor(s) should be considered when loading vehicles or trailers aboard Ro-Ro vessels?
A. Layout of decks
B. Vertical clearances
C. Tie-down and lashing
⚓ D. All of the above

010704/DG04150   **CARGO HANDLING**
Which of the following is/are TRUE regarding lashing requirements to secure vehicles aboard Ro-Ro vessels?
A. The securing of cargo on flats and trailers and in containers must be adequate to withstand both road and sea motions
B. The generally recommended lash angle cannot be greater than 45 degrees relative to the deck in any direction.
C. It is necessary for an adequate number of securing points on the vehicles themselves in order that lashings may be properly and safely utilized.
⚓ D. All the above

010705/DG04152   **CARGO HANDLING**
Which of the following statement(s) is/are TRUE regarding lashing requirements to secure vehicles aboard Ro-Ro vessels?
A. It is imperative that the securing of cargo on flats and trailers and in containers be adequate for both road and sea motions.
B. The movements experienced by road borne cargo differ significantly from the roll and sway movements of a ship at sea.
C. It is necessary for adequate number and strength of securing points on the vehicles themselves in order that lashings may be properly and safely utilized.
⚓ D. All the above

010706/DG04151   **CARGO HANDLING**

Which of the following statements is TRUE regarding lashing requirements to secure vehicles aboard Ro-Ro vessels?

A, It is NOT imperative that the securing of cargo on flats and trailers and in containers be adequate for BOTH road and sea motions.

B. The generally recommended lash angle should not be greater than 45 degrees relative to the deck in any direction.

C. For effective securing vehicles should be stowed athwartships whenever possible.

D. It is not necessary to lash automobiles since setting the brakes is sufficient to keep them from moving.

010707/DG04149   **CARGO HANDLING**

Which of the following statements is TRUE regarding lashing requirements to secure vehicles aboard Ro-Ro vessels?

A, The securing of cargo on flats and trailers must be adequate to withstand road motions only.

B. The movements experienced by road borne cargo are the same as the movements of a ship at sea.

C. The generally recommended lash angle is no greater than 45 degrees relative to the deck in any direction.

D. It is not necessary for an adequate number of securing points on the vehicles themselves since setting the brakes is sufficient.

010708/DG04109   **CARGO HANDLING**

Which operating procedure(s) should be adhered to on a Ro-Ro vessel?

A, One officer assigned to oversee the initial loading and lashing

B. All lashings should be completed before leaving port

C. Periodic inspection and retensioning of lashings during the voyage

D. All of the above

010709/DG04126   **CARGO HANDLING**

Which variable factor affects the initial lashing requirements aboard Ro-Ro vessels?

A, Number, position and angle of lashings

B. Vessel's draft

C. Port of origin

D. ABS requirements

010710/DG04124   **CARGO HANDLING**

Which variable factor affects the initial lashing requirements aboard Ro-Ro vessels?

A, Vessel's draft

B. Center of gravity of vehicle or cargo unit

C. Changes in humidity

D. Age of vehicle or cargo unit

010711/DG04125   **CARGO HANDLING**

Which variable factor affects the initial lashing requirements aboard Ro-Ro vessels?

A, Age of vehicle or cargo unit

B. Size and weight of vehicle/cargo unit

C. Reputation of shipper concerning condition of cargo

D. Air pressure in the vehicles tires

010712/DG04115   **CARGO STOWAGE IMO**

Entries should be made in a Ro-Ro vessel's cargo-securing device record book for _____.

A, procedures for accepting cargo securing devices

B. procedures for maintaining and repairing cargo-securing devices

C. record of cargo securing device inspections

D. All of the above

010713/DG04186   **CARGO HANDLING**

How could lashing gear used aboard Ro-Ro vessels be stowed when not in use?

A, Drape along brackets

B. Leave in place while back loading cargo to save time

C. Hang vertically in the paint locker

D. All of the above

010714/DG04185   **CARGO HANDLING**

How could lashing gear used aboard Ro-Ro vessels be stowed when not in use?

A, Drape along brackets

B. Hang vertically in a sheltered area

C. Stow in bins at hatch coming side

D. All of the above

010715/DG04184   **CARGO HANDLING**

Which of the following lashing gear used aboard Ro-Ro vessels should be stowed when not in use?

A, Chain

B. Wire rope

C. Webbing

D. All of the above

010716/DG04116   **CARGO HANDLING**

Onboard a Ro-Ro vessel many decks are used for the carriage of both rolling and container cargoes, as such it is most useful if a deck socket accepts both _____.

A, twist-Locks and lashing hooks

B. container locks and bridge fittings

C. bridge fittings and lashing hooks

D. twist-locks and container locks

010717/DG04142   **CARGO HANDLING**

The advantage(s) of using wire rope lashing on vehicles aboard Ro-Ro vessels is that it _____.

A, is Lighter than chain
B. has a good working life
C. is not affected by temperature
⚓ D. All of the above

010718/DG04119   **CARGO HANDLING**

The securing of passenger cars on a Ro-Ro vessel requires _____.

A, simple and lightweight equipment
B. low labor intensive equipment
C. specially designed equipment to avoid vehicle damage
⚓ D. All of the above

010719/DG04131   **CARGO HANDLING**

What is used when securing light vehicles aboard Ro-Ro vessels?

⚓ A, Buckle or ratchet tensioner
B. Chain
C. Wire
D. Manila rope

010720/DG04147   **CARGO HANDLING**

Which tensioning device is used with wire rope lashing to secure vehicles aboard Ro-Ro vessels?

A, Chain lever.
⚓ B. Adjust-a-matic tensioner
C. Buckle tensioner
D. Ratchet tensioner

010721/DG04143   **CARGO HANDLING**

Which tensioning device is used with wire rope lashing to secure vehicles aboard Ro-Ro vessels?

A, Chain lever
B. Buckle tensioner
⚓ C. Adjust-a-matic tensioner
D. Ratchet tensioner

010722/DG04130   **CARGO HANDLING**

Which lashing material is preferred when securing new cars aboard Ro-Ro vessels?

A, Chain lever or turnbuckle
⚓ B. Webbing
C. Wire
D. None of the above

010723/DG04129   **CARGO HANDLING**

Which lashing materials would be used in securing light vehicles aboard Ro-Ro vessels?

A, Chain lever or turnbuckle
⚓ B. Webbing
C. Chain
D. None of the above

010724/DG04146   **CARGO HANDLING**

Which of the following tensioning devices is used with webbing to secure light vehicles aboard Ro-Ro vessels?

A, Chain lever
⚓ B. Buckle tensioner
C. Adjust-a-matic tensioner
D. Turnbuckle

010725/DG04145   **CARGO HANDLING**

Which tensioning device is used with webbing to secure light vehicles aboard Ro-Ro vessels?

A, Chain lever
B. Turnbuckle
C. Adjust-a-matic tensioner
⚓ D. Ratchet tensioner

010726/DG04141   **CARGO HANDLING**

What is/are the advantage(s) of using web lashing on light vehicles aboard Ro-Ro vessels?

A, Good working life
B. Light and easy to handle
C. Flexible
⚓ D. All of the above

010727/DG04140   **CARGO HANDLING**

The disadvantage(s) of using web lashing on light vehicles aboard Ro-Ro vessels is that it _____.

A, deteriorates in sunlight
B. cuts on sharp edges
C. is vulnerable to damage and pilferage
⚓ D. All of the above

010728/DG04134   **CARGO HANDLING**

What may NOT be used when securing heavy vehicles aboard Ro-Ro vessels?

A, Chain lever
B. Turnbuckle
⚓ C. Webbing
D. Chain

RO-RO VESSEL SAFETY

010729/DG04188   **CARGO HANDLING**

The most important safety consideration during loading or discharge aboard a Ro-Ro vessel is _____.

A, having all crewmembers and longshoremen wear hard hats
⚓ B. the thorough ventilation of all cargo spaces
C. ensuring that visitors cannot come aboard
D. having the outboard anchor down

010730/DG04171 CARGO HANDLING

While loading or discharging vehicles, which is the most important safety consideration aboard a Ro-Ro vessel?

⚓ A, Preventing the asphyxiation of personnel below decks

B. Notifying the engine room prior to completing operations

C. Calling out the deck department for all hands periodically

D. Ensuring that a fuel barge cannot come alongside

RO-RO VESSEL PREPARATIONS & SECURING

010731/DG04175 CARGO HANDLING

Which of the following is NOT necessary, prior to loading or discharging cargo on a Ro-Ro vessel?

A, Turn on ventilation for cargo holds.

B. Lower the stern ramp.

⚓ C. Turn on the red cargo light.

D. Raise/open the stern door.

010732/DG04173 CARGO HANDLING

What should be done before energizing the cargo hold ventilation on a Ro-Ro vessel, prior to loading or discharging cargo?

A, Call out the deck department for all hands.

B. Notify the boarding agent.

⚓ C. Notify the engine room.

D. All of the above

010733/DG04174 CARGO HANDLING

What should be done immediately after putting down the stern ramp on a Ro-Ro vessel, prior to loading or discharging cargo?

A, Turn on the red cargo light.

B. Turn on pumproom ventilation.

C. Call out the deck department for all hands.

⚓ D. Raise/open the stern door.

010734/DG04178 CARGO HANDLING

Which of the following actions are stated in the correct order prior to loading or discharging cargo on a Ro-Ro vessel?

⚓ A, Lower the stern ramp, raise/open the stern door, turn on ventilation for cargo holds

B. Turn on ventilation for cargo holds, raise/open the stern door, lower the stern ramp

C. Turn on ventilation for cargo holds, lower the stern ramp, raise/open the stern door

D. Raise/open the stern door, lower the stern ramp, turn on ventilation for cargo holds

010735/DG04180 CARGO HANDLING

Which of the following actions are stated in the correct order prior to loading or discharging cargo on a Ro-Ro vessel?

A, Raise/open stern door, lower the stern ramp, turn on ventilation for cargo holds

⚓ B. Lower the stern ramp, raise/open stern door, turn on ventilation for cargo holds

C. Turn on ventilation for cargo holds, lower the stern ramp, raise/open stern door

D. Turn on ventilation for cargo holds, raise/open stern door, lower the stern ramp

010736/DG04177 CARGO HANDLING

Which of the following actions are stated in the correct order prior to loading or discharging cargo on a Ro-Ro vessel?

A, Turn on ventilation for cargo holds, lower the stern ramp, raise/open the stern door

B. Turn on ventilation for cargo holds, raise/open the stern door, lower the stern ramp

⚓ C. Lower the stern ramp, raise/open the stern door, turn on ventilation for cargo holds

D. Raise/open the stern door, lower the stern ramp, turn on ventilation for cargo holds

010737/DG04179 CARGO HANDLING

Which of the following actions are stated in the correct order prior to loading or discharging cargo on a Ro-Ro vessel?

A, Raise/open stern door, lower the stern ramp, turn on ventilation for cargo holds

B. Turn on ventilation for cargo holds, raise/open the stern door, lower the stern ramp

C. Turn on ventilation for cargo holds, lower the stern ramp, raise/open the stern door

⚓ D. Lower the stern ramp, raise/open the stern door, turn on ventilation for cargo holds

010738/DG04187 CARGO HANDLING

Which of the following is the stated proper sequence before commencing cargo operations aboard Ro-Ro vessels?

A, Start ventilation, lower the ramp, notify engine room

B. Lower the ramp, start ventilation, notify engine room

⚓ C. Notify engine room, lower the ramp, start ventilation

D. Start ventilation, notify engine room, lower the ramp

010739/DG04172   **CARGO HANDLING**
What should be done after putting down the ramp on a Ro-Ro vessel, prior to loading or discharging cargo?
A, Turn on red cargo light.
B. Turn on ventilation for cargo holds.
C. Call out the deck department for all hands.
D. None of the above

DRY CARGO SECURITY

CARRIAGE OF GOODS BY SEA

010740/DG01367   **MARINE CARGO OPS.**
Under the Carriage of Goods by Sea Act of 1936, a vessel will be liable for damage to cargo when the damage arises out of _____.
A. poor stowage of cargo in a container
B. fire caused by lightning
C. overloading
D. inherent vice

010741/DG01195   **MARINE CARGO OPS.**
Under the Carriage of Goods by Sea Act of 1936, a vessel will be liable for damage to a cargo when the damage arises from _____.
A. unseaworthiness when sailing
B. insufficient packing
C. quarantine delays
D. mismanagement of the vessel

010742/DG01477   **MARINE CARGO OPS.**
Under the Carriage of Goods by Sea Act of 1936, a vessel will be liable for damage to a cargo when the damage arises out of _____.
A. delays due to seizure of the vessel
B. fire caused by fault of the carrier
C. strikes or lockouts
D. improper stowage

010743/DG01202   **MARINE CARGO OPS.**
Under the Carriage of Goods by Sea Act of 1936, a vessel will be liable for damage to cargo when the damage arises from _____.
A. an act of war
B. lack of ventilation in transit
C. perils of the sea
D. an error in navigation

APPLICATION & PRACTICE

010744/DG00158   **MARINE CARGO OPS.**
A claim for cargo damages may be held against the ship owner if such damage is the result of failure of the ship's officers to _____.
A. correct all defects in the ship's construction
B. ensure the fitness and safety of cargo spaces
C. ensure adequate packaging of the cargo
D. prevent delays due to quarantine restrictions

010745/DG01627   **MARINE CARGO OPS.**
A claim for cargo damages may be held against the shipowner if such damage is the result of failure of the ship's officers to _____.
A. ensure the fitness and safety of cargo spaces
B. ensure adequate packaging of the cargo
C. prevent delays due to quarantine restrictions
D. correct all defects in the ship's construction

010746/DG01582   **MARINE CARGO OPS.**
Which is an example of failure to exercise due diligence?
A. Overloading
B. Sailing short of union manning requirements
C. Sailing with less than 30% reserve fuel oil supply
D. Sailing short of being full and down

010747/DG00124   **MARINE CARGO OPS.**
Bilge soundings indicate _____.
A. the amount of condensation in the hold
B. whether the cargo is leaking or not
C. whether the vessel is taking on water
D. All of the above

STOWAGE TECHNIQUES

010748/DG00148   **MARINE CARGO OPS.**
Overcarriage is best prevented by _____.
A. assuring heavy cargo is stowed low in the vessel
B. checking the vessel's load line calculations carefully
C. inspection of the hold at completion of discharge
D. stowing the cargo which is to be discharged last on the bottom

010749/DG01445   **MARINE CARGO OPS.**
What is an example of a fundamental objective of cargo stowage?
A. Load so the trim does not exceed 3 feet by the stern.
B. Make maximum use of existing dunnage.
C. Separate wet and dry cargoes into separate holds.
D. Prevent overcarriage by block stowage.

HYDROSCOPIC & NON-HYDROSCOPIC CARGOES

010750/DG00558   **MARINE CARGO OPS.**
A heated bulkhead has the effect on a hygroscopic commodity of _____.
A. causing moisture to accumulate against the bulkhead
B. lowering the vapor pressure of the commodity
C. lowering the dew point of the air
D. raising the vapor pressure of the commodity

010751/DG00448   **MARINE CARGO OPS.**

Hygroscopic cargoes should be ventilated when _____.

  ⚓ A. going from a warm to a cold climate
- B. the dew point of the outside air is greater than the dew point of the air in the hold
- C. the dew point of the air in the hold is very low
- D. the outside dew point is 60° F (16° C) and the cargo temperature is 54° F (12° C)

010752/DG00428   **MARINE CARGO OPS.**

Your vessel is going from a warm climate to a cold climate with a hygroscopic cargo. Which statement is TRUE?

  ⚓ A. You must ventilate constantly and vigorously to combat ship sweat.
- B. You should ventilate; there is little danger of ship sweat, but a possibility of cargo sweat.
- C. There is danger of heavy cargo sweat if you ventilate.
- D. There is little danger of any sweat problem.

010753/DG00418   **MMOH**

On a vessel proceeding from a very cold to a warm climate with a cargo of a nonhygroscopic nature in the holds, which is TRUE?

- A. Danger of heavy ship sweat exists; constant and vigorous ventilation is required.
  ⚓ B. There is danger of heavy cargo sweat if outside air is introduced by ventilation.
- C. There is little danger of ship's sweat, slight possibility of cargo sweat; moderate ventilation is needed.
- D. The possibility of any sweat problem, either cargo or ship, is remote.

010754/DG00438   **MARINE CARGO OPS.**

Your vessel is loaded with nonhygroscopic cargoes and is going from a cold to a warm climate. You should _____.

- A. start the exhaust blowers
- B. start the intake blowers
  ⚓ C. not ventilate the cargo holds
- D. ventilate the cargo holds

SWEAT DAMAGE & VENTILATION

010755/DG00478   **MARINE CARGO OPS.**

The moisture equilibrium chart can be used to determine the _____.

- A. absolute moisture content of the air surrounding a hygroscopic cargo when moisture equilibrium exists
  ⚓ B. dew point temperature that the air surrounding a hygroscopic commodity will have when in moisture equilibrium with that commodity
- C. enthalpy of the air surrounding a hydroscopic cargo which is in moisture equilibrium with the cargo
- D. temperature at which moisture equilibrium will occur in a cargo hold containing a hygroscopic cargo

010756/DG00488   **MARINE CARGO OPS.**

Which data can NOT be found on a moisture equilibrium chart?

- A. Dry bulb temperature
- B. Moisture content
- C. Vapor pressure
  ⚓ D. Wet bulb temperature

010757/DG00468   **MARINE CARGO OPS.**

Sweat damage in a hatch full of canned goods in cartons will occur when the _____.

- A. air temperature is higher than the temperature of the cargo
- B. air temperature is lower than the temperature of the cargo
  ⚓ C. dew point is higher than the temperature of the cargo
- D. dew point is lower than the temperature of the cargo

010758/DG00458   **MMOH**

Sweat damage will occur in a cargo hold containing cased machinery when the _____.

- A. air temperature of the hold is higher than the temperature of the outside air
  ⚓ B. dew point of the hold is higher than the temperature of the ship's skin
- C. dew point of the outside air is lower than the temperature of the cargo
- D. outside air temperature is colder than the temperature of the cargo

010759/DG00518   **MMOH**

Which factor is MOST important in preventing sweat damage within a cargo hold?

  ⚓ A. Dew point of the cargo hold
- B. Dew point of the outside atmosphere
- C. Outside air temperature
- D. Temperature of the cargo

010760/DG00498   **MARINE CARGO OPS.**

When the dew point of the outside air is higher than the dew point of the air in the cargo hold, you should _____.

A. energize the exhaust blowers
B. energize the intake blowers
⚓ C. not ventilate the cargo holds
D. ventilate the cargo holds

010761/DG00508   **MARINE CARGO OPS.**

When the dew point of the outside air is lower than or equal to the dew point of the air in the cargo hold, you should _____.

A. secure all ventilation
B. shut down the exhaust blowers
C. shut down the intake blowers
⚓ D. ventilate the cargo holds

DRY CARGO OPERATIONS COMPUTATIONS

STOWAGE FACTOR

010762/DG00778   **MARINE CARGO OPS.**

What is the stowage factor of a commodity whose density is 15 pounds per cubic foot?

A. 15
B. 45
C. 133
⚓ D. 149

010763/DG00768   **MARINE CARGO OPS.**

A cargo of canned foodstuff is packed in cartons. Each carton is 36 cubic feet and weighs 340 pounds. The stowage factor of the cargo is _____.

A. 9.5
B. 62
C. 212
⚓ D. 237

010764/DG02009   **THOMAS**

A cargo of canned foodstuffs is packed in cartons. Each carton is 36 cubic feet and weighs 380 pounds. What is the stowage factor of the cargo?

A. 9.5
B. 62
⚓ C. 212
D. 237

BROKEN STOWAGE

010765/DG00798   **MARINE CARGO OPS.**

How many cubic feet of space is required to stow 775 tons of a cargo with a stowage factor of 25? (estimated broken stowage is 15%)

A. 12,916
⚓ B. 22,794
C. 25,833
D. 29,397

010766/DG00858   **MARINE CARGO OPS.**

The lower hold of your vessel has a bale capacity of 60,000 cubic feet. How many tons of cotton in bales having a stowage factor of 85 can be stowed in the lower hold, assuming a broken stowage factor of 20%?

A. 141
⚓ B. 565
C. 706
D. 847

010767/DG00848   **MARINE CARGO OPS.**

You are loading a cargo of canned goods with a stowage factor of 65. If you allow 15% for broken stowage, how many tons can be loaded in a space of 55,000 cubic feet?

A. 687
⚓ B. 719
C. 846
D. 973

010768/DG00888   **MARINE CARGO OPS.**

You are going to load bales of wool having a stowage factor of 100 in #3 lower hold which has a bale cubic of 62,000. How many tons of the wool can be stowed in the compartment, assuming 10% broken stowage?

A. 520
⚓ B. 558
C. 620
D. 654

010769/DG00868   **MARINE CARGO OPS.**

You are going to load bales of wool having a stowage factor of 100 in #3 lower hold which has a bale cubic of 72,000. How many tons of the wool can be stowed in the compartment, assuming 10% broken stowage?

A. 493
B. 577
C. 602
⚓ D. 648

010770/DG00838   **MARINE CARGO OPS.**

You are going to load bales of wool having a stowage factor of 110 in #3 lower hold which has a bale cubic of 72,000. If broken stowage is figured at 15%, how many tons of the wool can be stowed?

⚓ A. 556
B. 654
C. 752
D. 770

010771/DG00878   **MARINE CARGO OPS.**

You are going to load bales of wool having a stowage factor of 96 in #3 lower hold which has a bale cubic of 84,000. How many tons of wool can be stowed in the compartment?

A. 577
B. 602
C. 654
⚓ D. 875

010772/DG00482   **THOMAS**

A lot of special cargo of similar cartons is to be loaded aboard your vessel. You examine one of the cartons of the lot shown. What is the total cubic space the consignment will occupy? (Assume no broken stowage.) See Diagram D042DG

A. 51 cubic feet (1.5 cubic meters)
⚓ B. 58 cubic feet (1.7 cubic meters)
C. 336 cubic feet (10 cubic meters)
D. 700 cubic feet (21 cubic meters)

010773/DG00752   **THOMAS**

A lot of special cargo of similar cartons as shown is to be loaded. What is the total cubic capacity the consignment will occupy if you assume 10% broken stowage? See Diagram D042DG

A. 51 cubic feet (1.5 cubic meters)
B. 58 cubic feet (1.7 cubic meters)
⚓ C. 65 cubic feet (2.0 cubic meters)
D. 336 cubic feet (10 cubic meters)

010774/DG03103   **THOMAS**

A case received for shipment has the markings shown. Each carton measures 13" x 15" x 23". What is the total cubic capacity the entire consignment will occupy? (Ignore broken stowage.) See Diagram D043DG

⚓ A. 779 cubic feet (22 cubic meters)
B. 992 cubic feet (28 cubic meters)
C. 1,047 cubic feet (30 cubic meters)
D. 112,125 cubic feet (3173 cubic meters)

010775/DG02155   **THOMAS**

A case received for shipment has the markings shown. Each carton measures 13" x 15" x 23". What is the total cubic capacity the entire consignment will occupy if you assume 10% broken stowage? See Diagram D043DG

A. 779 cubic feet (22 cubic meters)
⚓ B. 857 cubic feet (24 cubic meters)
C. 1047 cubic feet (30 cubic meters)
D. 112,125 cubic feet (3173 cubic meters)

010776/DG00808   **MARINE CARGO OPS.**

You are loading a cargo of cases into a hold which has a bale cubic of 44,000. The cargo consists of cases measuring 4 ft by 2 ft by 1.5 ft. Estimated broken stowage is 15%. What is the maximum number of cases which can be stowed in the hold?

A. 3096
⚓ B. 3116
C. 3136
D. 3156

010777/DG00788   **MARINE CARGO OPS.**

The lower hold of your vessel has a bale capacity of 45,000 cubic feet. How many cases of a cargo weighing 450 lbs. and measuring 2.5 feet by 3 feet by 3 feet could be stowed in the hold, assuming a broken stowage factor of 15 percent?

A. 300
B. 675
C. 1325
⚓ D. 1700

010778/DG00908   **MARINE CARGO OPS.**

You must load as much of a large shipment of case goods as possible into a hold which has 24,400 cubic feet of space. Each case measures 2 feet by 2 feet by 4 feet and weighs 448 pounds. If you allow for broken stowage of 15%, how many long tons can be loaded?

A. 54
B. 207
⚓ C. 259
D. 351

010779/DG00898   **MARINE CARGO OPS.**

You must load as much of a large shipment of case goods as possible into a hold which has 24,000 cubic feet of space. Each case measures 2 feet by 2-1/2 feet by 4 feet and weights 448 pounds. If you allow for broken stowage of 15%, how many long tons can be loaded?

A. 280
B. 233
⚓ C. 204
D. 190

010780/DG02039   **THOMAS**

There is a large shipment of case goods available to be loaded on your vessel. You are to load as many tons as possible in a hold which has 32,300 cubic feet left unfilled by cargo. Each case measures 2-feet high by 2-feet wide by 4-feet long and weighs 500 pounds. If you allow a broken stowage allowance of 10% of the 32,300 feet, what is the nearest whole number of tons which may be loaded?

A. 324 tons
B. 360 tons
C. 363 tons
⚓ D. 406 tons

010781/DG02172   **THOMAS**

The lower hold of your vessel has a bale cubic of 52,000 cu. ft. You will load a cargo of cases, each weighing 380 lbs. and measuring 3 ft. x 2 ft. x 2 ft. The estimated broken stowage is 15%. How many tons of cases can be loaded?

A. 137 tons
B. 161 tons
C. 625 tons
D. 969 tons

ESTIMATED CARGO WEIGHT

010782/DG02157   **THOMAS**

You are in a fresh water port loading logs with gear rated at 5 tons, and suspect the weight of the logs exceeds the SWL of the gear. The logs are floating in the water alongside the vessel and have 95% of their volume submerged. The average length of the logs is 15 feet and the average diameter is 4.4 feet. What is the nearest average weight of the logs, based on these average measurements?

A. 5.5 tons
B. 6.0 tons
C. 7.7 tons
D. 24.1 tons

CARGO CENTER OF GRAVITY

010783/DG00948   **MARINE CARGO OPS.**

Twenty-five hundred (2500) tons of iron ore with a stowage factor of 17 is stowed in a cargo hold. The dimensions of the hold are 55 feet long and 45 feet wide and 35 feet high. What is the height of the center of gravity of the ore above the bottom of the hold?

A. 7.8 feet
B. 8.6 feet
C. 17.1 feet
D. 34.6 feet

HEIGHT OF CARGO STOW

010784/DG00918   **MARINE CARGO OPS.**

Ten triangular piles of piping on the pier are to be loaded - each pile has a 20 foot base, is 15 feet high and 30 feet long. If the breadth of the hold is 60 feet and the piping is to be stowed fore and aft in a 30 foot space, how high will it stow?

A. 16.6 feet
B. 25.0 feet
C. 50.0 feet
D. 75.0 feet

010785/DG00938   **MARINE CARGO OPS.**

The deck load capacity of a compartment into which you intend to load a cargo of soft brick is 380 lbs. per sq. ft. The stowage factor of the brick is 21.3. Disregarding broken stowage, what is the maximum height the brick may be stacked without endangering the structure?

A. 1.7 feet
B. 3.6 feet
C. 5.0 feet
D. 7.1 feet

AREA & VOLUME

AREA OF A CIRCLE

010786/DG02283   ***BOWD 2; CHAP. 1**

What is the area of a circle with a radius of 2 feet after a sector of 86° has been removed?

A. 2.39 sq. ft
B. 3.02 sq. ft
C. 9.55 sq. ft
D. 12.57 sq. ft

010787/DG02273   ***BOWD 2; CHAP. 1**

What is the area of a circle with a radius of 4 feet after a sector of 111° has been removed?

A. 3.90 sq. ft
B. 8.67 sq. ft
C. 34.77 sq. ft
D. 50.27 sq. ft

010788/DG02238   ***BOWD 2; CHAP. 1**

What is the area of a circle with a radius of 12 feet after a sector of 60° has been removed?

A. 18.85 square feet
B. 75.40 square feet
C. 94.25 square feet
D. 376.99 square feet

010789/DG02253   ***BOWD 2; CHAP. 1**

What is the area of a circle with a radius of 17 feet after a sector of 57° has been removed?

A. 764.17 sq. ft
B. 190.66 sq. ft
C. 145.27 sq. ft
D. 36.85 sq. ft

010790/DG02242   ***BOWD 2; CHAP. 1**

What is the area of a circle with a radius of 21 feet after a sector of 120° has been removed?

A. 115.45 sq. ft
B. 230.91 sq. ft
C. 461.81 sq. ft
D. 923.63 sq. ft

010791/DG02387   *BOWD 2; CHAP. 1
What is the area of a circle with a diameter of 2 feet after a sector of 60° has been removed?
A. 0.25 square ft.
B. 0.52 square ft.
C. 2.09 square ft.
⚓ D. 2.62 square ft.

010792/DG02388   *BOWD 2; CHAP. 1
What is the area of a circle with a diameter of 4 feet after a sector of 120° has been removed?
A. 2.67 square ft.
B. 4.19 square ft.
⚓ C. 8.38 square ft.
D. 10.67 square ft.

010793/DG02351   *BOWD 2; CHAP. 1
What is the area of a circle with a diameter of 12 feet after a sector of 86° has been removed?
A. 108.57 square ft.
⚓ B. 86.08 square ft.
C. 28.65 square ft.
D. 27.14 square ft.

010794/DG02389   *BOWD 2; CHAP. 1
What is the area of a circle with a diameter of 17 feet after a sector of 111° has been removed?
A. 36.94 square ft.
⚓ B. 156.99 square ft.
C. 226.98 square ft.
D. 627.47 square ft.

010795/DG02354   *BOWD 2; CHAP. 1
What is the area of a circle with a diameter of 21 feet after a sector of 72° has been removed?
⚓ A. 277.09 square ft.
B. 149.43 square ft.
C. 69.27 square ft.
D. 52.78 square ft.

AREA OF A TRIANGLE

010796/DG02394   *BOWD 2; CHAP. 1
Determine the area of a triangle with a base of 3.5 feet and a height of 4.0 feet.
⚓ A. 7.0 square ft.
B. 7.5 square ft.
C. 11.5 square ft.
D. 14.0 square ft.

010797/DG02395   *BOWD 2; CHAP. 1
Determine the area of a triangle with a base of 4.7 feet and a height of 6.3 feet.
A. 29.6 square ft.
B. 26.2 square ft.
C. 18.5 square ft.
⚓ D. 14.8 square ft.

010798/DG02396   *BOWD 2; CHAP. 1
Determine the area of a triangle with a base of 5.8 feet and a height of 2.1 feet.
A. 12.2 square ft.
B. 7.9 square ft.
⚓ C. 6.1 square ft.
D. 3.0 square ft.

010799/DG02397   *BOWD 2; CHAP. 1
Determine the area of a triangle with a base of 6.7 feet and a height of 9.1 feet.
A. 61.0 square ft.
⚓ B. 30.5 square ft.
C. 22.9 square ft.
D. 15.8 square ft.

CIRCUMFERENCE OF A CIRCLE

010800/DG01762   *BOWD 2; CHAP. 1
What is the perimeter of a circle with a radius of 2.5 feet?
A. 7.86 ft
⚓ B. 15.71 ft
C. 19.63 ft
D. 22.71 ft

010801/DG01695   *BOWD 2; CHAP. 1
What is the perimeter of a circle with a radius of 3.7 feet?
A. 11.62 ft
B. 17.49 ft
⚓ C. 23.25 ft
D. 25.72 ft

010802/DG01687   *BOWD 2; CHAP. 1
What is the perimeter of a circle with a radius of 4.2 feet?
⚓ A. 26.39 ft
B. 21.19 ft
C. 17.81 ft
D. 13.20 ft

010803/DG01657   *BOWD 2; CHAP. 1
What is the perimeter of a circle with a radius of 5.1 feet?
A. 81.71 ft
B. 64.08 ft
C. 40.85 ft
⚓ D. 32.04 ft

VOLUME OF A CYLINDER
CYLINDRICAL TANK CAPACITY

010804/DG02342   ***BOWD 2; CHAP. 1**
How many tons of salt water can be loaded into a flat ended cylindrical tank with a diameter of 3 feet and a length of 8 feet?
⚓ A. 1.62
   B. 1.98
   C. 3.23
   D. 6.46

010805/DG02398   ***BOWD 2; CHAP. 1**
How many tons of salt water can be loaded into a flat-ended cylindrical tank with a diameter of 4.5 feet and a length of 8 feet?
   A. 1.82
⚓ B. 3.64
   C. 7.27
   D. 14.54

010806/DG01929   ***BOWD 2; CHAP. 1**
How many tons of salt water can be loaded into a flat-ended cylindrical tank with a diameter of 5 feet and a length of 10 feet?
   A. 22.44 T
   B. 11.22 T
   C. 7.48 T
⚓ D. 5.61 T

010807/DG01926   ***BOWD 2; CHAP. 1**
How many tons of salt water can be loaded into a flat-ended cylindrical tank with a diameter of 5 feet and a length of 12 feet?
⚓ A. 6.73 T
   B. 7.85 T
   C. 13.46 T
   D. 26.93 T

010808/DG01917   ***BOWD 2; CHAP. 1**
How many tons of salt water can be loaded into a flat-ended cylindrical tank with a diameter of 5 feet and a length of 14 feet?
   A. 31.42
   B. 15.71
⚓ C. 7.85
   D. 6.25

VOLUME OF A CONE

010809/DG01824   ***BOWD 2; CHAP. 1**
What is the volume in a cone with a base diameter of 4.5 feet and a height of 3 feet?
   A. 4.50 cubic ft.
   B. 7.12 cubic ft.
   C. 9.81 cubic ft.
⚓ D. 15.90 cubic ft.

010810/DG01827   ***BOWD 2; CHAP. 1**
What is the volume in a cone with a base diameter of 8 feet and a height of 6 feet?
⚓ A. 100.53 Cu. Ft
   B. 131.39 Cu. Ft
   C. 172.72 Cu. Ft
   D. 197.39 Cu. Ft

010811/DG01777   ***BOWD 2; CHAP. 1**
What is the volume in a cone with a base diameter of 23 feet and a height of 14 feet?
   A. 1,648.05 cubic ft.
⚓ B. 1,938.89 cubic ft.
   C. 2,908.33 cubic ft.
   D. 7,755.55 cubic ft.

010812/DG01772   ***BOWD 2; CHAP. 1**
What is the volume in a cone with a base diameter of 32 feet and a height of 21 feet?
   A. 8,444.60 cubic ft.
   B. 7,732.81 cubic ft.
⚓ C. 5,629.73 cubic ft.
   D. 703.72 cubic ft.

VOLUME OF A SPHERE

010813/DG02384   ***BOWD 2; CHAP. 1**
What is the volume of a sphere with a radius of 3 feet?
⚓ A. 113.08 cubic ft.
   B. 96.57 cubic ft.
   C. 37.69 cubic ft.
   D. 28.23 cubic ft.

010814/DG02367   ***BOWD 2; CHAP. 1**
What is the volume of a sphere with a radius of 5 feet?
   A. 4,188.00 cubic ft.
⚓ B. 523.60 cubic ft.
   C. 129.62 cubic ft.
   D. 65.44 cubic ft.

010815/DG02349   ***BOWD 2; CHAP. 1**
What is the volume of a sphere with a radius of 7 feet?
   A. 11,491.87 cubic ft.
⚓ B. 1,436.76 cubic ft.
   C. 963.72 cubic ft.
   D. 205.21 cubic ft.

010816/DG02346   ***BOWD 2; CHAP. 1**
What is the volume of a sphere with a radius of 11 feet?
   A. 506.75 cubic ft.
   B. 696.78 cubic ft.
⚓ C. 5,575.28 cubic ft.
   D. 44,593.82 cubic ft.

BOARD FEET

010817/DG00728   **MARINE CARGO OPS.**
How many board feet of dunnage are in a draft 4 feet wide, 1-1/2 feet high and 13 feet long?
A. 84
B. 756
⚓ C. 936
D. 1021

010818/DG00718   **MARINE CARGO OPS.**
How many board feet of dunnage would you estimate to be in a pile 5 feet wide, 1 foot high and 14 feet long?
A. 70
⚓ B. 840
C. 960
D. 1080

010819/DG00738   **MARINE CARGO OPS.**
How many board feet of dunnage are there in a draft 3 feet wide, 1-1/2 feet high, and 14 feet long?
A. 526
⚓ B. 756
C. 876
D. 906

010820/DG01672   **THOMAS**
You are to load a consignment of lumber. Each piece measures 2-inches thick, 10-inches wide and 16-feet long. There are 30,000 pieces in the shipment. How many board feet would be listed on the Bill of Lading?
⚓ A. 800,000
B. 1,200,000
C. 1,440,000
D. 14,400,000

010821/DG01705   **THOMAS**
You are to load a consignment of lumber. Each piece measures 3-inches thick, 12-inches wide and 16-feet long. There are 30,000 pieces in the shipment. How many board feet would be listed on the Bill of Lading?
A. 96,000
B. 1,200,000
⚓ C. 1,440,000
D. 14,400,000

RELATIVE HUMIDITY

010822/DG00548   **MARINE CARGO OPS.**
Using the graph shown, if the dry bulb temperature is 55° F (13° C) and the wet bulb is 50° F (10° C), what is the relative humidity? See Diagram D008DG
A. 55%
⚓ B. 70%
C. 75%
D. 82%

010823/DG01779   **CARGO HANDLING**
Using the graph shown, if the dry bulb temperature is 58°, and the wet bulb temperature is 53°, what is the relative humidity in a cargo hold? See Diagram D008DG
A. 56%
B. 61%
C. 66%
⚓ D. 75%

010824/DG01916   **CARGO HANDLING**
Using the graph shown, if the dry bulb temperature is 68°, and the wet bulb temperature is 65°, what is the relative humidity in a cargo hold? See Diagram D008DG
A. 66%
B. 74%
⚓ C. 82%
D. 90%

010825/DG02237   **CARGO HANDLING**
Using the graph in illustration D008DG, if the dry bulb temperature is 76° and the wet bulb temperature is 59°, what is the relative humidity in a cargo hold? See Diagram D008DG
⚓ A. 34%
B. 47%
C. 76%
D. 79%

010826/DG02282   **CARGO HANDLING**
Using the graph in illustration D008DG, if the dry bulb temperature is 77° and the wet bulb temperature is 69°, what is the relative humidity in a cargo hold? See Diagram D008DG
⚓ A. 67%
B. 70%
C. 77%
D. 81%

010827/DG00538   **MARINE CARGO OPS.**
Using the graph shown, if the dry bulb temperature is 80° F (27° C) and the wet bulb temperature is 70° F (21° C), what is the relative humidity in a cargo hold? See Diagram D008DG
A. 45%
B. 52%
⚓ C. 58%
D. 65%

010828/DG01617   **CARGO HANDLING**
Using the graph in illustration D008DG, if the dry bulb temperature is 84°, and the wet bulb temperature is 81°, what is the relative humidity in a cargo hold? See Diagram D008DG
A. 71%
B. 79%
C. 81%
⚓ D. 87%

010829/DG01697   **CARGO HANDLING**
Using the graph shown, if the dry bulb temperature is 85°, and the wet bulb temperature is 73°, what is the relative humidity in a cargo hold? See Diagram D008DG
A. 42%
⚓ B. 55%
C. 67%
D. 85%

010830/DG01991   **CARGO HANDLING**
Using the graph shown, if the dry bulb temperature is 91°, and the wet bulb temperature is 87°, what is the relative humidity in a cargo hold? See Diagram D008DG
A. 79%
⚓ B. 85%
C. 91%
D. 98%

010831/DG01967   **CARGO HANDLING**
Using the graph shown, if the dry bulb temperature is 92°, and the wet bulb temperature is 85°, what is the relative humidity in a cargo hold? See Diagram D008DG
⚓ A. 75%
B. 81%
C. 84%
D. 88%

010832/DG01830   **CARGO HANDLING**
Using the graph, if the dry bulb temperature is 76°, and the wet bulb temperature is 58°, what is the relative humidity in a cargo hold? See Diagram D008DG
⚓ A. 35%
B. 47%
C. 61%
D. 76%

010833/DG01810   **CARGO HANDLING**
Using the graph shown, if the dry bulb temperature is 98°, and the wet bulb temperature is 87°, what is the relative humidity in a cargo hold? See Diagram D008DG
A. 87%
B. 84%
C. 79%
⚓ D. 65%

DEW POINT

010834/DG00528   **BOWD**
Determine the dew point when the dry bulb temperature is 74° F (23° C) and the wet bulb temperature is 60° F (16° C). See Diagram D008DG
A. 14° F
B. 20° F
C. 28° F
⚓ D. 50° F

010835/DG02215   **BOWD**
Given a dry bulb temperature of 78° F and wet bulb temperature of 66.5° F, the dew point is _____. See Diagram D008DG
A. 47.0° F
B. 51.5° F
⚓ C. 59.0° F
D. 70.0° F

FULL & DOWN

010836/DG02087   **THOMAS**
A vessel has a deadweight carrying capacity of 10,500 tons. Fuel, water, and stores require 1500 tons. The cubic capacity is 500,000 cubic feet. Which cargo will put her full and down?
A. Slabs of zinc, SF 7.1
⚓ B. Rolls of barbed wire, SF 55.5
C. Barrels of tallow, SF 66.8
D. Bundles of rubber, SF 140.2

010837/DG00818   **MARINE CARGO OPS.**
Your vessel has a deadweight capacity of 5000 tons and a cubic capacity of 300,000 cu. ft. You are to load lead, with a stowage factor of 18, and cotton, with a stowage factor of 80. If you load full and down, how much cotton should you load?
A. 1613 tons
B. 2190 tons
C. 2810 tons
⚓ D. 3387 tons

010838/DG00828   **MARINE CARGO OPS.**
Your vessel's available bale cubic capacity is 625,000 and her available cargo capacity is 10,000 deadweight tons. Disregarding broken stowage, how many tons of pyrite (stowage factor - 13) and how many tons of cork (s.f. - 150) must be loaded to be full and down?
⚓ A. 6387 tons pyrite, 3613 tons cork
B. 6721 tons pyrite, 3279 tons cork
C. 7500 tons pyrite, 2500 tons cork
D. 9133 tons pyrite, 867 tons cork

TANK VESSEL CARGO OPERATIONS

LIQUID CARGO SAMPLING

010839/DG00339   **BAPTIST**
Oil product samples should be taken from the _____.
A. dock riser
B. ship's cargo tanks
C. shore tank discharge
⚓ D. All of the above

CARGO TANK GAUGING

010840/DG00219   **MARTON**
What refers to the depth of a petroleum product in a tank?
⚓ A. Innage
B. Outage
C. Thievage
D. Ullage

010841/DG00229   **MARTON**
Which refers to the depth of a petroleum product in a tank?
A. Outage
B. Ullage
C. Thievage
⚓ D. Innage

010842/DG00329   **MARTON**
Litmus paste is used in order to determine _____.
A. innage
⚓ B. thievage
C. ullage
D. the tank's datum point

010843/DG00099   **MARTON**
What is meant by "thieving" a petroleum cargo?
A. Siphoning off a few barrels of petroleum for shipboard use
⚓ B. Determining the amount of water (if any) in each cargo tank
C. Adjusting the cargo figures to coincide with the draft
D. Reducing the gross cargo calculations to net amounts

010844/DG00109   **MARTON**
What is meant by "thieving" a petroleum cargo?
A. Adjusting the cargo figures to coincide with the draft
⚓ B. Determining the amount of water (if any) in each cargo tank
C. Reducing the gross cargo calculations to net amounts
D. Siphoning off a few barrels of petroleum for shipboard use

010845/DG00257   **MARTON**
The distance between the surface of the liquid and the tank top in a cargo tank is called _____.
A. thievage
B. innage
⚓ C. ullage
D. tankage

010846/DG00089   **MARTON**
Ullage measurements are taken from the top of the liquid to _____.
A. the base of the expansion trunk
B. the base of the ullage port
C. a line scribed within the ullage port
⚓ D. an above-deck datum, usually the top of the ullage hole

010847/DG00069   **MARTON**
Ullages are measured from _____.
A. the tank ceiling
B. the tank top bushing
C. the thievage mark
⚓ D. an above deck datum

010848/DG00079   **MARTON**
Ullages on tankers are measured from _____.
⚓ A. an above-deck datum such as the top of the ullage pipe
B. the tank ceiling aboard transversely framed vessels
C. the tank top
D. a thievage mark below the edge of the deck

CHARACTERISTICS & SENSITIVITY OF LIQUID CARGOES

010849/DG00509   **MARTON; ISGOTT**
Which factor must be considered when determining the order of loading of dissimilar products through the same piping system aboard a tanker?
⚓ A. Contamination of the cargo
B. Flash points
C. Reid vapor pressures
D. Specific gravities

010850/DG00745   **BAPTIST**
When carrying a cargo of asphalt or molten sulfur, which are carried at temperatures of over 300° F, one of the biggest dangers is _____.
⚓ A. water in the tanks or pipelines
B. having the cargo too cool
C. explosion of vapors after discharge
D. inadequate ullage space

010851/DG00747   **BAPTIST**
When carrying a cargo of asphalt or molten sulfur, which are carried at temperatures of over 300° F, one of the biggest dangers is _____.
A. inadequate ullage space
B. having the cargo too cool
C. explosion of vapors after discharge
⚓ D. having to breathe the fumes

010852/DG00459   **MMOH; MARTON**
Petroleum cargo tanks should not be topped off at deck level when loading on a cold day because _____.
⚓ A. a subsequent temperature rise will cause the cargo to overflow
B. air pockets may cause the cargo to bubble out of the ullage hole
C. the increased viscosity of the product requires higher loading pressure which increases the chances of a spill
D. the tank valve may be stiff and a spill will occur before the valve can be closed

010853/DG00469   **MARTON**
With an increase in temperature the volume of flammable and combustible liquids _____.
⚓ A. expands
B. contracts
C. remains constant
D. remains constant if pressure remains constant

010854/DG00569   **MFPFFS**
In order to reduce the accumulation of static electricity while loading petroleum products, you should _____.
A. start to load at maximum pressure
⚓ B. start to load slowly
C. increase the air flow into the tank
D. use the overall method of loading only

010855/DG00319   **PTS**
Static electricity may be built up by the _____.
A. flow of petroleum through pipes
B. spraying or splashing of petroleum
C. settling of solids or water in petroleum
⚓ D. All of the above

010856/DG01169   **PTS**
Static electricity may be built up by the _____.
A. spraying or splashing of petroleum
B. settling of solids or water in petroleum
C. flow of petroleum through pipes
⚓ D. All of the above

010857/DG01159   **CG-174**
Which product is most likely to accumulate static electricity?
A. Crude oil
B. Hard asphalt
⚓ C. Lubricating oil
D. Residual fuel oil

010858/DG00119   **MARTON**
Sour crude oil _____.
⚓ A. contains high quantities of hydrogen sulfide
B. is diluted with other products for carriage
C. is lighter than other crudes
D. is less hazardous to load than other crudes

LIQUID CARGO TERMINOLOGY

010859/DG00139   **MARTON**
A "barrel" is a unit of liquid measure equivalent to _____.
A. 40 U.S. gallons at 50° F
⚓ B. 42 U.S. gallons at 60° F
C. 43 U.S. gallons at 65° F
D. 45 U.S. gallons at 75° F

010860/DG00149   **MARTON**
A standard net barrel of petroleum products is _____.
⚓ A. 42 gallons at 60° F
B. 48 gallons at 70° F
C. 50 gallons at 50° F
D. 60 gallons at 100° F

010861/DG00133   **MARTON**
The standard unit of liquid volume used in the petroleum industry, as well as the tanker industry, is a _____.
⚓ A. barrel
B. drum
C. gallon
D. liter

010862/DG00159   **MARTON**
What is the standard net barrel for petroleum products?
⚓ A. 42 gallons at 60° Fahrenheit
B. 48 gallons at 70° Fahrenheit
C. 50 gallons at 50° Celsius
D. 60 gallons at 100° Saybolt

010863/DG00032   **MFPFFS**
The explosive range of a fuel lies between the lower explosive limit and the _____.
A. flash point
B. ignition temperature
⚓ C. upper explosive limit
D. fire point

010864/DG00189   **MARTON; AMSM**
Reid vapor pressure is _____.
A. exerted by liquid cargo on the sides of a tank
B. exerted by liquid cargo on a cargo hose body
C. the lowest temperature and pressure that will cause a flammable liquid to give off vapors
⚓ D. a measurement of the amount of flammable vapors given off by a liquid at a certain temperature

010865/DG00042   **BAPTIST**
The vapor pressure of a substance _____.
A. decreases as temperature increases
⚓ B. increases with the temperature
C. is not affected by temperature
D. may increase or decrease as the temperature rises

010866/DG00380   **ISGOTT**
The (auto)ignition temperature is that temperature at which _____.
⚓ A. no spark or flame is required to ignite gas or vapor
B. a fuel begins to give off explosive vapors
C. a fuel if ignited will continue to burn
D. a 1% mixture of the fuel with air will explode

010867/DG00179   ***CHEM. DATA GUIDE; MARTON**
The minimum temperature required to ignite gas or vapor without a spark or flame being present is called _____.
A. flash point
B. fire point
⚓ C. autoignition temperature
D. lower explosive limit

010868/DG00169   ***CHEM. DATA GUIDE; MARTON**
The lowest temperature at which a liquid will give off sufficient vapors to form a flammable mixture with air is known as the _____.
A. fire point
⚓ B. flash point
C. lower explosive limit
D. threshold limit value

BUNKERING OPERATIONS

010869/DG00312   **MARTON**
If you are bunkering and you close off one tank in the line of tanks being filled, the rate of flow to other open tanks on the same line will _____.
⚓ A. increase
B. decrease
C. stop
D. remain constant

010870/DG01189   **MARTON**
When bunkering is complete, the hoses should be _____.
A. cleaned internally with a degreaser
B. washed out with hot soapy water
⚓ C. drained, blanked off, and stored securely
D. stowed vertically and allowed to drain

010871/DG00936   **MARTON**
A precaution you should take before bunkering is to _____.
A. plug the vents
B. plug the sounding pipes
⚓ C. plug the scuppers
D. close the lids on the vents

010872/DG01179   **MARTON**
The most likely time for oil pollution while bunkering is when _____.
⚓ A. final topping off is occurring
B. first starting to receive fuel
C. hoses are being blown down
D. hoses are disconnected and being capped

010873/DG00935   **MARTON**
The scuppers had been plugged as required at the time an oil spill occurs on deck. After shutting down the transfer, the engineroom should first be informed and then _____.
A. rig a fire hose and call for water on deck
⚓ B. spread an absorbent material, such as sawdust
C. remove the plugs from the scuppers
D. sound the general alarm

010874/DG02450   **CHAPMAN**
Which statement is FALSE concerning precautions during fueling operations?
A. All engines, motors, fans, etc. should be shut down when fueling.
B. All windows, doors, hatches, etc. should be closed.
C. A fire extinguisher should be kept nearby.
⚓ D. Fuel tanks should be topped off with no room for expansion.

010875/DG00940   **MARTON**
When selecting the fuel oil tanks for the "burn-out" of bunkers during a voyage consideration of all of the following must be taken with the EXCEPTION of _____.
⚓ A. flashpoint
B. stability
C. trim
D. list

010876/DG00953   **MARTON**
When bunkering at anchorage which of the following signals must be displayed?
A. A red flag by day, red light by night
⚓ B. A red flag by day ONLY
C. A red light by night ONLY
D. No signal required at anchorage

010877/DG00928   **MARTON**
Which of the signals listed is required to be displayed during the day while bunkering?
⚓ A. A red flag
B. A yellow flag
C. A red and yellow flag
D. A red light

010878/DG00932   **MARTON**
When bunkering at a dock which of the following signals must be displayed?
A. A yellow flag by day, red light by night
⚓ B. A red flag by day, red light by night
C. A green flag by day, green light by night
D. A red flag by day, a blue light by night

010879/DG00930   **MARTON**
Which of the signals listed is required to be displayed at night while bunkering at a dock?
⚓ A. One red light
B. Two red lights
C. One red light over a yellow light
D. One red light over a white light

CARGO TRANSFER OPERATIONS

010880/DG00299   **MARTON; MMOH**
Cargo transfer operations on a tank vessel need NOT be stopped when _____.
⚓ A. a tug comes alongside while the tanker is loading grade D and E cargoes
B. a large, fresh oil spill is discovered immediately adjacent to the side of the tanker
C. there is an electrical storm in the vicinity
D. there is a fire on the dock or on a nearby vessel

010881/DG00162   ***33 CFR 156.120 (m)**
Oil may NOT be transferred unless _____.
A. there are two certificated tankermen on each vessel
B. the vessel is equipped with constant-tension winches
⚓ C. discharge containment equipment (i.e. drip pans) are in place
D. All of the above

010882/DG00529   **MMOH; MARTON**
When loading a tanker, you should _____.
A. load only one tank at a time
B. keep the seamen on watch on standby in the mess room
C. keep a strain on the loading hoses
⚓ D. close valves by closing them down, reopening one or two turns, and re-closing

010883/DG00272   ***46 CFR 39.30-1 (i)**
When measuring the oxygen content of the cargo tanks prior to loading cargoes requiring vapor recovery, check it _____.
A. one meter from the tank bottom and one meter below the tank top
⚓ B. one half the ullage of the tank and one meter below the tank top
C. one half the ullage of the tank and one meter above the tank bottom
D. at three meter intervals from the tank top to the bottom

010884/DG00249   **CG-174**
Functions aboard a tanker or tank barge such as connecting, disconnecting, and topping off must be supervised by _____.
A. any certificated tankerman
B. the Master of the vessel
C. the officer of the watch
⚓ D. the person designated as "person in charge"

010885/DG00519   **MARTON**
What is NOT a precaution to be taken when topping off?
A. Reduce the loading rate.
⚓ B. Notify the engine room of the procedure.
C. Maintain communications with the dock man.
D. Give the operation your undivided attention.

010886/DG00439   **MARTON**
When loading bulk liquid cargo, what is the FIRST action you should take if a cargo valve jammed open?
A. Trip the pump relief valve.
⚓ B. Order the dock man to shut down.
C. Call the owner, operator, or terminal supervisor.
D. Run out the vessel's or terminal's fire hose.

010887/DG00449   **MARTON**
When loading bulk liquid cargo, what is the first action you should take if a cargo valve jammed open?
A. Call the owner, operator, or terminal supervisor.
B. Unplug the deck scuppers.
⚓ C. Order the dock man to shut down.
D. Run out the vessel's or terminal's fire hose.

DISCHARGE & STRIPPING OPERATIONS

010888/DG01129   **MARTON**

The main function of a stripping system is to _____.

A. maintain the temperature of the cargo throughout the vessel
B. dispose of dangerous vapors within the cargo tanks
C. increase the loading rate of the shoreside pumps
⚓ D. discharge liquid left in the cargo tanks after the main pumps have discharged the bulk

010889/DG00599   **MARTON**

When stripping a tank, excessive air in the suction line may cause _____.

A. an over pressurized line
B. back pressure
⚓ C. loss of suction
D. increase of suction

010890/DG04030   **BAPTIST**

While discharging a cargo, the stripping of the tanks falls behind schedule. This would indicate the _____.

A. main pumps are working at a high discharge pressure
⚓ B. main pumps are leaving too much oil in the tanks
C. stripping pump is not primed
D. stripping line is cross-connected to the main line

010891/DG04020   **MARTON**

You are on a tankship discharging oil. When all of the oil that the main cargo pumps can handle is pumped out of a tank, the remainder is _____.

A. stripped out and pumped directly ashore into the mainline as the remaining cargo tanks are pumped out with the main pumps
⚓ B. stripped to one tank and then pumped out with the main pumps
C. stripped out and pumped directly ashore after all the tanks have been emptied by the main pumps
D. gravitated to the centers from the wings and pumped out with the main pumps

BONDING CABLES

010892/DG00389   **ISGOTT**

When hooking up a cargo hose to your vessel's manifold, you should use a(n) _____.

A. international shore connection
⚓ B. insulating flange or single length of non-conducting hose
C. self-contained breathing apparatus
D. oxygen analyzer

TANK VESSEL TRIM & STABILITY

010893/DG00609   **MARTON**

While discharging a tanker, list can be controlled by _____.

A. shoreside personnel
B. using a center tank near the bow, discharging as necessary
⚓ C. using wing tanks near the longitudinal center, discharging as necessary
D. using the after peak tank, loading as necessary

010894/DG02569   **MARTON**

When discharging an oil cargo, the first consideration is to _____.

⚓ A. get the bow up
B. discharge from the wings first
C. discharge from the centerline tanks first
D. discharge from amidships first

010895/DG02609   **MARTON**

Which tanker discharge pattern would be the safest and most efficient?

A. Empty the forward tanks and start working aft, emptying each tank in sequence
⚓ B. Start discharging with most of the discharge coming from forward, but include some from midships and after tanks
C. Start pumping from forward, midships, and aft with the discharge distributed equally among the tanks
D. Start pumping from midships and then work forward and aft simultaneously as the midships tank is emptied

010896/DG00489   **MARTON**

Your tank vessel is fully loaded, and you find that she is down slightly by the head. To adjust the trim, you may _____.

A. add ballast aft
B. load more cargo aft
⚓ C. shift cargo aft
D. All of the above

010897/DG00479   **MARTON**

Your tank vessel is loaded down to her marks, and you find that she has too much trim by the stern. To adjust the trim you may _____.

A. add ballast forward
B. load more cargo forward
⚓ C. shift bunkers forward
D. All of the above

010898/DG00499   **MARTON**

Your tank vessel is loaded down to her marks, and you find that she has too much trim by the stern. To adjust the trim, you may _____.

- A. add ballast forward
- B. load more cargo forward
- ⚓ C. shift bunkers forward
- D. All of the above

010899/DG00559   **MARTON**

A vessel loads edible oil in a deep tank through a manhole at the mid-length of the tank. In order to fill the tank to maximum capacity, what trim should the vessel have?

- A. Down by the bow
- B. Down by the stern
- C. Down by either the bow or stern
- ⚓ D. In level trim

TANK VESSEL CARGO PIPING SYSTEMS

CARGO HOSES

010900/DG01109   **MFPFFS**

Pinching of the cargo hose between the vessel and the dock should be prevented by _____.

- ⚓ A. adjusting the hose supports
- B. laying out an excess length of hose on deck
- C. tying off the topping lifts and runners to winch heads
- D. All of the above

010901/DG01099   ***33 CFR 156.120**

To allow for the rise or fall in tide and for change in draft of a tankship during cargo transfer, cargo hoses must be suspended with _____.

- A. slings or saddles placed at 25-foot (8 meter) intervals
- ⚓ B. enough slack in their bight
- C. topping lifts and runners tied off to winches
- D. All of the above

010902/DG00549   **MARTON**

Your vessel is taking on cargo oil when a small leak develops in the hose. You order the pumping stopped. Before you resume pumping, you should _____.

- A. notify the terminal superintendent
- B. place a large drip pan under the leak and plug the scuppers
- C. repair the hose with a patch
- ⚓ D. replace the hose

CARGO PIPE FITTINGS

010903/DG01119   **MARTON**

A single fitting installed in a pipeline that either blanks off the pipe or allows a full flow passage of a liquid through the pipe is referred to as a _____.

- A. blind flange
- B. pivot coupling
- C. quick-release coupling
- ⚓ D. spectacle flange

010904/DG04442   **ISGOTT**

Insulating flanges minimize the dangers arising from _____.

- A, smoking on deck
- B. loading asphalt
- ⚓ C. accumulations of electrostatic charges
- D. tank over-pressurization

010905/DG00392   **ISGOTT**

Which statement is TRUE concerning insulating flanges?

- ⚓ A. They should be inspected and tested periodically to ensure that the insulation is clean and in good condition.
- B. Switching off a cathodic protection system may be substituted for using an insulating flange
- C. The measured resistance value after installation should be less than 1,000 ohms.
- D. After the insulating flange is installed, hot work may be performed on deck.

CARGO PIPING SYSTEMS

010906/DG02809   **MARTON**

The fitting at the end of a cargo line in a tank that allows suction to be taken close to the bottom of a tank is a _____.

- A. suction end
- B. strainer
- ⚓ C. bell-mouth
- D. vacuum valve

010907/DG03000   **MARTON**

The pipe used to connect two separate piping systems on a tank vessel is known as a _____.

- ⚓ A. crossover
- B. transfer
- C. connection
- D. junction

010908/DG00137   **MARTON**

The system of valves and cargo lines in the bottom piping network of a tank barge that connects one section of cargo tanks to another section is called a _____.

A. come-along

⚓ B. crossover

C. manifold

D. runaround

010909/DG01089   **MARTON**

The system of valves and cargo lines in the bottom piping network of a tank vessel that connects one section of cargo tanks to another section is called a _____.

⚓ A. crossover

B. runaround

C. come-along

D. manifold

010910/DG01079   **MARTON**

The system of valves and cargo lines in the bottom piping network of a tanker that connects one section of cargo tanks to another section is called a _____.

A. come-along

⚓ B. crossover

C. manifold

D. runaround

010911/DG03020   **MARTON**

The main underdeck pipeline on a tankship is connected to individual tanks by _____.

A. tank drops

B. line drops

C. crossovers

⚓ D. branch lines

010912/DG03010   **MARTON**

The piping that routes an oil cargo from the manifold directly to a cargo tank and serves only one tank is known as a _____.

A. cargo fill

B. filler line

⚓ C. tank drop

D. branch line

010913/DG03030   **MARTON**

The piping that routes an oil cargo from the manifold to underdeck pipelines is known as a _____.

A. cargo fill

⚓ B. line drop

C. transfer

D. branch line

010914/DG02662   **BAPTIST**

What will NOT increase friction of a liquid flowing in a pipe and cause a loss of suction head?

A. Bends in the piping

⚓ B. Slowing the pumping rate

C. Pipeline valves

D. Backing rings for pipe welds

CARGO VALVE OPERATION

010915/DG00869   **MARTON**

To ensure proper seating when closing a valve on a tank, the valve should be _____.

A. set up as tight as possible by hand

B. set up tight using a valve wrench

⚓ C. closed, opened a half turn, and then closed

D. closed against the stop and the locking pin inserted

010916/DG00859   **MMOH**

To insure proper seating when closing a valve on a tank, the valve should be _____.

A. closed against the stop and the locking pin inserted

⚓ B. closed, opened a half turn, and then closed again

C. set up as tight as possible by hand

D. set up tight using a valve wrench

CLASSIFICATION & USE OF VALVES

010917/DG03050   **MARTON**

Which characteristic is an advantage of a butterfly valve as compared to a gate valve?

A. Precise control over cargo flow

⚓ B. Quick operation

C. No resistance to cargo flow when open

D. Less maintenance required

010918/DG03060   **MARTON**

Which characteristic is an advantage of a butterfly valve as compared to a gate valve?

A. Precise adjustment of cargo flow

B. Faster rate of cargo flow

⚓ C. Easier operation

D. Less chance of leaks

010919/DG00839   **MARTON**

The valve on the discharge side of a cargo pump on a tank vessel will usually be a _____.

A. butterfly valve

B. spectacle valve

⚓ C. check valve

D. globe valve

010920/DG00849   **MARTON**

The valve on the discharge side of a cargo pump on a tank vessel will usually be a _____.

A. gate valve

B. butterfly valve

C. globe valve

⚓ D. check valve

010921/DG03070   **MARTON**

What is an advantage of a gate valve over a butterfly valve?

⚓ A. Less frequent maintenance
B. Faster operation
C. Cheaper
D. More compact

010922/DG00939   ***46 CFR 30.10-55; MARTON**

What is the purpose of pressure-vacuum relief valves?

A. Regulation of discharge pressure from cargo pumps
B. Maintaining constant velocity in cargo lines
C. Regulation of suction head on cargo pumps
⚓ D. To maintain a tank or void at atmospheric pressure

010923/DG00383   **MARTON**

What is TRUE of pressure/vacuum valves?

A. They are designed to provide for the flow of small volumes of tank atmospheres caused by thermal variations in a cargo tank.
B. They should operate in advance of the pressure/vacuum breakers.
C. They should be kept in good working order by regular inspection and cleaning.
⚓ D. All of the above

010924/DG00959   ***46 CFR 36.10-1**

A relief valve for a cargo pump is generally installed _____.

A. after the discharge valve
⚓ B. between the pump and discharge valve
C. after the suction valve
D. between the pump and suction valve

010925/DG00949   **MARTON**

Cargo pump relief valves are piped to the _____.

A. cargo pump pressure gauges
B. crossover lines interconnecting two pumps
⚓ C. suction side of pumps
D. atmosphere through pump vents

010926/DG00909   **MARTON**

What is the purpose of the relief valve of a cargo pump?

A. Provides for the removal of vapors
B. Allows two or more tanks to be filled at the same time
C. Provides for the emergency shutdown of the pump
⚓ D. Permits the return of cargo to the suction side of the pump

CARGO SYSTEM LINE-UP

010927/DG03080   **BAPTIST**

Which method should be used to warm up the pump turbines prior to discharge?

A. Lock the turbine rotor and slowly bleed in steam until operating temperature is reached
B. Run the pump at high speed with the discharge valves closed
C. Run the turbine at slow speed with the pump disconnected
⚓ D. Shut the discharge valve and run the pump at slow speed

TANK VESSEL CARGO PUMPING SYSTEMS

CARGO PUMPS (NON-POSITIVE DISPLACEMENT)

010928/DG00879   **MARTON**

Centrifugal pumps have what advantage(s) over reciprocating pumps?

A. They are less expensive.
B. They are smaller for equivalent pumping ability.
C. They pump more cargo in less time.
⚓ D. All of the above

010929/DG00142   **MARTON**

What is NOT an advantage of centrifugal pumps over reciprocating pumps?

A. They pump more cargo in less time.
B. They are smaller for equivalent pumping ability.
C. They are less expensive.
⚓ D. They require priming for stripping.

010930/DG00122   **MARTON**

You may be able to avoid loss of suction in a pump by _____.

A. using a full tank to keep the pump primed
B. opening the vent cock on the pump
C. closing down on the tank valve
⚓ D. All of the above

010931/DG00092   **MARTON**

You start a centrifugal cargo pump to discharge cargo. The pump works for a while and then loses suction. This could be caused by _____.

A. the pump running backwards
⚓ B. incomplete priming
C. the discharge head being too high
D. All of the above

010932/DG00112   MARTON
You start a centrifugal cargo pump to discharge cargo. The pump works for a while and then loses suction. This could NOT be caused by _____.
A. leaking shaft seals
B. air pockets in the liquid
⚓ C. high cargo level in the tanks
D. a leaking suction line

010933/DG00132   MARTON
What is a characteristic of all centrifugal cargo pumps?
A. They are self-priming.
⚓ B. Decreasing the speed of rotation will decrease the discharge pressure.
C. Opening the discharge valve wider will increase the discharge pressure.
D. All of the above

010934/DG00929   MARTON
All of the following steps are taken in starting a centrifugal pump, EXCEPT to _____.
⚓ A. set the relief valve
B. check the lubrication system
C. vent the pump casing
D. open the pump suction and discharge valves

010935/DG00809   MARTON
Which pump must always be primed?
⚓ A. Centrifugal pump
B. Reciprocating pump
C. Rotary pump
D. All of the above

010936/DG00819   MARTON
Which pump must be primed?
A. Rotary pump
B. Reciprocating pump
⚓ C. Centrifugal pump
D. All of the above

010937/DG00789   MARTON
Which statement about a centrifugal cargo pump is TRUE?
A. It is a positive displacement pump.
⚓ B. It must have a positive suction.
C. Increasing rotation speed will decrease discharge pressure.
D. All of the above

010938/DG00790   CG-174
Which statement is TRUE of centrifugal pumps aboard tank vessels?
A. They are positive displacement pumps.
⚓ B. They are gravity-fed.
C. They produce a pulsating flow.
D. They require more maintenance than a reciprocating pump.

010939/DG00779   MARTON
Which statement is TRUE of centrifugal pumps aboard tankers?
⚓ A. They are gravity-fed.
B. They are more expensive than reciprocating pumps.
C. They are positive displacement pumps.
D. They are used for stripping pumps.

010940/DG02892   MARTON
What is LEAST likely to be used to strip a cargo tank?
⚓ A. Centrifugal pump
B. Eductor
C. Rotary pump
D. Reciprocating pump

010941/DG00919   MARTON
A deepwell pump is a type of _____.
A. screw pump
⚓ B. centrifugal pump
C. eductor
D. gear pump

010942/DG00397   BAPTIST
Which statement is TRUE concerning deep well self-priming pumps?
A. When loading oil cargo, it is always loaded via the discharge line through to the pump until the tank is topped off.
⚓ B. Stripping systems are generally eliminated for the purposes of cargo handling.
C. In recent years deep well pumps have become increasingly unpopular in product tankers and medium size crude ships.
D. There is no danger of damaging the pump from overheating.

BOOSTER PUMPS

010943/DG00589   MARTON
The terminal indicates to you that they are going to use a booster pump to assist the discharging operation. You start the discharge and in a few minutes the pressure drops sharply. This could be a result of the _____.
⚓ A. booster pump coming on the line and discharging properly
B. booster pump failing to start
C. ship's pump speeding up
D. booster pump being lined up in the wrong direction

010944/DG00579   **MARTON**

The terminal indicates to you that they are going to use a booster pump to assist the discharging operation. You start the discharge, and in a few minutes the pressure drops sharply. This could be a result of the _____.

⚓ A. booster pump coming on the line and discharging properly
   B. booster pump failing to start
   C. booster pump being lined up in the wrong direction
   D. ship's pump speeding up

TANK CLEANING & CRUDE OIL WASHING OPERATIONS

TANK CLEANING & WATER WASHING

010945/DG00385   ***33 CFR 157.155; BAPTIST**

In controlling pollution, which action should be taken after all dirty ballast has been transferred to the slop tank and prior to discharge through the oily water separator?
   A. The clean tanks should be ballasted.
⚓ B. The slops should be allowed time to settle.
   C. Chemicals should be added to emulsify the oil.
   D. The dirty ballast tank is crude oil washed.

010946/DG01029   **MARTON**

When cleaning a tank by the Butterworth process, you should begin to pump out the slops _____.
   A. at the end of the drop schedule
⚓ B. when the process is started
   C. when the process is finished
   D. when the tank is clean

010947/DG02912   **MARTON**

When tank cleaning with a portable machine, the weight of the machine is suspended from _____.
   A. solid iron bars clamped to the Butterworth opening
⚓ B. the supply hose
   C. the suspension line, usually manila or natural fiber line
   D. a wire rope suspension line

010948/DG01039   **MARTON**

When cleaning cargo tanks with portable machines, how is the machine grounded?
   A. Bonding wires are secured from the machine to a convenient location on deck.
   B. The machines must maintain physical contact with the deck at the Butterworth opening.
⚓ C. The water supply hoses contain internal wires that act as conductors
   D. The water jets impinging on the vessel's structure form a pathway to ground.

010949/DG01049   **MARTON**

You have water washed your cargo tanks using the fixed machines. What should you do before using portable machines to clean areas screened from the wash of the fixed machine by structural members?
⚓ A. Ventilate the tank to eliminate any electrostatically charged mist.
   B. Attach the water supply hose to the portable machine after the cleaning head is positioned inside the tank.
   C. Insure that the tanks are not stripped until the final wash is started.
   D. Ground the fixed machines to eliminate any electrostatic buildup on the cleaning head.

CRUDE OIL WASHING OPERATIONS

010950/DG00649   ***33 CFR 157.164**

Before a tank is to be crude oil washed, the oxygen content in the tank must be measured at a position _____.
   A. immediately above the level of the oil
   B. at the top of the tank
   C. in the vent riser
⚓ D. one meter from the deck

010951/DG00629   ***33 CFR 157.155**

You are planning to use a crude oil washing system. What precaution must be taken with the source tank for the washing machines?
⚓ A. At least one meter must be decanted from the source tank.
   B. The oil in the source tank must be sampled for compatibility.
   C. The source tank must have been crude oil washed at least once in the past 150 days.
   D. The inert gas system must lower the oxygen content in the source tank to a maximum of 12%.

010952/DG00659   **MARTON**

You are planning to use the crude oil washing system on your tankship. What is required to prevent electrostatic buildup in the tanks?
   A. The portable machines must be set at the proper drop for the first wash before the fixed machines are used.
⚓ B. The source tank for the tank cleaning machines must have least one meter decanted from it.
   C. The inert gas system must reduce the oxygen content in the tanks to a maximum of 18%.
   D. The fixed machines must be operated simultaneously with the portable machines to equalize the electrostatic potential.

010953/DG04010   **MARTON**
You have completed a crude oil wash. What action should be taken with the oil in the lines running to the washing machines?
⚓ A, Open a COW nozzle forward and one aft and drain the line into the after tank by gravity
B. Blow the line out using compressed air
C. Pull a suction using the supply line pump
D. Close off all valves in the system and leave the oil in the line primed for the next crude oil wash

010954/DG00619   **MARTON**
What is NOT a requirement for the safe and effective use of a crude oil washing system?
A. Strip all tanks and remove the bottom residue.
B. Use an inert gas system while washing tanks.
⚓ C. Use portable washing machines to reach areas obscured by structural members in the tanks.
D. Decant one meter from the source tank for the tank cleaning machines.

010955/DG00639   ***33 CFR 157.138**
The complete details of a crude oil washing system aboard your vessel, including the operating sequences and procedures, design characteristics, a description of the system, and required personnel will be found in the _____.
A. Oil Transfer Procedures Manual
⚓ B. Crude Oil Washing Operations and Equipment Manual
C. Code of Federal Regulations
D. Crude Oil Washing addendum to the Certificate of Inspection

010956/DG01059   **MARTON**
You are cleaning the tanks after carrying a cargo of crude oil. Which statement is TRUE?
A. Washing water should be recirculated if possible because it has the same electric potential as the cargo tank being cleaned.
B. The hoses to portable cleaning machines should be disconnected before the machines are removed from the tank.
C. The principal hazard with steaming cargo tanks is raising the ambient temperature above the flame point of the cargo residue.
⚓ D. Steam cleaning and water washing are both capable of generating electrostatic charges within a tank.

TANK ENTRY PROCEDURES

GAS FREEING OPERATIONS

010957/DG03150   ***46 CFR 31.05-5; *46 CFR 35.01**
You are moving a gas free tank barge to dry dock for repairs. The barge must have onboard a valid _____.
A. Gas Free Certificate
⚓ B. Certificate of Inspection
C. Permit to Proceed and Hot Work Permit
D. All of the above

010958/DG01069   **MARTON**
Which step is NOT generally taken when gas-freeing a tank?
A. Washing the tank interior with sea water
⚓ B. Application of degreasing solvents
C. Removal of corrosion products and sludge
D. Fresh air ventilation

TANK VESSEL OPERATIONS COMPUTATIONS

LIQUID CARGO TANK VOLUME

010959/DG01019   **LADAGE**
A tank holds 400 tons of sea water when filled. How many tons of liquid of specific gravity 0.9300 will it hold when filled to 90% capacity?
⚓ A. 326.6
B. 343.2
C. 377.6
D. 390.2

LIQUID CARGO RATE

010960/DG00989   **MARTON**
You are loading 465,000 barrels of cargo oil. At 0900 you find that you have loaded 207,000 barrels. At 1030 you find that you have loaded 223,000 barrels. If you continue loading at the same rate, you will finish at approximately _____.
A. 2100 that night
B. 0730 the next day
⚓ C. 0910 the next day
D. 1215 the next day

010961/DG00999   **MARTON**
You are loading 530,000 barrels of cargo oil. At 0945 on 13 April, you find that you have loaded 202,000 barrels. At 1130, you find that you have loaded 223,000 barrels. If you continue at the same rate, you will finish at _____.
A. 1322, 13 April
B. 1920, 13 April
C. 1120, 14 April
⚓ D. 1305, 14 April

010962/DG01009   **MARTON**

You are loading 475,000 barrels of cargo oil. At 0800 on 8 July, you find that you have loaded 174,000 barrels. At 1000, you find that you have loaded 192,000 barrels. If you continue loading at the same rate, you will finish at approximately _____.

- A. 1752, 8 July
- B. 1940, 8 July
- C. 0143, 9 July
- ⚓ D. 1727, 9 July

010963/DG00072   **MARTON**

You are in the process of loading 465,000 barrels of cargo oil. At 1030, on 5 November, you gauge the vessel and find that you have loaded 203,000 barrels. At 1200 you find that you have loaded 218,000 barrels. If you continue loading at the same rate, you will finish at approximately _____.

- A. 1510, 5 November
- B. 1104, 6 November
- ⚓ C. 1242, 6 November
- D. 0735, 7 November

010964/DG00062   **MARTON**

You are in the process of loading 465,000 barrels of cargo oil. At 1030, on 5 November, you gauge the vessel and find that you have loaded 203,000 barrels. At 1200 you find that you have loaded 219,000 barrels. If you continue loading at the same rate, you will finish at approximately _____.

- A. 1510, 5 November
- B. 0140, 6 November
- ⚓ C. 1104, 6 November
- D. 0735, 7 November

COEFFICIENT OF EXPANSION GROSS & NET VOLUME

010965/DG00409   **MMOH**

A tanker is loaded with 5,000 barrels of petroleum. The cargo was loaded at a temperature of 70° F, and the coefficient of expansion is .0004. What is the net amount in barrels of cargo loaded?

- A. 4800
- ⚓ B. 4980
- C. 5020
- D. 5200

010966/DG01454   **MMOH**

Your ship has loaded 6,000 barrels of gasoline, at a cargo temperature of 50° F, departing New Jersey bound for Florida. API gravity is 55°. The volume correction factor (VCF) is .0006. How many barrels would you expect to unload if the cargo temperature is 90° F at the discharge port?

- A. 5,856
- B. 5,982
- C. 6,018
- ⚓ D. 6,144

010967/DG01554   **MMOH**

Your ship has loaded 8,000 barrels of gasoline at a cargo temperature of 36° C (97° F). API gravity is 54°. The volume correction factor (VCF) is .0006. You are bound for New Jersey from Ecuador. How many barrels would you expect to unload if the cargo temperature is 55° F at the discharge port?

- ⚓ A. 7,798
- B. 7,827
- C. 8,173
- D. 8,202

010968/DG01480   **MMOH**

Your ship has loaded 8,000 barrels of gasoline at a cargo temperature of 85° F, departing Aruba bound for New Jersey. API gravity is 55°. The volume correction factor (VCF) is .0006. How many barrels would you expect to unload if the cargo temperature is 50° F at the discharge port?

- A. 7,880
- ⚓ B. 7,832
- C. 8,168
- D. 8,120

010969/DG01432   **MMOH**

A tanker is loaded with 8,000 barrels of fuel oil. The temperature of the cargo is 50° F. API gravity is 37°. The volume correction factor (VCF) is .0005. What is the net amount in barrels of cargo loaded?

- ⚓ A. 8,040
- B. 8,016
- C. 7,984
- D. 7,960

010970/DG00429   **MARTON**

A tank is loaded with 9,000 barrels of gasoline. The temperature of the product is 90° F (32° C), and it has a coefficient of expansion of .0008. What is the net amount of cargo loaded?

- A. 8856 bbls
- ⚓ B. 8784 bbls
- C. 8820 bbls
- D. 9216 bbls

010971/DG01542 MMOH

Your ship has loaded 9,000 barrels of fuel oil at a cargo temperature of 35° C (95° F). API gravity is 44°. The volume correction factor (VCF) is .0005. You are bound to New Jersey from Venezuela. How many barrels would you expect to unload if the cargo temperature is 55° F at the discharge port?

A. 9,090
B. 9,180
⚓ C. 8,820
D. 8,910

010972/DG00969 MMOH

A tank is loaded with 9,000 barrels of gasoline. The temperature of the product is 80° F (27° C), and it has a coefficient of expansion of .0008. The net amount of cargo loaded is _____.

⚓ A. 8,856 barrels
B. 8,944 barrels
C. 9,072 barrels
D. 9,144 barrels

010973/DG01425 MMOH

A cargo of fuel oil is loaded whose temperature is 66° F. API gravity is 36°. The volume correction factor (VCF) is .0005. A cargo temperature of 80° F is expected at the discharge port. If 9,000 barrels were loaded, how many barrels would you expect to unload?

A. 8,910
B. 8,937
⚓ C. 9,063
D. 9,090

010974/DG00419 MMOH

A cargo of 10,000 barrels of gasoline is loaded at a temperature of 90° F, and a cargo temperature of 55° F, is expected on this voyage. It has a coefficient of expansion of .0006. How many barrels would you expect to discharge at your destination?

⚓ A. 9790
B. 9994
C. 10210
D. 10410

010975/DG01450 MMOH

Your ship departed Venezuela for New York, loaded with 10,000 barrels of crude oil, whose average cargo temperature was 30° C (86° F). API is 25°. The volume correction factor (VCF) is .00045. If this cargo is heated to 100° F prior to discharge, how many barrels will you offload?

A. 10,315
⚓ B. 10,063
C. 9,937
D. 9,685

010976/DG00979 MMOH

A cargo of oil has a coefficient of expansion of .0005 per degree F. If this cargo is loaded at 70° F, and a cargo temperature of 90° F is expected at the discharge port, how many barrels would you expect to unload if you loaded 10,000 barrels?

A. 9,900
B. 9,990
C. 10,010
⚓ D. 10,100

010977/DG01440 MMOH

A tanker is loaded with 12,000 barrels of #2 fuel oil. The temperature of the product is 88° F. API gravity is 39°. The volume correction factor (VCF) is .0005. The net amount of cargo in barrels, loaded is _____.

A. 12,168
B. 12,006
C. 11,994
⚓ D. 11,832

010978/DG01490 MMOH

Your ship has loaded 20,000 barrels of crude oil, departing Valdez, Alaska for San Francisco. When loaded the cargo temperature was 96° F. API was 15°. The volume correction factor (VCF) is .0004. If the cargo temperature is expected to be 56° F at the discharge port, how many barrels will be offloaded?

⚓ A. 19,680
B. 19,712
C. 20,288
D. 20,320

010979/DG01522 MMOH

Your ship has loaded 22,000 barrels of crude oil, departing Valdez, Alaska for Panama. When loaded the cargo temperature was 90° F. API was 15°. The volume correction factor (VCF) is .0004. If the cargo temperature is expected to be 100° F at the discharge port, how many barrels will be offloaded?

A. 21,252
B. 21,912
⚓ C. 22,088
D. 22,748

010980/DG01457 MMOH

Your ship has loaded 6,000 barrels of gasoline, at a cargo temperature of 50° F, departing New Jersey bound for Florida. API gravity is 55°. The volume correction factor (VCF) is .0006. How many gallons would you expect to unload if the cargo temperature is 90° F at the discharge port?

A. 337,920
B. 322,080
C. 295,952
⚓ D. 258,048

010981/DG01569   MMOH

Your ship has loaded 8,000 barrels of gasoline at a cargo temperature of 36° C (97° F). API gravity is 54°. The volume correction factor (VCF) is .0006. Your are bound for New Jersey from Ecuador. How many gallons would you expect to unload if the cargo temperature is 55° F at the discharge port?

A. 451,110
B. 428,890
C. 344,484
⚓ D. 327,533

010982/DG01485   MMOH

Your ship has loaded 8,000 barrels of gasoline at a cargo temperature of 85° F, departing Aruba bound for New Jersey. API gravity is 55°. The volume correction factor (VCF) is .0006. How many gallons would you expect to unload if the cargo temperature is 50° F at the discharge port?

A. 449,240
B. 430,760
C. 343,056
⚓ D. 328,944

010983/DG01437   MMOH

A tanker is loaded with 8,000 barrels of fuel oil. The temperature of the cargo is 50° F. API gravity is 37°. The volume correction factor (VCF) is .0005. What is the net amount in gallons of cargo loaded?

A. 334,320
⚓ B. 337,680
C. 437,800
D. 442,200

010984/DG01547   MMOH

Your ship has loaded 9,000 barrels of fuel oil at a cargo temperature of 35° C (95° F). API gravity is 44°. The volume correction factor (VCF) is .0005. You are bound for New Jersey from Venezuela. How many gallons would you expect to unload if the cargo temperature is 55° F at the discharge port?

⚓ A. 370,440
B. 385,560
C. 485,100
D. 504,900

010985/DG01428   MMOH

A cargo of fuel oil is loaded whose temperature is 66° F. API gravity is 36°. The volume correction factor (VCF) is .0005. A cargo temperature of 80° F is expected at the discharge port. If 9,000 barrels were loaded, how many gallons would you expect to unload?

A. 375,354
⚓ B. 380,646
C. 491,535
D. 498,465

010986/DG01453   MMOH

Your ship departed Venezuela for New York, loaded with 10,000 barrels of crude oil, whose average cargo temperature was 30° C (86° F). API is 25°. The volume correction factor (VCF) is .00045. If this cargo is heated to 100° F prior to discharge, how many gallons will you offload?

A. 417,354
⚓ B. 422,646
C. 546,535
D. 553,465

010987/DG01447   MMOH

A tanker is loaded with 12,000 barrels of #2 fuel oil. The temperature of the product is 88° F. API gravity is 39°. The volume correction factor (VCF) is .0005. The net amount of cargo in gallons, loaded is _____.

⚓ A. 496,944
B. 511,056
C. 650,760
D. 669,240

010988/DG01507   MMOH

Your ship has loaded 20,000 barrels of crude oil, departing Valdez, Alaska for San Francisco. When loaded the cargo temperature was 96° F. API was 15°. The volume correction factor (VCF) is .0004. If the cargo temperature is expected to be 56° F at the discharge port, how many gallons will be offloaded?

A. 1,117,600
B. 1,082,400
C. 853,440
⚓ D. 826,560

010989/DG01535   MMOH

Your ship has loaded 22,000 barrels of crude oil, departing Valdez, Alaska for Panama. When loaded the cargo temperature was 90° F. API was 15°. The volume correction factor (VCF) is .0004. If the cargo temperature is expected to be 100° F at the discharge port, how many gallons will be off loaded?

A. 1,214,840
B. 1,205,160
⚓ C. 927,696
D. 920,304

LONGITUDINAL BENDING STRESS

010990/DG01897   **STABILITY DATA REFERENCE BOOK; SALMON PAGE No. 3**

The tankship Northland is loaded as shown. Use the salmon colored pages in the Stability Data Reference Book to determine the hogging numeral.

LONGITUDINAL BENDING STRESSES (PSI)

NO.	DESCRIPTION	TONS
1.	FORE PEAK	0
2.	DEEP TANK P/S	0
3.	FWD STORES	6
4.	FWD BUNKERS	1600
5.	FWD COFFERDAM	0
6.	#1 CARGO TANK	4659
7.	#2 CARGO TANK	5280
8.	#3 CARGO TANK	5489
9.	#4 CARGO TANK	0
10.	BRIDGE CREW	3
11.	BRIDGE STORES	12
12.	BRIDGE F.W.	10
13.	#5 CARGO TANK	5196
14.	#6 BALLAST TANK	2400
15.	#7 CARGO/BALLAST TANK	5319
16.	#8 CARGO/BALLAST TANK	5400
17.	#9 CARGO/BALLAST TANK	6000
18.	#10 CARGO TANK	5361
19.	#11 CARGO TANK	4952
20.	AFT COFFERDAM	0
21.	AFT BUNKERS	850
22.	AFT SETTLERS	360
23.	DISTILLED WATER	50
24.	AFT STORES	75
25.	AFT CREW	7
26.	F.W. AFT	57
27.	AFT PEAK	0

A. 43.19 numeral
B. 46.56 numeral
C. 49.92 numeral
D. 55.72 numeral

010991/DG01502   **STABILITY DATA REFERENCE BOOK; SALMON PAGE No. 3**

The tankship Northland is loaded as shown. Use the salmon colored pages in the Stability Data Reference Book to determine the hogging numeral.

LONGITUDINAL BENDING STRESSES (PSI)

NO.	DESCRIPTION	TONS
1.	FORE PEAK	0
2.	DEEP TANK P/S	0
3.	FWD STORES	6
4.	FWD BUNKERS	1600
5.	FWD COFFERDAM	0
6.	#1 CARGO TANK	5229
7.	#2 CARGO TANK	5193
8.	#3 CARGO TANK	4229
9.	#4 CARGO TANK	5116
10.	BRIDGE CREW	3
11.	BRIDGE STORES	12
12.	BRIDGE F.W.	15
13.	#5 CARGO TANK	3956
14.	#6 BALLAST TANK	1628
15.	#7 CARGO/BALLAST TANK	5929
16.	#8 CARGO/BALLAST TANK	6012
17.	#9 CARGO/BALLAST TANK	0
18.	#10 CARGO TANK	5417
19.	#11 CARGO TANK	3257
20.	AFT COFFERDAM	0
21.	AFT BUNKERS	900
22.	AFT SETTLERS	325
23.	DISTILLED WATER	56
24.	AFT STORES	75
25.	AFT CREW	7
26.	F.W. AFT	57
27.	AFT PEAK	375

⚓ A. 49.73 numeral
　 B. 52.76 numeral
　 C. 55.29 numeral
　 D. 57.93 numeral

010992/DG02560
STABILITY DATA REFERENCE BOOK; SALMON PAGE No. 3

The tankship Northland is loaded as shown. Use the salmon colored pages in the Stability Data Reference Book to determine the hogging numeral.

LONGITUDINAL BENDING STRESSES (PSI)

NO.	DESCRIPTION	TONS
1.	FORE PEAK	0
2.	DEEP TANK P/S	0
3.	FWD STORES	6
4.	FWD BUNKERS	1600
5.	FWD COFFERDAM	0
6.	#1 CARGO TANK	4759
7.	#2 CARGO TANK	5288
8.	#3 CARGO TANK	5463
9.	#4 CARGO TANK	0
10.	BRIDGE CREW	3
11.	BRIDGE STORES	10
12.	BRIDGE F.W.	10
13.	#5 CARGO TANK	5486
14.	#6 BALLAST TANK	2408
15.	#7 CARGO/BALLAST TANK	5446
16.	#8 CARGO/BALLAST TANK	2410
17.	#9 CARGO/BALLAST TANK	5454
18.	#10 CARGO TANK	5349
19.	#11 CARGO TANK	5026
20.	AFT COFFERDAM	0
21.	AFT BUNKERS	800
22.	AFT SETTLERS	360
23.	DISTILLED WATER	50
24.	AFT STORES	75
25.	AFT CREW	7
26.	F.W. AFT	65
27.	AFT PEAK	0

A. 101.02 numeral
B. 91.36 numeral
C. 72.43 numeral
D. 52.79 numeral

010993/DG02176

STABILITY DATA REFERENCE BOOK; SALMON PAGE No. 3

The tankship Northland is loaded as shown. Use the salmon colored pages in the Stability Data Reference Book to determine the hogging numeral.

LONGITUDINAL BENDING STRESSES (PSI)

NO.	DESCRIPTION	TONS
1.	FORE PEAK	749
2.	DEEP TANK P/S	1747
3.	FWD STORES	6
4.	FWD BUNKERS	2867
5.	FWD COFFERDAM	338
6.	#1 CARGO TANK	0
7.	#2 CARGO TANK	0
8.	#3 CARGO TANK	0
9.	#4 CARGO TANK	0
10.	BRIDGE CREW	3
11.	BRIDGE STORES	10
12.	BRIDGE F.W.	10
13.	#5 CARGO TANK	0
14.	#6 BALLAST TANK	2595
15.	#7 CARGO/BALLAST TANK	3315
16.	#8 CARGO/BALLAST TANK	2595
17.	#9 CARGO/BALLAST TANK	2595
18.	#10 CARGO TANK	0
19.	#11 CARGO TANK	0
20.	AFT COFFERDAM	239
21.	AFT BUNKERS	859
22.	AFT SETTLERS	360
23.	DISTILLED WATER	60
24.	AFT STORES	80
25.	AFT CREW	7
26.	F.W. AFT	71
27.	AFT PEAK	394

A. 91.42 numeral
B. 85.60 numeral
C. 79.23 numeral
D. 74.73 numeral

010994/DG00443 **STABILITY DATA REFERENCE BOOK; SALMON PAGE No. 3**

The tankship Northland is loaded as shown. Use the salmon colored pages in the Stability Data Reference Book to determine the hogging numeral.

LONGITUDINAL BENDING STRESSES (PSI)

NO.	DESCRIPTION	TONS
1.	FORE PEAK	0
2.	DEEP TANK P/S	0
3.	FWD STORES	6
4.	FWD BUNKERS	1600
5.	FWD COFFERDAM	0
6.	#1 CARGO TANK	5229
7.	#2 CARGO TANK	5193
8.	#3 CARGO TANK	4229
9.	#4 CARGO TANK	5116
10.	BRIDGE CREW	3
11.	BRIDGE STORES	12
12.	BRIDGE F.W.	15
13.	#5 CARGO TANK	2956
14.	#6 BALLAST TANK	1628
15.	#7 CARGO/BALLAST TANK	0
16.	#8 CARGO/BALLAST TANK	0
17.	#9 CARGO/BALLAST TANK	6012
18.	#10 CARGO TANK	5417
19.	#11 CARGO TANK	3257
20.	AFT COFFERDAM	0
21.	AFT BUNKERS	900
22.	AFT SETTLERS	325
23.	DISTILLED WATER	56
24.	AFT STORES	75
25.	AFT CREW	7
26.	F.W. AFT	57
27.	AFT PEAK	375

A. 86.72 numeral
B. 89.98 numeral
⚓ C. 91.40 numeral
D. 93.18 numeral

010995/DG02734 **STABILITY DATA REFERENCE BOOK; SALMON PAGE No. 3**

The tankship Northland is loaded as shown. Use the salmon colored pages in the Stability book to determine the hogging numeral.

LONGITUDINAL BENDING STRESSES (PSI)

NO.	DESCRIPTION	TONS
1.	FORE PEAK	0
2.	DEEP TANK P/S	0
3.	FWD STORES	6
4.	FWD BUNKERS	2867
5.	FWD COFFERDAM	0
6.	#1 CARGO TANK	3596
7.	#2 CARGO TANK	3996
8.	#3 CARGO TANK	4128
9.	#4 CARGO TANK	4146
10.	BRIDGE CREW	0
11.	BRIDGE STORES	0
12.	BRIDGE F.W.	0
13.	#5 CARGO TANK	0
14.	#6 BALLAST TANK	0
15.	#7 CARGO/BALLAST TANK	1821
16.	#8 CARGO/BALLAST TANK	2328
17.	#9 CARGO/BALLAST TANK	2303
18.	#10 CARGO TANK	4042
19.	#11 CARGO TANK	3798
20.	AFT COFFERDAM	0
21.	AFT BUNKERS	850
22.	AFT SETTLERS	340
23.	DISTILLED WATER	60
24.	AFT STORES	80
25.	AFT CREW	7
26.	F.W. AFT	70
27.	AFT PEAK	0

A. 98.23 numeral
⚓ B. 95.70 numeral
C. 84.46 numeral
D. 81.37 numeral

010996/DG04056   STABILITY DATA REFERENCE BOOK; SALMON PAGE No. 3

The tankship Northland is loaded as shown. Use the salmon colored pages in the Stability Data Reference Book to determine the sagging numeral.

LONGITUDINAL BENDING STRESSES (PSI)

NO.	DESCRIPTION	TONS
1.	FORE PEAK	0
2.	DEEP TANK P/S	0
3.	FWD STORES	6
4.	FWD BUNKERS	2867
5.	FWD COFFERDAM	0
6.	#1 CARGO TANK	3596
7.	#2 CARGO TANK	3996
8.	#3 CARGO TANK	4128
9.	#4 CARGO TANK	4146
10.	BRIDGE CREW	0
11.	BRIDGE STORES	0
12.	BRIDGE F.W.	0
13.	#5 CARGO TANK	0
14.	#6 BALLAST TANK	0
15.	#7 CARGO/BALLAST TANK	1821
16.	#8 CARGO/BALLAST TANK	2328
17.	#9 CARGO/BALLAST TANK	2303
18.	#10 CARGO TANK	4042
19.	#11 CARGO TANK	3798
20.	AFT COFFERDAM	0
21.	AFT BUNKERS	850
22.	AFT SETTLERS	340
23.	DISTILLED WATER	60
24.	AFT STORES	80
25.	AFT CREW	7
26.	F.W. AFT	70
27.	AFT PEAK	0

A. 89.75 numeral
B. 40.18 numeral
C. 28.62 numeral
⚓ D. 22.44 numeral

010997/DG03776   **STABILITY DATA REFERENCE BOOK; SALMON PAGE No. 3**

The tankship Northland is loaded as shown. Use the salmon colored pages in the Stability Data Reference Book to determine the sagging numeral.

LONGITUDINAL BENDING STRESSES (PSI)

NO.	DESCRIPTION	TONS
1.	FORE PEAK	749
2.	DEEP TANK P/S	1747
3.	FWD STORES	6
4.	FWD BUNKERS	2867
5.	FWD COFFERDAM	338
6.	#1 CARGO TANK	0
7.	#2 CARGO TANK	0
8.	#3 CARGO TANK	0
9.	#4 CARGO TANK	0
10.	BRIDGE CREW	3
11.	BRIDGE STORES	10
12.	BRIDGE F.W.	10
13.	#5 CARGO TANK	0
14.	#6 BALLAST TANK	2595
15.	#7 CARGO/BALLAST TANK	3315
16.	#8 CARGO/BALLAST TANK	2595
17.	#9 CARGO/BALLAST TANK	2595
18.	#10 CARGO TANK	0
19.	#11 CARGO TANK	0
20.	AFT COFFERDAM	239
21.	AFT BUNKERS	859
22.	AFT SETTLERS	360
23.	DISTILLED WATER	60
24.	AFT STORES	80
25.	AFT CREW	7
26.	F.W. AFT	71
27.	AFT PEAK	394

⚓ A. 29.70 numeral

    B. 33.63 numeral

    C. 49.82 numeral

    D. 58.33 numeral

010998/DG00992 **STABILITY DATA REFERENCE BOOK; SALMON PAGE No. 3**

The tankship Northland is loaded as shown. Use the salmon colored pages in the Stability Data Reference Book to determine the sagging numeral.

LONGITUDINAL BENDING STRESSES (PSI)

NO.	DESCRIPTION	TONS
1.	FORE PEAK	0
2.	DEEP TANK P/S	0
3.	FWD STORES	6
4.	FWD BUNKERS	1600
5.	FWD COFFERDAM	0
6.	#1 CARGO TANK	5229
7.	#2 CARGO TANK	5193
8.	#3 CARGO TANK	4229
9.	#4 CARGO TANK	5116
10.	BRIDGE CREW	3
11.	BRIDGE STORES	12
12.	BRIDGE F.W.	15
13.	#5 CARGO TANK	2956
14.	#6 BALLAST TANK	1628
15.	#7 CARGO/BALLAST TANK	0
16.	#8 CARGO/BALLAST TANK	0
17.	#9 CARGO/BALLAST TANK	6012
18.	#10 CARGO TANK	5417
19.	#11 CARGO TANK	3257
20.	AFT COFFERDAM	0
21.	AFT BUNKERS	900
22.	AFT SETTLERS	325
23.	DISTILLED WATER	56
24.	AFT STORES	75
25.	AFT CREW	7
26.	F.W. AFT	57
27.	AFT PEAK	375

A. 29.49 numeral
⚓ B. 31.97 numeral
C. 33.61 numeral
D. 35.12 numeral

010999/DG01015   **STABILITY DATA REFERENCE BOOK; SALMON PAGE No. 3**

The tankship Northland is loaded as shown. Use the salmon colored pages in the Stability Data Reference to determine the sagging numeral.

LONGITUDINAL BENDING STRESSES (PSI)

NO.	DESCRIPTION	TONS
1.	FORE PEAK	0
2.	DEEP TANK P/S	0
3.	FWD STORES	6
4.	FWD BUNKERS	1600
5.	FWD COFFERDAM	0
6.	#1 CARGO TANK	5229
7.	#2 CARGO TANK	5193
8.	#3 CARGO TANK	4229
9.	#4 CARGO TANK	5116
10.	BRIDGE CREW	3
11.	BRIDGE STORES	12
12.	BRIDGE F.W.	15
13.	#5 CARGO TANK	3956
14.	#6 BALLAST TANK	1628
15.	#7 CARGO/BALLAST TANK	5929
16.	#8 CARGO/BALLAST TANK	6012
17.	#9 CARGO/BALLAST TANK	0
18.	#10 CARGO TANK	5417
19.	#11 CARGO TANK	3257
20.	AFT COFFERDAM	0
21.	AFT BUNKERS	900
22.	AFT SETTLERS	325
23.	DISTILLED WATER	56
24.	AFT STORES	75
25.	AFT CREW	7
26.	F.W. AFT	57
27.	AFT PEAK	375

A. 71.07 numeral
B. 74.95 numeral
C. 77.56 numeral
D. 78.29 numeral

011000/DG03208   **STABILITY DATA REFERENCE BOOK; SALMON PAGE No. 3**

The tankship Northland is loaded as shown. Use the salmon colored pages in the Stability Data Reference Book to determine the sagging numeral.

LONGITUDINAL BENDING STRESSES (PSI)

NO.	DESCRIPTION	TONS
1.	FORE PEAK	0
2.	DEEP TANK P/S	0
3.	FWD STORES	6
4.	FWD BUNKERS	1600
5.	FWD COFFERDAM	0
6.	#1 CARGO TANK	4759
7.	#2 CARGO TANK	5288
8.	#3 CARGO TANK	5463
9.	#4 CARGO TANK	0
10.	BRIDGE CREW	3
11.	BRIDGE STORES	10
12.	BRIDGE F.W.	10
13.	#5 CARGO TANK	5486
14.	#6 BALLAST TANK	2408
15.	#7 CARGO/BALLAST TANK	5446
16.	#8 CARGO/BALLAST TANK	2410
17.	#9 CARGO/BALLAST TANK	5454
18.	#10 CARGO TANK	5349
19.	#11 CARGO TANK	5026
20.	AFT COFFERDAM	0
21.	AFT BUNKERS	800
22.	AFT SETTLERS	360
23.	DISTILLED WATER	50
24.	AFT STORES	75
25.	AFT CREW	7
26.	F.W. AFT	65
27.	AFT PEAK	0

A. 72.42 numeral

⚓ B. 78.98 numeral

C. 83.46 numeral

D. 91.48 numeral

011001/DG02051   STABILITY DATA REFERENCE BOOK; SALMON PAGE No. 3

The tankship Northland is loaded as shown. Use the salmon colored pages in the Stability Data Reference Book to determine the sagging numeral.

LONGITUDINAL BENDING STRESSES (PSI)

NO.	DESCRIPTION	TONS
1.	FORE PEAK	0
2.	DEEP TANK P/S	0
3.	FWD STORES	6
4.	FWD BUNKERS	1600
5.	FWD COFFERDAM	0
6.	#1 CARGO TANK	4659
7.	#2 CARGO TANK	5280
8.	#3 CARGO TANK	5498
9.	#4 CARGO TANK	0
10.	BRIDGE CREW	3
11.	BRIDGE STORES	12
12.	BRIDGE F.W.	10
13.	#5 CARGO TANK	5196
14.	#6 BALLAST TANK	2400
15.	#7 CARGO/BALLAST TANK	5319
16.	#8 CARGO/BALLAST TANK	5400
17.	#9 CARGO/BALLAST TANK	6000
18.	#10 CARGO TANK	5361
19.	#11 CARGO TANK	4952
20.	AFT COFFERDAM	0
21.	AFT BUNKERS	850
22.	AFT SETTLERS	360
23.	DISTILLED WATER	50
24.	AFT STORES	75
25.	AFT CREW	7
26.	F.W. AFT	57
27.	AFT PEAK	0

A. 81.79 numeral
B. 85.02 numeral
C. 89.68 numeral
⚓ D. 91.92 numeral

CARGO MISCELLANEOUS VESSELS

011002/DG00258   *46 CFR 98.25-40; *46 CFR 98.25-45
Your U.S. tankship is designed to carry anhydrous ammonia in bulk. The keel was laid in 1980. Which statement concerning the carriage of this cargo is TRUE?
- A. A flammable gas detection system must be installed in each cargo pump room.
- ⚓ B. The cargo may be gauged by automatic float type devices.
- C. Carriage of this cargo is authorized by issuance of an IMO Certificate.
- D. Aluminum, copper, zinc, and mercury are allowed in valve parts in contact with the cargo.

011003/DG02493   *46 CFR 98.25-40; *46 CFR 98.25-45
Your U.S. tankship is designed to carry anhydrous ammonia in bulk. The keel was laid in 1980. Which statement concerning the carriage of this cargo is TRUE?
- A. A flammable gas detection system must be installed in each cargo pump room.
- B. Tanks may not be located "on deck".
- C. Carriage of this cargo is authorized by issuance of an IMO Certificate.
- ⚓ D. Aluminum and copper alloys are prohibited from being in valve parts in contact with the cargo.

011004/DG00080   *46 CFR 98.30-9
You are on a cargo vessel carrying portable tanks of dangerous cargoes in bulk. Which statement is TRUE?
- A. If the tanks are pumped out while remaining on board, each hose connection must have a minimum of three bolts.
- B. If the tanks are off loaded, no more than two tanks may be lifted together in a hoist.
- C. When transferring sulfuric acid, you must display a red flag by day whether at anchor or moored.
- ⚓ D. All electrical equipment within 10 feet horizontally must be explosion proof or intrinsically safe.

011005/DG00040   *46 CFR 98.30-37
You are on a cargo vessel carrying toluol in bulk in portable tanks. Which is a requirement for pumping the toluol?
- A. Hose connections to the tank must be made with a minimum of three bolts.
- ⚓ B. There must be water pressure on the fire main.
- C. You must shut down if another vessel comes alongside.
- D. If transferring at anchor, you must display a red flag by day and a red light at night.

011006/DG00407   *46 CFR 148.01-7
You are carrying cargoes of crotonaldehyde, phosphoric acid, and morpholine on your multiple-product tankship. Which of the following statements is TRUE?
- ⚓ A. Each of the cargoes must be segregated from the other by at least two barriers.
- B. The minimum protective clothing required for taking samples of phosphoric acid is goggles or a face shield.
- C. Aluminum, copper, and zinc are prohibited in all valve parts in contact with these cargoes.
- D. The required warning sign must have the legend "cancer hazard" added to it.

011007/DG00010   *46 CFR 148.01-7
You are scheduled to load a bulk shipment of steel turnings. Which statement is TRUE?
- ⚓ A. The primary hazard of this cargo is that it is subject to spontaneous heating and ignition.
- B. The shipping papers should describe this cargo as "Waste; steel borings".
- C. After loading, you may not sail if the temperature in each hold of steel turnings exceeds 130° F.
- D. This cargo may not be transported in bulk unless a special permit is issued by the Coast Guard.

011008/DG02278   *46 CFR 148.01-7
You will load and carry a bulk cargo of sulfur at ambient temperature. Which statement is true?
- A. Wooden covers must be laid over the bilge wells to prevent the sulfur from entering the bilges.
- ⚓ B. Bulk sulfur may be carried without a special permit providing the vessel complies with all applicable regulations.
- C. The major characteristic of this cargo is that it forms sulfuric acid upon contact with water.
- D. Other hazardous material may not be stowed in the same hold as the sulfur but may be carried on deck above the hold.

011009/DG00323   *46 CFR 148.02-3; *49 CFR 176.39
You are transporting dangerous cargo on your vessel. The regulations require you to _____.
- ⚓ A. periodically inspect it and make an entry in a log
- B. keep a warning sign posted nearby
- C. keep a fire hose run out and ready for use if needed
- D. allow no chipping or painting in the vicinity of the cargo

011010/DG00510   *46 CFR 148.02-3

You have loaded dangerous cargo on your vessel and must fill out a Dangerous Cargo Manifest. In which publication would you find the requirements to complete this form?

A. 33 CFR - Navigation and Navigable Waters

⚓ B. 46 CFR - Shipping

C. IMCO - Intergovernmental Maritime Consultative Organization

D. IMDG - International Maritime Dangerous Goods

011011/DG01408   *46 CFR 148.03-11

Which statement about the carriage of solid hazardous materials in bulk is TRUE?

A. A special permit issued by the Coast Guard is required before the cargoes in this subpart are loaded.

⚓ B. Other hazardous materials cargo must not be stowed on deck above a hold in which a solid hazardous material in bulk is loaded.

C. A certificate issued by ABS will be accepted as evidence that the vessel complies with all applicable loading regulations.

D. The shipping papers can be used in lieu of a Dangerous Cargo Manifest for a vessel carrying solid hazardous materials in bulk.

011012/DG00020   *46 CFR 150; Table 1

You are carrying triethylamine, methyl methacrylate and isoprene in your multiple-product tankship. Which of the following statements is true?

⚓ A. Isoprene may be carried in a cargo tank adjacent to either of the other two cargoes.

B. Methyl methacrylate may not be carried in a tank adjacent to a pump room.

C. Methyl methacrylate must usually be heated to maintain its stability.

D. Portable thermometers are not permitted to be used to take the cargo temperature of triethylamine.

011013/DG02348   *46 CFR 150

You are on a multiple-product chemical tanker and will carry cargoes of allyl alcohol, benzene, and propanolamine. Which of the following is true?

A. All of these cargoes are mutually compatible.

B. Benzene may not be carried in a tank adjacent to either of the other two cargoes.

⚓ C. Allyl alcohol is incompatible with propanolamine but both are compatible with benzene.

D. Propanolamine is compatible with allyl alcohol but must be segregated from benzene.

011014/DG02385   *46 CFR 150

You are on a multiple-product chemical tanker and will carry cargoes of butyric acid, propylene oxide, and octyl alcohol. Which statement is true?

A. Butyric acid is incompatible with octyl alcohol but not propylene oxide.

⚓ B. Propylene oxide may not be stowed in a tank adjacent to butyric acid.

C. All of these cargoes are compatible.

D. Octyl alcohol is incompatible with both butyric acid and propylene oxide.

011015/DG02375   *46 CFR 150; *CHEM. DATA GUIDE

You are on a multiple-product chemical tanker and will carry cargoes of ethanolamine, methyl acrylate, and glycerine. Which statement is true?

A. All of these cargoes are mutually incompatible.

B. Glycerine may be stowed adjacent to methyl acrylate but must be segregated from ethanolamine.

C. Methyl acrylate and ethanolamine are compatible but both must be segregated from glycerine.

⚓ D. Glycerine is compatible with both of the other cargoes.

011016/DG02299   *46 CFR 150

You are on a multiple-product chemical tanker and will carry cargoes of isophorone, ethylenediamine, and creosote. Which of the following is TRUE?

⚓ A. All of these cargoes are compatible.

B. Isophorone is incompatible with ethylenediamine but may be stowed adjacent to creosote.

C. All of these cargoes are incompatible.

D. Ethylenediamine is compatible with isophorone but both are incompatible with creosote.

011017/DG00120   *46 CFR 150; Table 1

You are on a multiple-product tankship and scheduled to load a cargo classed as an aromatic amine. This cargo is incompatible with cargoes classed as _____.

⚓ A. organic anhydrides

B. ketones

C. phenols

D. esters

011018/DG00090   *46 CFR 150.130

You are on a multiple-product chemical tanker. The loading plan includes cargoes of diethylenetriamine and formamide. Which statement concerning the stowage of these cargoes is TRUE?

A. They must be separated by a void space or empty tank.

B. The cargoes must have individual venting systems.

C. The valves in common piping systems must be chained closed and locked.

⚓ D. The minimum segregation required is a single bulkhead.

011019/DG00030   ***46 CFR 150.130**

You are planning the stowage of two incompatible products on your multiple-product tankship. What will NOT provide the minimum required segregation?

    A.   Empty tank

⚓ B.   Solid (non-intercostal) bulkhead

    C.   Diagonally adjacent tanks

    D.   Tank containing a third cargo compatible with the other two

011020/DG00252   ***46 CFR 150.160**

You have orders to load cargoes of carbon disulfide, diisopropylamine and pyridine on your multi-product tankship. Which statement is true?

    A.   Carbon disulfide may be carried in NOS. 1 and 2 center tanks and diisopropylamine in NOS. 1 and 2 wing tanks.

⚓ B.   Pyridine and diisopropylamine may not be carried in tanks having a common header vent.

    C.   Pyridine must be separated from carbon disulfide by two barriers (cofferdams, voids, empty tanks, etc.).

    D.   A tank of diisopropylamine may be used to separate a tank of pyridine from a tank of carbon disulfide.

011021/DG00952   ***46 CFR 150.160**

You have orders to load cargoes of carbon disulfide, diisopropylamine and pyridine on your multi-product tankship. Which statement is TRUE?

    A.   Carbon disulfide may be carried in NOS. 1 and 2 center tanks and diisopropylamine in NOS. 1 and 2 wing tanks.

    B.   Pyridine and diisopropylamine may be carried in tanks having a common header vent.

⚓ C.   Pyridine need not be separated from carbon disulfide by two barriers (cofferdams, voids, empty tanks, etc.).

    D.   A tank of carbon disulfide may be used to separate a tank of pyridine from a tank of diisopropylamine.

011022/DG02710   ***46 CFR 150.160**

You have orders to load cargoes of carbon disulfide, diisopropylamine and pyridine on your multi-product tankship. Which statement is TRUE?

    A.   Carbon disulfide may be carried in NOS. 1 and 2 center tanks and diisopropylamine in NOS. 1 and 2 wing tanks.

    B.   Pyridine and diisopropylamine may be carried in tanks having a common header vent.

⚓ C.   Diisopropylamine must be separated from carbon disulfide by two barriers (cofferdams, voids, empty tanks, etc.)

    D.   A tank of carbon disulfide may be used to separate a tank of pyridine from a tank of diisopropylamine.

011023/DG03541   ***46 CFR 150.160**

You have orders to load cargoes of carbon disulfide, diisopropylamine and pyridine on your multi-product tankship. Which statement is TRUE?

    A.   Carbon disulfide may be carried in NOS. 1 and 2 center tanks and diisopropylamine in NOS. 1 and 2 wing tanks.

    B.   Pyridine and diisopropylamine may be carried in tanks having a common header vent.

    C.   Carbon disulfide must be separated from pyridine by two barriers (cofferdams, voids, empty tanks, etc.).

⚓ D.   A tank of pyridine may be used to separate a tank of carbon disulfide from a tank of diisopropylamine.

011024/DG00060   ***46 CFR 151.50-72**

You are on a vessel designed to carry compressed gasses in bulk with a cargo of butadiene. Which statement is TRUE?

    A.   The ullage must be padded with compressed air at a minimum pressure of 2 psig.

⚓ B.   Silver and copper are prohibited in the parts of valves and fittings in contact with the cargo.

    C.   The cargo tank may be sampled only when the tank is being filled.

    D.   The shipping document must specify the exact quantity of butadiene being carried.

011025/DG00581   ***46 CFR 153.8**

The Certificate of Inspection for your tankship authorizes the carriage of grade A and lower products. Which chemical may NOT be carried unless it is specifically endorsed on the Certificate of Inspection?

    A.   Amylene

    B.   Diisobutyl Phthalate

    C.   Oleic acid

⚓ D.   Vinyl acetate

011026/DG00070   ***46 CFR 153.440**

You are on a tankship designed to carry molten sulfur. Which statement is TRUE?

    A.   There must be two portable toxic vapor detectors on board.

    B.   The cargo tank ventilation system must maintain the H2S vapor concentration at 1.85% or more by volume.

⚓ C.   Cargo temperature may be taken by portable thermometers.

    D.   The pressure in the heating coils in the tanks must be less than that of the cargo exerted on them.

011027/DG00110   *46 CFR 153.465

What is NOT required as special safety equipment on a tankship carrying hazardous cargoes in bulk?

A. Shower and eyewash fountain

B. Equipment to lift an injured person from a pumproom

⚓ C. Two portable vapor detectors suitable for the cargoes carried

D. A safety locker adjacent to the emergency shutdown station

011028/DG00140   *46 CFR 153.500

Your tankship is carrying a 30% solution of hydrogen peroxide. The cargo containment system must have a permanent inert gas system. While discharging this cargo the inert gas system must maintain a minimum pressure of _____.

⚓ A. 0.5 psig

B. 3.0 psig

C. 5.0 psig

D. atmospheric pressure

011029/DG00170   *46 CFR 153.900

Which is NOT required on a tankship carrying hazardous liquid cargoes in bulk?

A. A copy of 46 CFR parts 35 and 150

⚓ B. Certificate of Adequacy for the hazardous cargoes carried

C. Certificate of Inspection issued under the Tank Vessel Regulations

D. Cargo piping plan showing loading rates for all applicable cargo lines

011030/DG01712   *46 CFR 153.912

You are to load styrene in bulk, which is subject to self-polymerization. You must _____.

A. not carry any cargo in the tanks surrounding the tank loaded with styrene

B. inject nitrogen to pad any ullage above the styrene to prevent contact with oxygen

⚓ C. be furnished with a Certificate of Inhibition to be maintained on the bridge

D. use heating coils to maintain the styrene within the temperatures specified by the shipper

011031/DG03126   *46 CFR 153.912

Your tankship is carrying a cargo of styrene. Which of the following is NOT a requirement for carriage of this cargo?

⚓ A. P/V valves with galvanized parts must be replaced.

B. Authorization to carry styrene must be endorsed on the Certificate of Inspection.

C. You must have a "Certificate of Inhibition" provided by the shipper.

D. The cargo tank heating coils must be blanked off.

011032/DG00150   *46 CFR 153.932

Protective clothing must be worn while sampling hazardous cargo on a tankship, and as a minimum includes _____.

A. a hood or hard hat

⚓ B. a face mask or goggles

C. boots

D. chemical resistant gloves

011033/DG01405   *46 CFR 153, Table 1

You are on a multiple-product chemical tanker with orders to load diethylamine. What is NOT a requirement for transporting this cargo?

A. You must have two toxic vapor detectors or the pumproom must meet special requirements.

⚓ B. You must have a containment system made out of stainless steel other than types 416 and 422.

C. If you are carrying propionic acid also, the venting systems must be segregated.

D. Each crew member must be provided with an emergency escape breathing apparatus.

011034/DG01303   *46 CFR 153, Table 1

You are on a multiple-product chemical tanker with orders to load diethylamine. What is NOT a requirement for transporting this cargo?

A. You must have two toxic vapor detectors or the pumproom must meet special requirements.

B. Each crew member must be provided with an emergency escape breathing apparatus.

⚓ C. You must have a containment system made out of stainless steel other than types 416 and 422.

D. If you are also carrying allyl alcohol, the venting systems don't have to be segregated.

011035/DG00180   *46 CFR 153.981

Your tank vessel is loading a hazardous cargo. The allowance for expansion is based on ambient temperatures of what maximum range?

A. 0° C to 100° C

B. -10° C to 90° C

⚓ C. -18° C to 46° C

D. -40° C to 50° C

011036/DG00327   *46 CFR 153.1002

You are on a multiple product tankship and carrying methyl acrylate, diethanolamine, and triethylamine. Which statement is TRUE?

A. Methyl acrylate may be loaded in a tank adjacent to diethanolamine but not triethylamine.

⚓ B. The heating coils to the cargo tank loaded with methyl acrylate must be blanked off.

C. Valve components made of aluminum, copper, or zinc may not be in contact with the cargoes.

D. Each crew member working on deck must have an emergency escape breathing apparatus.

011037/DG00130   ***46 CFR 154.1810**
You are on a vessel carrying liquefied butadiene in bulk. Which document is NOT required to be either in the wheelhouse or easily accessible to the person on watch while underway?
⚓ A. Cargo manual
   B. Cargo information card
   C. Certificate of Inspection
   D. Shipping document

011038/DG00190   ***46 CFR 154.1815**
You are on a vessel that carries liquefied gasses in bulk. The person on watch is required to have what information about the cargo easily accessible?
   A. Port of loading
   B. Exact quantity on board
   C. Name and address of consignee
⚓ D. Firefighting procedures

011039/DG01272   ***46 CFR 197**
You are on a tankship carrying benzene in bulk. Which statement is TRUE?
   A. No other cargoes may be carried due to the possibility of contamination by a carcinogen.
   B. The crew quarters must have positive-pressure ventilation to prevent the fumes from entering the living spaces.
   C. Benzene is not a cancer-causing agent.
⚓ D. Personnel working in regulated areas must use respirators.

HAZARDOUS MATERIALS REGULATIONS

011040/DG00500   ***49 CFR 171.16**
What would NOT require that a detailed report of the release of hazardous cargo be made to the Department of Transportation?
   A. The valve on an empty portable tank that contained acetone is accidentally opened and some of the residue escapes to the open sea.
   B. A carboy of nitric acid is broken on deck while loading and is flushed overboard with no injury or damage.
⚓ C. Part of your deck cargo of five gallon cans of paint is damaged and leaking so you jettison them to eliminate the fire hazard.
   D. Heavy weather causes damage to packages of a hazardous liquid that is subsequently pumped out at sea through the bilge pumping system.

011041/DG00340   ***49 CFR 172.101**
Argon is classified as a _____.
   A. corrosive
   B. flammable gas
   C. flammable liquid
⚓ D. nonflammable gas

011042/DG00749   ***49 CFR 172.101**
Butadiene, inhibited, is labeled as a _____.
   A. combustible liquid
⚓ B. flammable gas
   C. flammable liquid
   D. flammable solid

011043/DG00135   ***49 CFR 172.101; IMDG**
Corrosive liquids and acids should have which kind of label?
   A. Skull and crossbones
   B. Yellow and white
   C. Red and white
⚓ D. White and black

011044/DG01940   ***49 CFR 172.415; *49 CFR 172.528**
Nonflammable gases should have what kind of label?
   A. Skull and crossbones
   B. White
⚓ C. Green
   D. Red

011045/DG01874   ***49 CFR 172.101**
The label required for magnesium scrap is _____.
   A. oxidizer
   B. yellow
   C. corrosive
⚓ D. None of the above

011046/DG00360   ***49 CFR 172.101; *49 CFR 172.431**
The label required on containers carrying barium oxide in an international shipment must read _____.
⚓ A. Poison
   B. Spontaneously Combustible
   C. Radioactive
   D. Infectious Substance

011047/DG04038   ***49 CFR 172.102**
Which cargo would require a dangerous cargo manifest?
⚓ A. Cotton
   B. Wheat
   C. Sugar
   D. Lumber

011048/DG01752   ***49 CFR 172.102**
Your containership has a container displaying a hazardous cargo placard. The placard has the number 2199 on it. This indicates that it is carrying what cargo?
   A. Furan
⚓ B. Phosphine
   C. Adiponitrile
   D. Xylenol

011049/DG01692   *49 CFR 172.102

Your containership has a container displaying a hazardous cargo placard. The placard has the number 2206 on it. This indicates that it is carrying what cargo?

⚓ A. Isocyanates, n.o.s.
B. Propadiene, inhibited
C. Xylenol
D. Hexanols

011050/DG01775   *49 CFR 172.102

Your containership has a container displaying a hazardous cargo placard. The placard has the number 2224 on it. This indicates that it is carrying what cargo?

A. Hexanol
B. Acrylic acid
⚓ C. Benzonitrile
D. Propadiene, inhibited

011051/DG01702   *49 CFR 172.102

Your containership has a container displaying a hazardous cargo placard. The placard has the number 2282 on it. This indicates that it is carrying what cargo?

A. Isoheptene
B. Phosphine
C. Furan
⚓ D. Hexanols

011052/DG01338   *49 CFR 172.200

A "dangerous cargo manifest" is needed for you to carry a combustible cargo. You should obtain the shipping papers to make this "manifest" from the _____.

A. manufacturer
B. ABS
C. Coast Guard
⚓ D. shipper

011053/DG02131   *49 CFR 172.203

If you carry packaged hazardous cargoes on a break bulk vessel bound foreign, you must _____.

A. stow the hazardous cargoes on deck available for jettisoning if necessary
B. remove the hazardous cargo labels from a portable tank after the tank is emptied
⚓ C. have the shipping papers indicate the proper shipping name and the technical name of n.o.s. cargoes
D. log the receipt of hazardous cargoes in the Official Logbook

011054/DG00410   *49 CFR 172.336

You are loading a cargo tank on your container ship. The tank displays the red label shown. Which statement is TRUE? See Diagram D023DG

⚓ A. The tank contains propylene.
B. The tank's volume is 1077 cubic feet.
C. There are three tanks in the shipment.
D. The tank contains an oxidizing material.

011055/DG00390   *49 CFR 172.101; *49 CFR 172.403

A package contains nitric acid solution and is radioactive. The radiation level at the package surface is .36 millirems per hour. How should this package be labeled?

A. Radioactive II and oxidizer
B. Radioactive II and poison
⚓ C. Radioactive I and corrosive
D. Fissile class I

011056/DG03325   *49 CFR 172.419

Flammable liquids should have what kind of label?

A. Skull and crossbones
B. Yellow
⚓ C. Red
D. White

011057/DG00320   *49 CFR 172.420

Containers of flammable solids should be conspicuously labeled by the shipper with a _____.

A. green label
⚓ B. red and white label
C. orange label
D. yellow label

011058/DG00400   *49 CFR 172.514; *49 CFR 172.558

You are on a containership carrying a tank container that had been filled with sodium hydroxide solution. The container is empty but has not been cleaned. Which, if any, placard is required?

A. No placard is required; the tank openings must be sealed
B. Empty placard with corrosive placard
C. Residue label with the UN number
⚓ D. Black and white corrosive placard

011059/DG02528   *49 CFR 176.30

Which entry on a dangerous cargo manifest concerning the classification of a cargo is correct?

⚓ A. Class 8
B. Class 3 - flammable liquid
C. Division 2.2 - nonflammable gas
D. All of the above are correct

011060/DG02516   *49 CFR 176.30 (a)

Which statement about the dangerous cargo manifest, carried on a ship, is TRUE?

A. The manifest must be made up by the Master or other designated ship's officer.
B. Shipments of hazardous and non-hazardous cargo may be listed on the manifest if they are destined for the same consignee.
⚓ C. The manifest must be kept in a designated holder on or near the bridge.
D. The type of label(s) required for each cargo must be indicated.

011061/DG00330 *46 CFR 148.02-3; *49 CFR 176.39
You have completed a Dangerous Cargo Manifest for dangerous cargoes loaded on board. It should be kept in a conspicuous location _____.
A. in the radio room
B. in the ship's office
⚓ C. on or near the bridge
D. outside the Captain's stateroom

011062/DG02546 *49 CFR 176.30
The dangerous cargo manifest does NOT indicate _____.
A. the stowage location of hazardous material aboard the vessel
B. a description of the packaging (drums, boxes, etc.)
C. UN identification numbers
⚓ D. the net weight of each hazardous cargo

011063/DG02524 *49 CFR 176.30 (a) (5) (i); *49 CFR 171.14
Which entry on a dangerous cargo manifest concerning the classification of a cargo is NOT correct?
A. Class 8
⚓ B. Division 3.1
C. Division 2.3
D. All of the above are incorrect

011064/DG02496 *49 CFR 176.30
Which statement about the dangerous cargo manifest is FALSE?
A. The manifest must be made up by the carrier, agents, and any person designated for this purpose.
⚓ B. Shipments of hazardous and non-hazardous cargoes may be listed on the manifest if they are destined for the same consignee.
C. The manifest must be kept in a designated holder on or near the bridge.
D. The hazard class of each cargo must be indicated.

011065/DG00430 *49 CFR 176.39
On a manned vessel carrying packaged hazardous cargo, the hazardous materials shall be inspected _____.
A. every 24 hours unless equipped with a fire detecting system
B. prior to entry into a U.S. port
C. after stowage is complete
⚓ D. All of the above

011066/DG00450 *49 CFR 176.39
Once a vessel has loaded packaged hazardous cargo, the cargo spaces shall be inspected. The spaces shall also be inspected at least once in every 24 hours. The only exception to daily inspection is when _____.
⚓ A. a vessel is equipped with an automatic smoke or fire detecting system
B. the cargo hatches are of steel construction
C. the cargo is of a nonflammable type
D. there is sufficient fire protection located on the main deck adjacent to the cargo hatch

011067/DG00195 *49 CFR 176.39 (a)
You are transporting dangerous cargo on your vessel. The Dangerous Cargo Manifest must be signed by the _____.
A. shipper
B. U.S. Coast Guard Marine Inspector
⚓ C. Master or his authorized representative
D. Master only

011068/DG00155 *49 CFR 176.39 (a)
You are transporting dangerous cargo on your vessel. You must inspect this cargo _____.
⚓ A. daily
B. daily, at sea only
C. after encountering rough weather
D. after loading and prior to arrival in port only

011069/DG00440 *49 CFR 176.48 (c)
If a Master must jettison a container loaded with hazardous material, he must, as soon as possible, notify the _____.
A. National Cargo Bureau
B. Environmental Protection Agency
C. National Hazardous Chemical Response Center
⚓ D. nearest Captain of the Port

011070/DG04006 *49 CFR 176.54
No hot work shall be performed on board a vessel with hazardous materials as cargo unless the work is approved by the _____.
A. American Bureau of Shipping
⚓ B. local U.S. Coast Guard Captain of the Port
C. National Cargo Bureau
D. harbormaster

011071/DG00420 *49 CFR 176.72 (a)
In handling break bulk hazardous materials, it is forbidden to use _____.
A. cargo nets
⚓ B. metal bale hooks
C. pallets
D. slings

011072/DG00460 *49 CFR 176.74 (a)
When stowing hazardous materials on deck, lashing of such cargo is permitted if _____.
- A. a wooden bin is constructed of at least 2-inch dunnage and bolted together
- B. the cargo is lashed to the adjacent guard rails
- ⚓ C. the lashings are secured to deck pad eyes
- D. there is at least 3 inches of dunnage on deck

011073/DG00620 *49 CFR 176.76
You are on a container vessel. What concerning the handling and stowage of containerized hazardous materials is TRUE?
- ⚓ A. Open-bed containers may be used to transport hazardous materials if the cargo is properly secured.
- B. A portable cargo tank of a flammable, cryogenic liquid may not be in transit for a period exceeding its marked rated holding time unless the liquid is inhibited.
- C. A portable cargo tank containing a cryogenic liquid must be shipped on deck unless forced ventilation is provided to the 'tween-decks.
- D. A container loaded with packages of tear gas would display a placard reading "Irritant."

011074/DG00600 *49 CFR 176.76
You are on a containership. Which statement about the stowage of hazardous materials in containers is TRUE?
- A. The containers provide automatic segregation of hazardous materials except for class A explosives.
- B. All packages within a container must be marked "This End Up" to indicate the correct stowage.
- ⚓ C. A refrigerated container with a fuel tank containing a flammable liquid must be stowed on deck.
- D. Packages of liquids within a container should be stowed on top of packages of solids to prevent crushing.

011075/DG01003 *49 CFR 176.80 (b)
You are on a containership. The cargo includes a container of small arms ammunition, a container of lead-acid storage batteries and a container of methyl acetylene bottles. Which statement is TRUE?
- A. The storage batteries must be stowed on deck away from the ammunition.
- B. The storage batteries must be at least ten horizontal feet away from the methyl acetylene.
- C. The ammunition must be separated from the methyl acetylene by at least one hold.
- ⚓ D. No separation is required because freight containers are exempted.

011076/DG00560 *49 CFR 176.83
You are loading a cargo that includes cylinders of acetylene aboard your break bulk vessel. Which statement is true?
- ⚓ A. The cylinders must be stowed at least 10 horizontal feet from corrosive materials in the same space.
- B. Stowage in the upper deck-deck is considered to be the equivalent of "on deck" stowage for this cargo.
- C. The cylinders must have a red label for flammability and a green label for compressed gas.
- D. The cylinders may be protected from the radiant heat of the Sun by laying a tarp on them.

011077/DG00267*49 CFR 176.83; Table *49 CFR 176.83 (b)
Which statement is NOT true concerning the stowage of class 1 explosives?
- A. Class 1.1 explosives may be stowed with class 9 dangerous substances
- B. Class 1.4 explosives must be "separated from" a stow of class 5.1 oxidizing materials.
- ⚓ C. Class 1.4 explosives may not be stowed in the same hold with class 6.1 poisons.
- D. Class 1.4 explosives must be "separated from" a stow of class 8 corrosive materials.

011078/DG00273 *49 CFR 176.137
You will load class 1.2 commercial explosives and need to construct a portable magazine. The magazine MUST _____.
- A. be made of metal
- ⚓ B. be elevated with skids 10cm (3.9 inches) above the deck
- C. have a hinged cover
- D. be fastened with nails or screws

011079/DG01060 *49 CFR 176.156 (a)
You receive a package, for shipment aboard your vessel, containing Class 1 explosives. The package is damp, moldy and stained. You must _____.
- ⚓ A. refuse to accept the package
- B. note the exception(s) on the Bill of Lading
- C. replace the packaging material before stowage
- D. seek the approval of the USCG Captain of the Port

011080/DG00260 *49 CFR 176.156 (a)
You receive a package, for shipment aboard your vessel, containing Class 1 explosives. The package is damp, moldy and stained. You must _____.
- A. have the U.S.C.G. Captain of the Port approve the shipment
- B. note an exception on the Bill of Lading
- C. repair or replace the packaging before stowage
- ⚓ D. seek the shipper's advice with regard to withdrawal, repair, or replacement

011081/DG00480   *49 CFR 176.905 (a) (1)*

What is NOT a requirement for the preparation of used, gasoline-propelled cars if they are to be carried as ordinary cargo and not as hazardous cargo?

- A. The engine must be run until it dies from lack of fuel.
- ⚓ B. The fuel tank must be inerted with CO2.
- C. The ignition key may not be in the ignition.
- D. The vehicle must be inspected for fuel leaks.

CHEMICAL DATA GUIDE FOR BULK SHIPMENT BY WATER (CIM 16616.6)

011082/DG00049   *46 CFR 30.10-22; MARTON*

Flammable liquid means any liquid which gives off flammable vapors at or below _____.

- A. 40° F (4.4° C)
- ⚓ B. 80° F (26.7° C)
- C. 110° F (43.3° C)
- D. 150° F (65.6° C)

011083/DG01708   *46 CFR 30.10-22*

For the purpose of regulating tank vessels, flammable liquids are liquids which will _____.

- ⚓ A. give off flammable vapors at or below 80° F (27° C)
- B. have a Reid vapor pressure of 18 pounds or more
- C. give off flammable vapors only above 80° F (27° C)
- D. sustain combustion at a temperature at or below 100° F (38° C)

011084/DG00709   **MMOH, CHEM. DATA GUIDE**

The designations A, B, C, D, and E grades of cargo refer to the _____.

- A. degrees of quality of petroleum products
- ⚓ B. flash point range and Reid vapor pressure index of petroleum products
- C. grades of crude oil
- D. pour point, color, and viscosity index of petroleum products

011085/DG01698   ***CHEM. DATA GUIDE; MARTON**

A flammable liquid having a Reid vapor pressure of 8-1/2 P.S.I.A. or less and a flash point of 80° F or below is grade _____.

- A. A
- B. B
- ⚓ C. C
- D. D

011086/DG00059   ***46 CFR 30.10-15; MARTON**

Combustible liquid is defined as any liquid having a flash point above _____.

- A. 40° F (4° C)
- ⚓ B. 80° F (27° C)
- C. 110° F (43° C)
- D. 150° F (66° C)

011087/DG00039   ***46 CFR 30.10-15; MARTON**

Combustible liquids are divided into how many grades?

- A. One
- ⚓ B. Two
- C. Three
- D. Four

011088/DG01718   ***CHEM. DATA GUIDE; MARTON**

A combustible liquid with a flash point of 90° F would be grade _____.

- A. B
- B. C
- ⚓ C. D
- D. E

011089/DG00152   ***46 CFR 30.10-15; MARTON**

A petroleum liquid has a flash point of 135° Fahrenheit. This liquid is classed as a grade _____.

- A. B flammable liquid
- B. C flammable liquid
- ⚓ C. D combustible liquid
- D. E combustible liquid

011090/DG00729   ***CHEM. DATA GUIDE; MARTON**

A petroleum liquid has a flash point of 85° F. This is a grade _____.

- A. B flammable liquid
- B. C flammable liquid
- ⚓ C. D combustible liquid
- D. E combustible liquid

011091/DG01678   ***CHEM. DATA GUIDE; MARTON**

Grade D combustible liquids have a maximum flash point of _____.

- A. 109° F
- B. 100° F
- ⚓ C. 149° F
- D. 80° F

011092/DG01688   ***CHEM. DATA GUIDE; MARTON**

Grade E combustible liquids have a flash point of _____.

- A. 80° F to 150° F
- ⚓ B. 150° F or above
- C. 60° F to 100° F
- D. 90° F to 120° F

011093/DG02986   ***CHEM. DATA GUIDE**

Sulfuric acid is a _____.

- A. clear syrupy liquid with no odor
- ⚓ B. colorless-to-brown liquid with a choking odor when hot
- C. colorless liquid with a pleasant fruity odor
- D. whitish liquid with a faint, pleasant odor

011094/DG03079　　　　*CHEM. DATA GUIDE
What is a solid at ambient temperature?
A.　Aniline
B.　Formic acid
C.　Methyl chloride
⚓ D.　Napthalene

011095/DG03610　　　　*CHEM. DATA GUIDE
You have a tow of chemical barges. The mate reports an ammonia smell around the head of the tow. You would suspect a leak in the barge carrying _____.
A.　methyl chloride
B.　heptane
C.　propanolamine
⚓ D.　morpholine

011096/DG04029　　　　*CHEM. DATA GUIDE
Which statement is TRUE concerning toluene?
A,　Its Reid Vapor Pressure is 9.4.
B.　The boiling point is 174° F.
⚓ C.　It is an aromatic hydrocarbon.
D.　It is classified as a grade A flammable liquid.

011097/DG00739　　　　*CHEM. DATA GUIDE
Camphor oil is classified as a grade _____.
A.　A
B.　C
⚓ C.　D
D.　E

011098/DG00370　　　　*CHEM. DATA GUIDE
Cottonseed oil is classed as a _____.
⚓ A.　combustible liquid
B.　flammable liquid
C.　flammable solid
D.　poison B

011099/DG00719　　　MMOH; *CHEM. DATA GUIDE
Most crude oils are classified as grade _____.
A.　A or B
B.　B
⚓ C.　C or D
D.　E

011100/DG04064　　　　*CHEM. DATA GUIDE
Which statement concerning castor oil is TRUE?
A,　It has a Reid vapor pressure of 9.5.
B.　It has a specific gravity of 1.3.
C.　The boiling point is 215° F (102° C).
⚓ D.　It is a grade E combustible liquid.

011101/DG03046　　　　*CHEM. DATA GUIDE
What is an explosion hazard when exposed to flame?
A.　Formic acid
B.　Nitrous oxide
C.　Tallow
⚓ D.　Toluene

011102/DG03077　　　　*CHEM. DATA GUIDE
The flash point of vinyl chloride is _____.
⚓ A.　-108° F (-78° C)
B.　-20° F (-29° C)
C.　32° F (0° C)
D.　97° F (36° C)

011103/DG04066　　　　*CHEM. DATA GUIDE
What is the MOST irritating to the skin?
A,　Carbon disulfide
B.　Ethyl alcohol
C.　Isoprene
⚓ D.　Oleum

011104/DG04068　　　　*CHEM. DATA GUIDE
What produces the MOST dangerous vapors?
⚓ A,　Anhydrous ammonia
B.　Camphor oil
C.　Methyl alcohol
D.　Pentane

011105/DG03078　　　　*CHEM. DATA GUIDE
Another name for coal naphtha that would appear on a dangerous cargo manifest is _____.
⚓ A.　benzene
B.　tar
C.　middle oil
D.　toluene

GENERAL SAFETY PRACTICES

011106/DG02114　　　　MARINE CARGO OPS.
All handling and stowage of packaged hazardous materials on board a domestic vessel engaged in foreign trade shall be done under the supervision of _____.
A.　a U.S. Coast Guard Marine Inspector
⚓ B.　an officer assigned to the vessel
C.　the American Bureau of Shipping
D.　the National Cargo Bureau

011107/DG02151　　　　MARINE CARGO OPS.
Many dangerous cargoes are stowed on deck because of the _____.
A.　danger to crew and cargo
B.　necessity of periodic inspection
C.　possible need to jettison
⚓ D.　All of the above

011108/DG02110   **MARINE CARGO OPS.**
Your ship is carrying hazardous cargo. During a daily inspection, you notice that some of the cargo has shifted and several cases are broken. You should FIRST _____.
- A. call out the deck gang to jettison the cargo
- B. log the facts in the rough log and inform the Chief Mate later
- C. make a determination of the seriousness of the breakage, and do what you think best
- ⚓ D. report the facts immediately to the Master, who will make a decision

BASIC PRINCIPLES OF WATCHKEEPING (ROUTINE OPERATIONS)

LOOK-OUT RESPONSIBILITIES

011109/DG00174   **AMSM**
A proper look-out must be kept _____.
A. only in fog
B. only between the hours of sunset and sunrise
C. only when entering and leaving port
⚓ D. at all times

011110/DG03540   **AMSM**
While on duty as a look-out, which other duty may you perform?
A. Sweep down the fo'c'sle
B. Paint any area near your station
C. Overhaul a block, as long as it is at your look-out station
⚓ D. None of the above

011111/DG01245   **WATCHSTAND GUIDE; STCW**
While on watch at sea you must maintain a proper lookout at all times. On a 700-foot cargo vessel being hand-steered during daylight hours in good visibility and clear of any navigational hazards, the lookout may be _____.
A. the helmsman
⚓ B. the mate on watch
C. Either A or B
D. Neither A nor B

011112/DG01255   **WATCHSTAND GUIDE; STCW**
While on watch at sea you must maintain a proper lookout at all times. You are on a 200-foot cargo vessel with an unobstructed view astern from the steering position. The vessel is being hand-steered during daylight hours in good visibility and clear of any navigational hazards. The lookout may be _____.
A. the helmsman
B. the officer on watch
⚓ C. Either A or B
D. Neither A nor B

011113/DG00867   *46 CFR 15.845; *46 CFR 15.850
Who may perform as a lookout?
A. A member of the engineering watch
⚓ B. A member of the navigational watch
C. A member of the Stewards Department
D. All of the above

011114/DG03530   **AMSM**
Which is NOT a duty of a look-out?
A. Refuse to talk to others, except as required by duty.
B. Remain standing during your watch.
C. Report every sighting.
⚓ D. Supervise any deck work going on in the area.

011115/DG00093   **AMSM**
A lookout can leave his station _____.
⚓ A. only when properly relieved
B. at the end of the watch
C. 15 minutes before the end of the watch
D. at any time

011116/DG00613   **AMSM**
A lookout can leave his station _____.
A. at the end of the watch
⚓ B. only when properly relieved
C. at any time
D. 15 minutes before the end of the watch

011117/DG01132   **AMSM**
A lookout can leave his station _____.
A. at the end of the watch
B. at any time
⚓ C. ONLY when properly relieved
D. 15 minutes before the end of the watch

011118/DG02316   **AMSM**
A lookout can leave his/her station _____.
A. at any time
B. at the end of the watch
C. 15 minutes before the end of the watch
⚓ D. only when properly relieved

011119/DG03550   **AMSM**
When can a look-out leave his duty station?
A. 15 minutes before the end of the watch
B. At the end of the watch
⚓ C. When properly relieved
D. At any time

011120/DG00604   **INT. MARITIME DICTIONARY**
The term "lee side" refers to the _____.
A. side of the vessel exposed to the wind
⚓ B. side of the vessel sheltered from the wind
C. port side
D. starboard side

LOOK-OUT TECHNIQUES

011121/DG02745   **AMSM**
While standing look-out at night, a dim light on the horizon will be seen quickest by looking _____.
⚓ A. a little above the horizon
B. directly towards the light
C. a little below the horizon
D. quickly above then quickly below the horizon

011122/DG00184   AMSM
You are standing look-out duty at night. A dim light on the horizon will be seen quickest by looking _____.
A. at an area just a little below the horizon
B. at the horizon, where the sky and water appear to meet
⚓ C. a little above the horizon
D. well below the horizon

011123/DG03560   AMSM
What should look-outs report?
A. Discolored water
B. Shoals
C. Floating objects
⚓ D. All of the above

LOOK-OUT REPORTS (BELLS)

011124/DG00154   AMSM
A look-out at the bow sights an object on your port side. How many bell strokes should he sound?
A. One
⚓ B. Two
C. Three
D. Four

011125/DG00144   AMSM
The lookout sights a vessel dead ahead. This should be reported on the bell with _____.
A. one bell
B. two bells
⚓ C. three bells
D. four bells

LOOK-OUT REPORTS (RELATIVE BEARINGS)

011126/DG00164   AMSM
A look-out should report objects sighted using _____.
A. true bearings
B. magnetic bearings
C. gyro bearings
⚓ D. relative bearings

011127/DG00194   AMSM
A vessel spotted at 45° relative can be reported as _____.
A. on the starboard beam
⚓ B. broad on the starboard bow
C. 4 points forward of starboard bow
D. 4 points abaft the starboard beam

011128/DG03570   AMSM
As look-out, you spot an object 45° off your port bow. You should report the object as _____.
⚓ A. broad on the port bow
B. 3 points on the port bow
C. 3 points forward of the port beam
D. on the port beam

STEERING PRACTICES & TECHNIQUES

011129/DG00031   AMSM
An embarked Pilot _____.
⚓ A. is a specialist hired for his local navigational knowledge
B. is solely responsible for the safe navigation of the vessel
C. relieves the Master of his duties
D. relieves the officer of the watch

011130/DG01242   WATCHSTAND GUIDE
You are a watchstanding mate and have come to the bridge to relieve the watch while underway at sea. The watch should not be transferred _____.
A. during an engine speed change
⚓ B. during a navigational course change
C. unless the helm is in the "hand" mode
D. All of the above

011131/DG01237   WATCHSTAND GUIDE
You are a watchstanding mate and have come to the bridge to relieve the watch. After reviewing the chart and having been briefed by the off-going mate, you are now ready to effect the relief. The watch is officially transferred to you after _____.
A. you state the vessel's charted position, present course and port of destination
B. the mate being relieved tells you the vessel's course and speed and states that you have the watch
⚓ C. you say, "I relieve you" and you state the course per gyro and magnetic compasses
D. the mate being relieved says, "You have the conn" and you state the ship's course

011132/DG01247   WATCHSTAND GUIDE
You are on watch and the Pilot has the conn. The Master has temporarily gone below. The Pilot orders a course change which you are certain will put the vessel into imminent danger. Your first action should be to _____.
⚓ A. countermand the order and immediately notify the Master
B. make an appropriate entry in the deck log concerning the Pilot's order
C. immediately call the Master and await further orders from him
D. immediately sound a short ring on the general alarm

011133/DG01243   **WATCHSTAND GUIDE; STCW**

You are on watch at sea and find it prudent to call the Master to the bridge due to traffic congestion. The moment that the Master officially relieves you of the conn is whenever _____.

  A.   a watchstander announces "Captain's on the bridge"

  B.   you call the Captain to the bridge in a traffic situation

⚓ C.   the Master specifically informs you that he has the conn

  D.   the Captain states the course being steered

011134/DG01253   **WATCHSTAND GUIDE**

You are preparing to relieve the mate on watch while underway at sea. The watch should not be transferred _____.

  A.   during an engine speed change

  B.   while the Master is on the bridge

⚓ C.   during a collision avoidance maneuver

  D.   All of the above

011135/DG02156   **AMSM**

You are standing watch on entering port and the Master gives a rudder command which conflicts with a rudder command from the Pilot. You should ensure the helmsman _____.

⚓ A.   obeys the Master

  B.   obeys the Pilot

  C.   brings the rudder to a position midway between the two conflicting positions

  D.   asks the Pilot if he has relinquished control

011136/DG03681   **AMSM**

While you are on watch entering port, the Master gives the helmsman a rudder command which conflicts with a rudder command from the Pilot. You should make sure the helmsman _____.

  A.   obeys the Pilot

⚓ B.   obeys the Master

  C.   asks you for instructions

  D.   brings the rudder to a point midway between the two conflicting positions

011137/DG02883   **AMSM**

While you are on watch entering port, the Master gives the helmsman a rudder command which conflicts with a rudder command from the Pilot. You should make sure the helmsman _____.

  A.   brings the rudder to a point midway between the two conflicting positions

  B.   obeys the Pilot

  C.   asks you for instructions

⚓ D.   obeys the Master

011138/DG01235   **AMSM; MMOH**

You are on watch entering port while the pilot has the conn. The pilot gives a steering command to the helmsman who partially repeats the command. You should immediately _____.

⚓ A.   repeat the Pilot's command and ensure that the helmsman repeats it completely

  B.   ask the Pilot to repeat the command since the helmsman failed to hear it completely

  C.   observe the helmsman's wheel action to be sure that it complies with the Pilot's command

  D.   ignore the helmsman's response as long as it was close to what the Pilot ordered

011139/DG03201   **AMSM**

You are on watch entering port, and the Master gives the helmsman a rudder command which conflicts with a rudder command from the Pilot. You should make sure the helmsman _____.

  A.   obeys the Pilot

  B.   asks you for instructions

⚓ C.   obeys the Master

  D.   brings the rudder to a point midway between the two conflicting positions

011140/DG01267   **AMSM; MMOH**

You are on watch while your vessel is entering port with a pilot conning. The pilot gave a steering command to the helmsman who failed to acknowledge it by repeating the order. You have now enunciated the pilot's order to the helmsman and there is still no response. If the helmsman continues on the original course, you should immediately _____.

⚓ A.   take the helm and expedite the maneuver that the pilot ordered

  B.   ask the Pilot to repeat the command since the helmsman failed to hear it

  C.   tell the helmsman to ask the Pilot to repeat any command that he fails to hear or understand

  D.   repeat the Pilot's command a second time and notify the Master

011141/DG01233   **AMSM; MMOH**

You are on watch while your vessel is entering port with a pilot conning. The pilot gives a steering command to the helmsman who fails to acknowledge it by repeating the command. You should immediately _____.

  A.   notify the Master

  B.   ask the Pilot to repeat the command since the helmsman failed to hear it

  C.   tell the helmsman to ask the Pilot to repeat any command that he fails to hear or understand

⚓ D.   repeat the Pilot's command and ensure that the helmsman repeats it exactly

011142/DG00187   **AMSM**

You are standing the wheel watch on entering port and the Master gives you a rudder command which conflicts with a rudder command from the Pilot. What should you do?
A. Ask the Pilot if he relinquishes control.
B. Obey the Pilot.
⚓ C. Obey the Master.
D. Bring the rudder to a position midway between the two conflicting positions.

011143/DG03580   **AMSM**

You are standing the wheelwatch on entering port and the Master gives you a rudder command which conflicts with a rudder command from the Pilot. What should you do?
⚓ A. Obey the Master.
B. Obey the Pilot.
C. Bring the rudder to a position midway between the two conflicting orders.
D. Ask the Pilot if he relinquishes control.

011144/DG02399   **AMSM**

You are standing wheel watch on entering port and the Master gives you a rudder command which conflicts with a rudder command from the Pilot. What should you do?
A. Obey the Pilot.
B. Bring the rudder to a position midway between the two conflicting positions.
C. Ask the Pilot if he relinquishes control.
⚓ D. Obey the Master.

011145/DG01075   **AMSM**

You are standing wheelwatch on entering port, and the Master gives you a rudder command that conflicts with a rudder command from the Pilot. What should you do?
A. Obey the Pilot
⚓ B. Obey the Master
C. Ask the Pilot for guidance
D. Bring the rudder to midships

011146/DG02181   **SEATECH**

When relieving the helm, the new helmsman should know the _____.
⚓ A. course per magnetic steering compass
B. gyro error
C. variation
D. maximum rudder angle previously used

011147/DG02694   **SEATECH**

When relieving the helm, the new helmsman should know the _____.
A. gyro error
⚓ B. course per magnetic steering compass
C. variation
D. maximum rudder angle previously used

011148/DG02567   **SEATECH**

When relieving the helm, the new helmsman should know the _____.
A. variation
B. gyro error
⚓ C. course per magnetic steering compass
D. maximum rudder angle previously used

011149/DG04379   **SEATECH**

When relieving the helm, the new helmsman should know the _____.
A, maximum rudder angle previously used
B. gyro error
C. variation
⚓ D. course per magnetic steering compass

011150/DG01557   **SEATECH**

When relieving the helm, the new helmsman should find it handy to know the _____.
⚓ A. amount of helm carried for a steady course
B. variation in the area
C. leeway
D. deviation on that heading

011151/DG02792   **SEATECH**

When relieving the helm, the new helmsman should find it handy to know the _____.
A. variation in the area
⚓ B. amount of helm carried for a steady course
C. leeway
D. deviation on that heading

011152/DG01839   **SEATECH**

When relieving the helm, the new helmsman should find it handy to know the _____.
A. leeway
B. variation in the area
⚓ C. amount of helm carried for a steady course
D. deviation on that heading

011153/DG02045   **SEATECH**

When relieving the helm, the new helmsman will find it helpful to know the _____.
A. deviation on that heading
B. variation in the area
C. leeway
⚓ D. amount of helm carried for a steady course

011154/DG01257   **WATCHSTAND GUIDE**
You are a watchstanding mate and have come to the bridge to relieve the watch. After reviewing the chart and having been briefed by the off-going mate, you are now ready to effect the relief. Which of the following is exemplary of the statement that would officially transfer the watch?
A. You say to the mate going off watch, "Destination New York, course 283°, speed 16 knots."
B. The mate being relieved says, "You now have the watch, course 147°, speed 15 knots."
C. The mate being relieved says, "All in apparent good order, course 068° per gyro, 075° per standard."
⚓ D. You say to the mate going off watch, "I relieve you, course 321° per gyro, 316° per standard."

011155/DG00634   **AMSM**
The "iron mike" is a(n) _____.
A. pilot
B. speaker
C. standby wheel
⚓ D. automatic pilot

011156/DG00077   **AMSM**
When steering a vessel, a good helmsman will _____.
A. use as much rudder as possible to keep the vessel on course
B. apply rudder to move the compass card towards the lubbers line when off course
⚓ C. repeat back to the watch officer any rudder commands before executing them
D. keep the rudder amidships except when changing course

011157/DG03590   **AMSM**
When steering a vessel, a good helmsman does NOT _____.
⚓ A. use as much rudder as possible to maintain course
B. consider steering a vessel a highly responsible job
C. use as little rudder as possible to maintain course
D. advise his relief of the course being steered

011158/DG03165   **AMSM**
When steering a vessel, a good helmsman does NOT _____.
A. consider steering a vessel a highly responsible job
⚓ B. use as much rudder as possible to keep the vessel on course
C. use as little rudder as possible to keep the vessel on course
D. advise his relief of the course being steered

011159/DG03411   **AMSM**
When steering a vessel, a good helmsman does NOT _____.
A. consider steering a vessel a highly responsible job
B. use as little rudder as possible to maintain course
⚓ C. use as much rudder as possible to keep the vessel on course
D. advise his relief of the course being steered

011160/DG04067   **AMSM**
When steering a vessel, a good helmsman does NOT _____.
A, use as little rudder as possible to maintain course
B. advise his relief of the course being steered
C. consider steering a vessel a highly responsible job
⚓ D. use as much rudder as possible to maintain course

HELM COMMANDS
011161/DG01452   **ENCY. NAUT. KNOW.**
The helm command "Check her" means _____.
A. test the steering control
B. read the compass heading
C. stop the swing using hard over rudder
⚓ D. slow the swing using moderate rudder

011162/DG01323   **AMSM**
Ease the rudder means to _____.
⚓ A. decrease the rudder angle
B. move the rudder slowly in the direction of the most recent rudder command
C. bring the rudder amidships
D. steer the course which is your present heading

011163/DG00442   **AMSM**
Ease the rudder means to _____.
A. move the rudder slowly in the direction of the most recent rudder command
⚓ B. decrease the rudder angle
C. bring the rudder amidships
D. steer the course which is your present heading

011164/DG00254   **AMSM**
Ease the rudder means to _____.
A. move the rudder slowly in the direction of the most recent rudder command
B. bring the rudder amidships
⚓ C. decrease the rudder angle
D. steer the course which is your present heading

011165/DG01815   **AMSM**
Ease the rudder means to _____.
A. steer the course which is your present heading
B. move the rudder slowly in the direction of the most recent rudder command
C. bring the rudder amidships
⚓ D. decrease the rudder angle

011166/DG02752   SEATECH
Which is a correct reply to a Pilot's request, "How's your head"?
⚓ A. Passing 040°
   B. Steady
   C. Checked
   D. Eased to 15° rudder

011167/DG01719   SEATECH
What is a CORRECT reply to a pilot's request, "How's your head"?
   A. Steady
   B. Eased to 10° rudder
   C. Checked
⚓ D. Passing 50°

011168/DG01157   SEATECH
What is a correct reply to a pilot's request, "How's your head"?
   A. Steady
⚓ B. Passing 150°
   C. Checked
   D. Eased to 5° rudder

011169/DG00575   SEATECH
What is a correct reply to a pilot's request, "How's your head"?
   A. Steady
   B. Checked
⚓ C. Passing 200°
   D. Eased to 10° rudder

011170/DG00244   AMSM
Hard right rudder means _____.
⚓ A. put the rudder over to the right all the way
   B. jam the rudder against the stops
   C. meet a swing to the right, then return to amidships
   D. put the rudder over quickly to 15° right rudder

011171/DG02805   AMSM
Hard right rudder means _____.
   A. jam the rudder against the stops
⚓ B. put the rudder over to the right all the way
   C. meet a swing to the right, then return to amidships
   D. put the rudder over quickly to 15 degrees right rudder

011172/DG02356   AMSM
Hard right rudder means _____.
   A. jam the rudder against the stops
   B. meet a swing to the right, then return to amidships
⚓ C. put the rudder over to the right all the way
   D. put the rudder over quickly to 15 degrees right rudder

011173/DG02144   AMSM
Hard right rudder means _____.
   A. jam the rudder against the stops
   B. put the rudder over quickly to 15 degrees right rudder
   C. meet a swing to the right, then return to amidships
⚓ D. put the rudder over to the right all the way

011174/DG01889   AMSM
The helm command "Nothing to the left" means do NOT _____.
   A. use left rudder
⚓ B. steer left of the ordered course
   C. steer right of the ordered course
   D. leave any buoys on the port side

011175/DG01941   AMSM
The helm command "Left twenty" means _____.
   A. change course twenty degrees to the left
⚓ B. put the rudder left twenty degrees
   C. put the rudder hard left for the first twenty degrees of swing
   D. put the rudder left twenty degrees and then ease back as the vessel starts swinging

011176/DG00214   AMSM
The helm command "meet her" means _____.
⚓ A. use rudder to check the swing
   B. decrease the rudder angle which is on
   C. steer more carefully
   D. note the course and steady on that heading

011177/DG00332   AMSM
The helm command "Meet her" means _____.
   A. steer more carefully
⚓ B. use rudder to check the swing
   C. decrease the existing rudder angle
   D. note the course and steady on that heading

011178/DG02817   AMSM
The command "meet her" means the helmsman should _____.
   A. decrease the rudder angle
   B. steer more carefully
⚓ C. use rudder to slow the vessel's swing
   D. note the course and steady on that heading

011179/DG02951   AMSM
The helm command "meet her" means _____.
   A. decrease the rudder angle
   B. note the course and steady on that heading
   C. steer more carefully
⚓ D. use rudder to check the swing

011180/DG00592   **AMSM**

When a helmsman receives the command "Right 15 degrees rudder," the helmsman's immediate reply should be _____.

⚓ A. Right 15 degrees rudder
   B. Aye-Aye Sir
   C. Rudder is right 15 degrees
   D. No reply is necessary, just carry out the order.

011181/DG03600   **AMSM**

A helmsman receives the command "Right 15 degrees rudder." The helmsman's IMMEDIATE reply should be _____.

   A. Aye-Aye Sir
⚓ B. Right 15 degrees rudder
   C. Rudder is right 15 degrees
   D. No reply is necessary, just carry out the order

011182/DG01092   **AMSM**

When a helmsman receives the command "Right 15 degrees rudder," the helmsman's immediate reply should be _____.

   A. Rudder is right 15 degrees
   B. Aye-Aye Sir
⚓ C. Right 15 degrees rudder
   D. No reply is necessary, just carry out the order.

011183/DG04390   **AMSM**

When a helmsman receives the command "Right 15 degrees rudder," the helmsman's immediate reply should be _____.

   A, Rudder is right 15 degrees
   B. Aye-Aye Sir
   C. No reply is necessary, just carry out the order
⚓ D. Right 15 degrees rudder

011184/DG02007   **AMSM**

The helm command "shift your rudder" means _____.

   A. double your rudder angle or go to full rudder
⚓ B. change from right rudder to left rudder an equal number of degrees
   C. bring your rudder amidships
   D. check the swing of the vessel

011185/DG00234   **AMSM**

The helm command "shift your rudder" means _____.

   A. double your rudder angle or go to full rudder
   B. bring your rudder amidships
⚓ C. change from right rudder to left rudder, or vice versa, an equal number of degrees
   D. check the swing of the vessel

011186/DG02268   **AMSM**

The helm command "shift your rudder" means _____.

   A. check the swing of the vessel
   B. double your rudder angle or go to full rudder
   C. bring your rudder amidships
⚓ D. change from right rudder to left rudder, or vice versa, an equal number of degrees

011187/DG01287   **AMSM**

The term "shift the rudder" means _____.

⚓ A. change from right (left) to left (right) rudder an equal amount
   B. use right or left rudder
   C. check, but do not stop the vessel from swinging
   D. put the rudder amidships

011188/DG01525   **AMSM**

The term "shift the rudder" means _____.

   A. use right or left rudder
⚓ B. change from right (left) to left (right) rudder an equal amount
   C. check, but do not stop the vessel from swinging
   D. put the rudder amidships

011189/DG01725   **AMSM**

The term "shift the rudder" means _____.

   A. use right or left rudder
   B. check, but do not stop the vessel from swinging
⚓ C. change from right (left) to left (right) rudder an equal amount
   D. put the rudder amidships

011190/DG00224   **AMSM**

The term "Shift the Rudder" means _____.

   A. put the rudder amidships
   B. use right or left rudder
   C. check, but do not stop the vessel from swinging
⚓ D. change from right to left or left or right

011191/DG01829   **AMSM**

The term "shift your rudder" means _____.

⚓ A. change from right rudder to left rudder an equal number of degrees
   B. double your rudder angle or go to full rudder
   C. bring your rudder amidships
   D. check the swing of the vessel

011192/DG00204   **AMSM**

What does the helm command "shift the rudder" mean?

⚓ A. Put the rudder over to the opposite side, the same number of degrees it is now.
   B. Put the rudder amidships and hold the heading steady as she goes.
   C. Shift the rudder control to the alternate steering method.
   D. Stop the swing of the ship.

011193/DG00345   **AMSM**

What does the helm command "shift the rudder" mean?

A. Put the rudder amidships and hold the heading steady as she goes.

⚓ B. Put the rudder over to the opposite side, the same number of degrees it is now.

C. Shift the rudder control to the alternate steering method.

D. Stop the swing of the ship.

011194/DG00632   **AMSM**

What does the helm command "shift the rudder" mean?

A. Stop the swing of the ship.

B. Shift the rudder control to the alternate steering method.

⚓ C. Put the rudder over to the opposite side, the same number of degrees that it is now.

D. Put the rudder amidships and hold the heading steady as she goes.

011195/DG00987   **AMSM**

What does the helm command "shift the rudder" mean?

A. Stop the swing of the ship.

B. Shift the rudder control to the alternate steering method.

C. Put the rudder amidships and hold the heading steady as she goes.

⚓ D. Put the rudder over to the opposite side, the same number of degrees it is now.

011196/DG01641   **AMSM**

The helm command "Steady as you go" means _____.

⚓ A. steer the course you are on now

B. steer the course when the swing stops

C. maintain the rate of swing

D. don't allow the vessel to swing off course so much

STEERING SYSTEMS

011197/DG00974   **AMSM; MMOH**

The "Port-Off-Stbd" selector switch on an autopilot steering stand is used to _____.

A. change from hand electric steering to automatic gyro

⚓ B. change over one steering system to the other

C. change over hand electric steering to non-followup

D. change over the port to the starboard bow thruster

011198/DG00972   **AMSM; MMOH**

The "rudder adjustment" control on an autopilot steering stand is used to _____.

A. align the rudder angle indicator with the true rudder angle

⚓ B. set the number of degrees of rudder per degree of course error

C. set the departure from base course before actuating the rudder

D. set the rate at which the rudder responds

011199/DG00973   **AMSM; MMOH**

The "weather adjustment" control on an autopilot steering stand is used to _____.

A. allow leeway according to the weather conditions

B. proportionally set the number of degrees of rudder response per degree of course error

⚓ C. set the null band or dead zone signal before actuating the rudder

D. set the speed at which the rudder responds

011200/DG00983   **AMSM; MMOH**

When a vessel is on autopilot steering, the "weather " control is adjusted to compensate for which severe weather effect on a vessel?

⚓ A. Yaw

B. Roll

C. Pitch

D. Leeway

011201/DG01667   **AMSM; MMOH;**
                                          SPERRY INSTR. MANUAL

When the gyro-pilot is used for steering, what control is adjusted to compensate for varying sea conditions?

A. Rudder control

B. Sea control

C. Lost motion adjustment

⚓ D. Weather adjustment

011202/DG01000   **AMSM; MMOH**

The "Mode" selector switch can be positioned and select all of the following EXCEPT _____.

⚓ A. weather adjustments

B. hand-electric steering

C. automatic gyro

D. non-followup control

011203/DG00975   **AMSM; MMOH**

The "Mode" selector switch on the autopilot steering stand is used to select any of the following with the EXCEPTION of _____.

A. automatic pilot steering

B. hand-electric steering

C. non-followup steering

⚓ D. rudder adjustment

011204/DG00997 AMSM; MMOH

When steering by hand, which of the following may be a functional input to the steering gear as a result of turning the wheel?

⚓ A. Non-followup
B. Rudder adjustment
C. Weather adjustment
D. All the above may be activated

011205/DG00998 AMSM; MMOH

When steering on autopilot which of the following input conditions may NOT have an effect on the control of the steering gear?

⚓ A. Non-followup
B. Rudder adjustment
C. Weather adjustment
D. All the above may be activated

BASIC PRINCIPLES OF WATCHKEEPING (EMERGENCY OPERATIONS)

FIRE & EMERGENCY

011206/DG00822 MFPFFS

You are on watch at sea at night and a fire breaks out in #3 hold. What should be done IMMEDIATELY?

⚓ A. Shut down the cargo hold ventilation.
B. Proceed to the space and determine the extent of the fire.
C. Flood the space with C02 from the fixed fire fighting system.
D. Cool the deck to contain the fire.

011207/DG00104 MFPFFS

You are on watch at sea at night when a fire breaks out in #3 hold just forward of the bridge. You would NOT _____.

A. call the Master
⚓ B. proceed to the space and inspect the extent of the fire
C. shut down the cargo hold ventilation
D. sound the fire alarm signal to roust out all hands

011208/DG00922 MFPFFS

You are on watch at sea at night, and a fire breaks out in #3 hold. What would you NOT do immediately?

A. Shut down the cargo hold ventilation.
B. Sound the fire alarm signal to rouse out all hands.
C. Call the Master.
⚓ D. Proceed to the space and inspect the extent of the fire.

STEERING GEAR FAILURE

011209/DG01002 AMSM; MMOH

While steering by autopilot you notice that the vessel has deviated 15 degrees from course and there is no corrective rudder being applied. As a standard operating procedure you should _____.

A. adjust the setting of the rudder adjustment
B. adjust the setting of the weather adjustment
C. immediately engage the trick wheel
⚓ D. switch to the other steering system

011210/DG00965 AMSM; MMOH

While steering by autopilot you notice that the vessel has deviated 15 degrees from course and there is no corrective rudder being applied. As a standard operating procedure you should first _____.

A. check the setting of the rudder adjustment
B. check the setting of the weather adjustment
⚓ C. switch to hand steering
D. immediately engage the trick wheel

011211/DG00967 AMSM; MMOH

While steering by autopilot you notice that the vessel is deviating from the given course and there is no follow up with corrective rudder action to return to the proper heading. The emergency operating procedure should require you to immediately change operation from _____.

⚓ A. gyro to hand
B. hand to gyro
C. gyro to control
D. control to hand

011212/DG01227 SPERRY INSTRUCTION MANUAL

You have the "conn" at the time the helmsman who is steering by hand reports that the rudder is not responding to the wheel. Your FIRST action should be to _____.

⚓ A. shift the selector switch to the other steering pump
B. signal the engineroom to stop the engines
C. call the engineroom
D. call the Master

011213/DG00985 AMSM; MMOH

You have the "conn" at the time the helmsman who is steering by hand reports that the rudder is not responding to the wheel. Your FIRST action should be to _____.

A. call the engineroom and report that you have lost steering
B. signal the engineroom to stop the engines
⚓ C. shift the selector switch to the other steering system
D. call the Master

011214/DG01232   SPERRY INSTRUCTION MANUAL
You have the "conn" at the time the helmsman who is steering by hand reports that the rudder is not responding to the wheel. Your FIRST action should be to _____.
A. check that the wheel is firmly connected to the shaft
B. signal the engineroom to "Standby the Engines"
C. set the "Mode" switch to "Auto" and steer by auto-pilot
⚓ D. switch to the other steering pump

011215/DG00134   MMOH
Your ship is steaming at night on gyro-pilot when you notice that the vessel's course is slowly changing to the right. Which action should you take FIRST?
A. Call the Master.
⚓ B. Change to hand steering.
C. Notify the engine room of the steering malfunction.
D. Send the Quartermaster to the emergency steering station.

011216/DG00627   AMSM
Your ship is steaming at night with the gyro-pilot engaged when you notice that the vessel's course is slowly changing to the right. What action should you take FIRST?
⚓ A. switch to hand steering
B. shift steering to the emergency steering station
C. call the Master
D. notify the engineroom

011217/DG01668   AMSM
Your ship is steaming at night with the gyro-pilot engaged. You notice that the vessel's course is slowly changing to the right. Which action should you take FIRST?
A. Notify the engine room of the steering malfunction.
⚓ B. Change to hand steering.
C. Call the Master.
D. Send the Quartermaster to the emergency steering station.

MAN OVERBOARD PROCEDURES
011218/DG02553   MSRS
The key to rescuing a man overboard is _____.
A. good equipment
B. a dedicated crew
⚓ C. well-conducted drills
D. good communication

011219/DG01575   MSRS
The key to rescuing a man overboard is _____.
A. good communication
B. a dedicated crew
C. good equipment
⚓ D. well-conducted drills

011220/DG01365   MSRS
A person who sees someone fall overboard should _____.
⚓ A. call for help and keep the individual in sight
B. run to the radio room to send an emergency message
C. immediately jump in the water to assist the individual
D. go to the bridge for the distress flares

011221/DG01600   MSRS; KNIGHTS; AMSM
A person who sees someone fall overboard should _____.
⚓ A. call for help and keep the individual in sight
B. immediately jump in the water to assist the individual
C. run to the radio room to send an emergency message
D. go to the bridge for the distress flares

011222/DG02596   MSRS
A person who sees someone fall overboard should _____.
A. immediately jump into the water to assist the individual
⚓ B. call for help and keep the individual in sight
C. run to the radio room to send an emergency message
D. go to the bridge for the distress flares

011223/DG02076   MSRS
A person who sees someone fall overboard should _____.
A. immediately jump in the water to assist the individual
B. go to the bridge for the distress flares
C. run to the radio room to send an emergency message
⚓ D. call for help and keep the individual in sight

011224/DG01945   AMSM
One of your crew members falls overboard from the starboard side. You should IMMEDIATELY _____.
A. apply left rudder
⚓ B. throw the crew member a life preserver
C. begin backing your engines
D. position your vessel to windward and begin recovery

011225/DG02124   **KNIGHTS**
You are on watch aboard a vessel heading NW, with the wind from dead ahead, in heavy seas. You notice a man fall overboard from the starboard bow. Which action would NOT be appropriate?
A. Hard right rudder
B. Throw a lifebuoy to the man, if possible
C. Send a man aloft
⚓ D. Get the port boat ready

011226/DG01192   **AMSM**
A person has fallen overboard and is being picked up with a lifeboat. If the person appears in danger of drowning, the lifeboat should make _____.
A. an approach from leeward
B. an approach from windward
⚓ C. the most direct approach
D. an approach across the wind

011227/DG01270   **WSM**
When a man who is conscious has fallen overboard is being picked up by a lifeboat, the boat should approach with the wind _____.
A. astern and the victim just off the bow
B. ahead and the victim just off the bow
C. just off the bow and the victim to windward
⚓ D. just off the bow and the victim to leeward

011228/DG01265   **CHAPMAN**
You are picking up an unconscious person that has fallen overboard in a fresh breeze. For safety reasons a small craft should approach with the _____.
A. victim to leeward
⚓ B. victim to windward
C. wind on your port side
D. wind on your starboard side

WILLIAMSON TURN

011229/DG02081   **NICHOLLS**
A seaman is reported missing in the morning and was last seen after coming off the mid-watch. Which type of turn would you use to return to the track-line steamed during the night?
⚓ A. Williamson
B. Racetrack
C. 180° turn
D. Anderson

011230/DG02064   **KNIGHTS**
While underway in thick fog you are on watch and hear the cry "man overboard". Which type of maneuver should you make?
A. figure eight turn
B. Round turn
C. Racetrack turn
⚓ D. Williamson turn

011231/DG00720   **MMOH**
You suspect that a crewmember has fallen overboard during the night and immediately execute a Williamson turn. What is the primary advantage of this maneuver under these circumstances?
⚓ A. You will be on a reciprocal course and nearly on the track-line run during the night.
B. The turn provides the maximum coverage of the area to be searched.
C. The turn enables you to reverse course in the shortest possible time.
D. You have extra time to maneuver in attempting to close in on the man for rescue.

011232/DG00730   **MMOH**
In a Williamson turn, the rudder is put over full until the _____.
A. vessel has turned 90° from her original course
⚓ B. vessel has turned 60° from her original course
C. vessel is on a reciprocal course
D. emergency turn signal sounds

011233/DG00630   **MMOH**
You are doing a Williamson turn. Your vessel has swung about 60° from the original course heading. You should _____.
A. put the rudder amidships and check the swing
B. stop the engines and prepare to maneuver to pick up the man in the water
⚓ C. shift your rudder
D. increase to maximum speed

011234/DG02070   **KNIGHTS**
Which statement about the Williamson turn is FALSE?
⚓ A. It requires the highest degree of shiphandling skills to accomplish.
B. It is the slowest of the methods used in turning the vessel.
C. It is the best turn to use when the victim is not in sight due to reduced visibility.
D. It returns the vessel to the original track-line on a reciprocal course.

011235/DG00710   **SHIPHAND**
Which statement is FALSE, concerning the Williamson turn?
A. In a large vessel (VLCC) much of the headway will be lost thereby requiring little astern maneuvering.
B. When the turn is completed, the vessel will be on a reciprocal course and nearly on the original track line.
C. The initial actions are taken at well defined points and reduce the need for individual judgment.
⚓ D. The turn will return the vessel to the man's location in the shortest possible time.

011236/DG00802   **MMOH**

You are on watch at sea on course 090° T. A man falls overboard on your starboard side. You immediately start a Williamson Turn. Which action is NOT a part of a Williamson Turn?

⚓ A. Stop the engines until clear of the man.
   B. Come right full rudder until the vessel heads 150° T.
   C. Shift the helm to left full rudder.
   D. Continue with left rudder until on course 270° T.

011237/DG00114   **MMOH**

You are on watch at sea on course 090° T. A man falls overboard on your starboard side. You immediately start a Williamson Turn. Which step is NOT a part of a Williamson Turn?

   A. Step 1: Come right full rudder until the vessel heads 150° T.
⚓ B. Step 2: Stop the engines until clear of the man.
   C. Step 3: Shift the helm to left full rudder.
   D. Step 4: Continue with left rudder until on course 270° T.

ENGINE RESPONSE

011238/DG02597   **CHAPMAN**

On a small boat, if someone fell overboard and you did not know over which side the person fell, you should _____.

   A. immediately reverse the engines
⚓ B. stop the propellers from turning and throw a ring buoy over the side
   C. increase speed to full to get the vessel away from the person
   D. first put the rudder hard over in either direction

RUDDER RESPONSE

011239/DG00650   **AMSM**

A crew member has just fallen overboard off your port side. Which action should you take?

   A. Immediately put the rudder over hard right.
⚓ B. Immediately put the rudder over hard left.
   C. Immediately put the engines astern.
   D. Wait until the stern is well clear of the man and then put the rudder over hard right.

011240/DG00002   **AMSM**

You are standing the wheelwatch when you hear the cry, "Man overboard starboard side". You should instinctively _____.

⚓ A. give full right rudder
   B. give full left rudder
   C. put the rudder amidships
   D. throw a life ring to mark the spot

011241/DG00005   **AMSM**

You are standing the wheelwatch when you hear the cry, "Man overboard starboard side". You should instinctively _____.

   A. give full left rudder
⚓ B. give full right rudder
   C. put the rudder amidships
   D. throw a life ring to mark the spot

011242/DG03095   **AMSM**

You are standing the wheelwatch when you hear the cry, "Man overboard starboard side". You should instinctively _____.

   A. give full left rudder
   B. put the rudder amidships
⚓ C. give full right rudder
   D. throw a life ring to mark the spot

011243/DG04440   **AMSM**

You are standing the wheelwatch when you hear the cry, "Man overboard, starboard side". You should be instinctively _____.

   A, give full left rudder
   B. throw a life ring to mark the spot
   C. put the rudder amidships
⚓ D. give full right rudder

011244/DG00660   **MMOH**

You receive word that a person has fallen overboard from the starboard side. You should FIRST _____.

   A. notify the Master
⚓ B. put the wheel hard right
   C. put the engines full astern
   D. sound the man overboard alarm

RACE TRACK TURN (OVAL)

011245/DG02106   **KNIGHTS**

A racetrack turn would be better than a Williamson turn in recovering a man overboard if _____.

   A. the man has been missing for a period of time
⚓ B. the sea water is very cold and the man is visible
   C. there is thick fog
   D. the wind was from astern on the original course

011246/DG02130   **KNIGHTS**

In a racetrack turn, to recover a man overboard, the vessel is steadied for the SECOND time after a turn of how many degrees from the original heading?

   A. 60°
   B. 135°
   C. 180°
⚓ D. 360°

011247/DG02095   **KNIGHTS**

You are using a racetrack turn to recover a man overboard. The vessel is first steadied when how many degrees away from the original heading?

A. 60° to 70°
B. 90°
C. 135°
⚓ D. 180°

ANDERSON TURN (ROUND)

011248/DG02113   **KNIGHTS**

One major advantage of the round turn maneuver in a man overboard situation is that it _____.

⚓ A. is the fastest method
B. is easy for a single-screw vessel to perform
C. requires the least shiphandling skills to perform
D. can be used in reduced visibility

011249/DG00995   **KNIGHTS**

The maneuver which will return your vessel in the shortest time to a person who has fallen overboard is _____.

⚓ A. a single turn with hard rudder
B. engine(s) crash astern, no turn
C. a Williamson Turn
D. two 180° turns

011250/DG01465   **KNIGHTS**

The maneuver which will return your vessel in the shortest time to a person who has fallen overboard is _____.

A. engine(s) crash astern, no turn
⚓ B. a single turn with hard rudder
C. a Williamson Turn
D. two 180° turns

011251/DG02336   **KNIGHTS**

The maneuver which will return your vessel in the shortest time to a person who has fallen overboard is _____.

A. engine(s) crash astern, no turn
B. two 180° turns
C. a Williamson Turn
⚓ D. a single turn with hard rudder

011252/DG02127   **KNIGHTS**

The maneuver which will return your vessel to a person who has fallen overboard in the shortest time is _____.

A. a Williamson Turn
B. engine(s) crash astern, no turn
⚓ C. a single turn with hard rudder
D. two 180° turns

011253/DG01995   **KNIGHTS**

The single turn method of returning to a man overboard should be used ONLY if _____.

A. the man is reported missing rather than immediately seen as he falls overboard
⚓ B. the vessel is very maneuverable
C. the conning officer is inexperienced
D. a boat will be used to recover the man

SCHARNOW TURN

011254/DG03719   **MERSAR**

Besides saving distance along the track line, another advantage of the Scharnow Turn over the Williamson Turn in a man overboard situation is because _____.

⚓ A. it is faster
B. it can be used in both the immediate action and the delayed action situations
C. in fog, if the turn is started as soon as the man goes over, the vessel will be at the point where he went over when the turn is completed
D. it returns the vessel to the original track line on a reciprocal course

011255/DG03614   **MERSAR**

While you are on watch, you learn that a crewman has not been seen on board for the past three hours. Which type of turn is best in this man-overboard situation?

A. Round
⚓ B. Scharnow
C. Racetrack
D. Single turn of 180°

011256/DG03484   **MERSAR**

You are on watch and see a man fall overboard. Which man-overboard turn should NOT be used in this situation?

⚓ A. Scharnow
B. Single turn
C. Racetrack
D. Williamson

011257/DG03434   **MERSAR**

The Scharnow turn should be used in a man overboard situation only when _____.

A. the man can be kept in sight from the bridge while maneuvering
B. the turn is started immediately when the man goes over
⚓ C. there has been sufficient time elapsed since the man went over to complete the maneuver
D. the vessel has twin screws to assist in making the turn

011258/DG03820   **MERSAR**
When making a Scharnow turn, the _____.
- A. rudder must be put over towards the side the man went over
- B. initial turn direction is away from the side the man went over
- ⚓ C. rudder is put hard over and the initial turn is maintained until about 240° from the original course
- D. man overboard must be not more than 300 feet astern when starting the turn

HANDLING LIFEBOATS UNDER SAIL

011259/DG01360   **AMSM**
What are reef points used for?
- ⚓ A. Reduce the area of a sail
- B. Keep the sail taut in light airs
- C. Reduce the draft if the boat runs aground
- D. Increase the strength of the mast

SEARCH & RESCUE PATTERNS

011260/DG02128   **MERSAR**
Several merchant ships are arriving at the scene of a distress incident. One of the them must assume the duties of the Coordinator Surface Search (CSS). Which of the following statements is TRUE?
- A. CSS duties are always assumed by passenger vessels, dry cargo vessels, or tankers in that order of precedence.
- ⚓ B. The CSS must be established by mutual agreement between the ships concerned.
- C. A tank vessel should never be assigned CSS duties unless only tank vessels are present.
- D. The first vessel to arrive at the distress incident is designated as the CSS.

011261/DG02772   ***PUB 117**
The Coordinator Surface Search (CSS) in a SAR situation should display by night _____.
- A. deck lights forward and aft
- B. a white light over two red lights
- C. a red light, white light, and blue light in a vertical line
- ⚓ D. a distinctive signal promulgated by the CSS

011262/DG02888   ***PUB 117**
The Coordinator Surface Search in a SAR situation should display by day _____.
- ⚓ A. the code flags FR
- B. a black ball over a black diamond shape
- C. code flag Quebec over a black ball
- D. two black diamond shapes in a vertical line

011263/DG01198   **MERSAR**
The most probable position of the object of a search at any given time is the _____.
- ⚓ A. datum position
- B. incident position
- C. reported position
- D. dead-reckoning position

011264/DG02139   **MERSAR**
You are proceeding to the area of reported distress. When you arrive at the reported position, the vessel in distress is not sighted. What type of search should be conducted?
- A. Sector search
- ⚓ B. Expanding square
- C. Track crawl
- D. Parallel track search

011265/DG01555   **MERSAR**
When carrying out a parallel track search pattern, the course of the search units should normally be which of the following?
- ⚓ A. In the same direction as the anticipated drift
- B. In the opposite direction of the anticipated drift
- C. Perpendicular to the line of anticipated drift
- D. Downwind

011266/DG02019   **MERSAR**
A man was sighted as he fell overboard. After completing a Williamson turn, the man is not sighted. What type of search should be conducted?
- A. Expanding circle
- ⚓ B. Sector search
- C. Parallel track pattern
- D. Datum-drift search

011267/DG01742   **MERSAR**
You should conduct a sector search under which of the following circumstances?
- ⚓ A. The search target is sighted and then lost.
- B. More than one vessel is available for a search.
- C. The search object is a target that will be readily detected by radar.
- D. An aircraft is available to assist a surface vessel.

011268/DG01990   **MERSAR**

Upon receipt of a distress message, a merchant vessel is bound to proceed to the scene of the distress. Under which of the following cases would this NOT be true?

A. The vessel would arrive at the distress scene more than 36 hours after the receipt of the initial distress message.

B. There are vessels closer to the distress scene that are proceeding to assist.

⚓ C. The Master of the vessel in distress has requisitioned another vessel, and that vessel has accepted the requisition.

D. You are on a tank vessel and the distress involves a major fire on board the other vessel.

HELICOPTER OPERATIONS

011269/DG00690   **AMSM**

A rescue helicopter's hoist area should have a radius of at least _____.

A. 6 feet of clear deck

B. 10 feet of clear deck

C. 25 feet of clear deck

⚓ D. 50 feet of clear deck

011270/DG01807   **MERSAR**

When evacuating a seaman by helicopter lift, which statement is TRUE?

A. Evacuation should be from an area forward of the bridge.

B. The vessel should be slowed to bare steerageway.

C. If the hoist is at the stern, booms extending aft at the stern should be cradled with the topping lifts hove taut.

⚓ D. The litter should not be touched until it has been grounded.

011271/DG00670   **KNIGHTS**

You must evacuate a seaman by helicopter lift. Which statement is TRUE?

A. The ship should be stopped with the wind off the beam while the helicopter is hovering overhead.

B. The basket or stretcher must not be allowed to touch the deck.

C. The tending line of the litter basket should be secured to the ship beyond the radius of the helicopter blades.

⚓ D. The hoist line should be slack before the basket or stretcher is hooked on.

011272/DG01282   **MERSAR**

When evacuating a seaman by helicopter lift, the vessel should be _____.

A. stopped with the wind dead ahead

B. stopped with the wind on the beam

⚓ C. underway with the wind 30° on the bow

D. underway on a course to provide no apparent wind

011273/DG01737   **MERSAR**

When evacuating a seaman by helicopter lift, which course should the ship take?

A. Downwind so that the apparent wind is close to nil.

⚓ B. A course that will keep a free flow of air, clear of smoke, over the hoist area.

C. A course that will have the hoist area in the lee of the superstructure.

D. With the wind dead ahead because the helicopter is more maneuverable when going into the wind.

011274/DG01782   **MERSAR**

When evacuating a seaman by helicopter lift, which statement is TRUE?

A. The vessel should be stopped with the wind dead ahead during the hoisting operation.

⚓ B. Flags should be flown to provide a visual reference as to the direction of the apparent wind.

C. The drop line should be grounded first then secured as close to the hoist point as possible.

D. The hoist area should be located as far aft as possible so the pilot will have a visual reference while approaching.

011275/DG00680   **KNIGHTS**

You must medevac a critically injured seaman by helicopter hoist. Which statement is TRUE?

A. The ship's relative wind should be from dead ahead at 10 to 30 knots.

⚓ B. The deck crew at the hoist point should not wear baseball hats.

C. The helicopter's drop line should be secured to the ship not more than 15 feet from the hoist position.

D. When using a "horse collar", the bight of the loop should be around the chest of the injured seaman.

ALLIED NAVAL CONTROL SHIPPING (NCS)

011276/DG00277   ***PUB 117**

Allied Naval Control of Shipping (NCS) has been established. Which statement is TRUE?

A. The Naval Control of Shipping Organization of each nation will serve their own ships only.

B. Allied ships, which are at sea when an emergency is declared, will all be controlled by a central authority.

C. The conduct of US-flag ships in an allied port will be controlled by US NCS authorities.

⚓ D. After Naval Control of Shipping has been established, permission to sail must come from local naval authorities or consular officers.

011277/DG00405   *PUB 117
At the establishment of Naval Control of Shipping (NCS), ships at sea will _____.
A. stop and await further orders
B. attempt to make their way to the nearest port of a friendly nation and await further instructions
C. continue voyages unless in danger areas defined in the advisory or supplemental message
D. keep radio silence

011278/DG02900   *PUB 117
Which statement about Naval Control of Shipping in wartime is TRUE?
A. It is mandatory in wartime.
B. It is mandatory in hazardous areas and voluntary in other areas.
C. It is mandatory only for vessels sailing in convoy.
D. It is mandatory for vessels bound foreign and voluntary for vessels in the coastwise trade.

011279/DG00280   *PUB 117
Your ship is in a neutral port when full Naval Control of Shipping is established. You may expect to be boarded and instructed by a(n) _____.
A. U.S. Naval Control of Shipping Officer
B. allied Naval Control of Shipping Officer
C. Consular Shipping Advisors (CONSA)
D. Any of the above

011280/DG02476   *PUB 117
At the outbreak of war your ship is caught in an enemy port. Which statement is FALSE?
A. You should attempt to contact U.S. Consular officials.
B. You should attempt to clear for sea before your ship is interned.
C. You should resist boarding by local officials.
D. You should try to send a Ship Hostile Action Report to the NGA (formerly NIMA).

011281/DG02769   *PUB 117
You will be advised of any hazardous areas due to the fallout of a nuclear explosive by a message with the code word _____.
A. MERWARN
B. NUCLEAR
C. FALLOUT
D. FALLWARN

011282/DG02956   *PUB 117
You are proceeding under NCS (Naval Control of Shipping) and wish to send a message concerning an initial enemy contact. Which precedence would you assign this message?
A. Z (FLASH)
B. P (PRIORITY)
C. R (ROUTINE)
D. O (IMMEDIATE)

011283/DG02481   *PUB 117
You are proceeding under NCS (Naval Control of Shipping) and wish to send a message concerning an initial enemy contact. Which precedence would you assign this message?
A. P (PRIORITY)
B. Z (FLASH)
C. R (ROUTINE)
D. O (IMMEDIATE)

011284/DG01845   *PUB 117
You are proceeding under NCS (Naval Control of Shipping) and wish to send a message concerning an initial enemy contact. Which precedence would you assign this message?
A. O (IMMEDIATE)
B. P (PRIORITY)
C. Z (FLASH)
D. R (ROUTINE)

011285/DG02202   *PUB 117
You are proceeding under NCS (Naval Control of Shipping) and wish to send a message concerning an initial enemy contact. Which precedence will you assign this message?
A. O (IMMEDIATE)
B. P (PRIORITY)
C. R (ROUTINE)
D. Z (FLASH)

011286/DG02311   *PUB 117
In a national emergency, when communicating via the Navy, messages are sent by precedence. A message designated FLASH will be delivered within _____.
A. 10 minutes
B. 3 hours
C. 30 minutes
D. 6 hours

011287/DG02931   *PUB 117
In a national emergency, when communicating via the Navy, messages are sent by precedence. A message designated FLASH will be delivered within _____.
A. 6 hours
B. 10 minutes
C. 3 hours
D. 30 minutes

011288/DG03173   *PUB 117

In a national emergency, when communicating via the Navy, messages are sent by precedence. A message designated FLASH will be delivered within _____.

- A. 6 hours
- B. 3 hours
- C. 10 minutes
- D. 30 minutes

011289/DG01872   *PUB 117

In a national emergency, when communicating via the Navy, messages are sent by precedence. A message designated FLASH will be delivered within _____.

- A. 3 hours to start of business the following day
- B. 1 to 6 hours
- C. 30 minutes to 1 hour
- D. less than 10 minutes

011290/DG02052   *PUB 117

You are proceeding under NCS (Naval Control of Shipping) when it becomes necessary to send a distress message. Which precedence would you assign this message?

- A. O (IMMEDIATE)
- B. P (PRIORITY)
- C. R (ROUTINE)
- D. Z (FLASH)

011291/DG03323   *PUB 117

You are proceeding under NCS (Naval Control of Shipping) when it becomes necessary to send a distress message. Which precedence would you assign this message?

- A. P (PRIORITY)
- B. O (IMMEDIATE)
- C. R (ROUTINE)
- D. Z (FLASH)

011292/DG02935   *PUB 117

You are proceeding under NCS (Naval Control of Shipping) when it becomes necessary to send a distress message. Which precedence would you assign this message?

- A. R (ROUTINE)
- B. P (PRIORITY)
- C. O (IMMEDIATE)
- D. Z (FLASH)

011293/DG01707   *PUB 117

You are proceeding under NCS (Naval Control of Shipping) when it becomes necessary to send a distress message. What precedence would you assign this message?

- A. R (ROUTINE)
- B. Z (FLASH)
- C. P (PRIORITY)
- D. O (IMMEDIATE)

011294/DG00047   *PUB 117

You are proceeding under NCS (Naval Control of Shipping) and wish to send a message warning of a hurricane. Which precedence would you assign this message?

- A. O (IMMEDIATE)
- B. P (PRIORITY)
- C. R (ROUTINE)
- D. Z (FLASH)

011295/DG00502   *PUB 117

You are proceeding under NCS (Naval Control of Shipping) and wish to send a message warning of a hurricane. Which precedence would you assign this message?

- A. Z (FLASH)
- B. O (IMMEDIATE)
- C. R (ROUTINE)
- D. P (PRIORITY)

011296/DG01512   *PUB 117

You are proceeding under NCS (Naval Control of Shipping) and wish to send a message warning of a hurricane. Which precedence would you assign this message?

- A. R (ROUTINE)
- B. Z (FLASH)
- C. O (IMMEDIATE)
- D. P (PRIORITY)

011297/DG02303   *PUB 117

You are proceeding under NCS (Naval Control of Shipping) and wish to send a message warning of a hurricane. Which precedence would you assign this message?

- A. P (PRIORITY)
- B. Z (FLASH)
- C. R (ROUTINE)
- D. O (IMMEDIATE)

011298/DG02287   *PUB 117

In a national emergency, when communicating via the Navy, messages are sent by precedence. A message designated IMMEDIATE will be delivered within _____.

⚓ A. 30 minutes
   B. 3 hours
   C. 6 hours
   D. 10 minutes

011299/DG02547   *PUB 117

In a national emergency, when communicating via the Navy, messages are sent by precedence. A message designated IMMEDIATE will be delivered within _____.

   A. 6 hours
⚓ B. 30 minutes
   C. 3 hours
   D. 10 minutes

011300/DG01846   *PUB 117

In a national emergency, when communicating via the Navy, messages are sent by precedence. A message designated IMMEDIATE will be delivered within _____.

   A. 3 hours to start of business the following day
   B. 1 to 6 hours
⚓ C. 30 minutes to 1 hour
   D. 10 minutes if possible

011301/DG03061   *PUB 117

In a national emergency, when communicating via the Navy, messages are sent by precedence. A message designated IMMEDIATE will be delivered within _____.

   A. 6 hours
   B. 3 hours
   C. 10 minutes
⚓ D. 30 minutes

011302/DG02977   *PUB 117

You are proceeding under NCS (Naval Control of Shipping) when you wish to send a message concerning your ships diversion. Which precedence would you assign this message?
⚓ A. P (PRIORITY)
   B. Z (FLASH)
   C. R (ROUTINE)
   D. O (IMMEDIATE)

011303/DG03075   *PUB 117

You are proceeding under NCS (Naval Control of Shipping) when you wish to send a message concerning your ships diversion. Which precedence would you assign this message?
   A. O (IMMEDIATE)
⚓ B. P (PRIORITY)
   C. R (ROUTINE)
   D. Z (FLASH)

011304/DG02158   *PUB 117

You are proceeding under NCS (Naval Control of Shipping) when you wish to send a message concerning your ships diversion. Which precedence would you assign this message?
   A. O (IMMEDIATE)
   B. R (ROUTINE)
⚓ C. P (PRIORITY)
   D. Z (FLASH)

011305/DG01871   *PUB 117

You are proceeding under NCS (Naval Control of Shipping) when you wish to send a message concerning your ships diversion. Which precedence would you assign this message?
   A. O (IMMEDIATE)
   B. Z (FLASH)
   C. R (ROUTINE)
⚓ D. P (PRIORITY)

011306/DG01974   *PUB 117

In a national emergency, when communicating via the Navy, messages are sent by precedence. A message designated PRIORITY will be delivered within _____.

⚓ A. 3 hours
   B. 30 minutes
   C. 6 hours
   D. 10 minutes

011307/DG01722   *PUB 117

In a national emergency, when communicating via the Navy, messages are sent by precedence. A message designated PRIORITY will be delivered within _____.

   A. 6 hours
⚓ B. 3 hours
   C. 30 minutes
   D. 10 minutes

011308/DG02274   *PUB 117

In a national emergency, when communicating via the Navy, messages are sent by precedence. A message designated PRIORITY will be delivered within _____.

A. 6 hours
B. 30 minutes
C. 3 hours
D. 10 minutes

011309/DG03219   *PUB 117

In a national emergency, when communicating via the Navy, messages are sent by precedence. A message designated PRIORITY will be delivered within _____.

A. 6 hours
B. 10 minutes
C. 30 minutes
D. 3 hours

011310/DG03293   *PUB 117

You are proceeding under NCS (Naval Control of Shipping) and wish to send a message by rapid transmission which does not require a higher precedence. Which precedence would you assign this message?

A. R (ROUTINE)
B. P (PRIORITY)
C. O (IMMEDIATE)
D. Z (FLASH)

011311/DG02785   *PUB 117

You are proceeding under NCS (Naval Control of Shipping) and wish to send a message by rapid transmission which does not require a higher precedence. Which precedence would you assign this message?

A. P (PRIORITY)
B. R (ROUTINE)
C. O (IMMEDIATE)
D. Z (FLASH)

011312/DG04053   *PUB 117

You are proceeding under NCS (Naval Control of Shipping) and wish to send a message by rapid transmission which does not require a higher precedence. Which precedence would you give this message?

A, O (IMMEDIATE)
B. P (PRIORITY)
C. R (ROUTINE)
D. Z (FLASH)

011313/DG01901   *PUB 117

You are proceeding under NCS (Naval Control of Shipping) and wish to send a message by rapid transmission which does not require a higher precedence. Which precedence would you assign this transmission?

A. O (IMMEDIATE)
B. Z (FLASH)
C. P (PRIORITY)
D. R (ROUTINE)

011314/DG00035   *PUB 117

In a national emergency, when communicating via the Navy, messages are sent by precedence. A message designated ROUTINE will be delivered within _____.

A. 6 hours
B. 3 hours
C. 30 minutes
D. 10 minutes or less

011315/DG00009   *PUB 117

Defense plans may cause the operation of electronic aids to navigation to be suspended with _____.

A. no notice
B. one day's notice
C. a week's notice
D. thirty (30) days notice

011316/DG01203   *PUB 117

Under defense plans, operation of electronic aids may be temporarily suspended with _____.

A. one day's notice
B. no notice
C. thirty (30) day's notice
D. a week's notice

011317/DG04011   *PUB 117

Under defense plans, operation of electronic aids may be temporarily suspended with _____.

A, thirty (30) day's notice
B. a week's notice
C. one day's notice
D. no notice

011318/DG01662   *PUB 117

Under defense plans, operation of electronic aids to navigation may be temporarily suspended with _____.

A. one day's notice
B. thirty (30) days notice
C. no notice
D. a week's notice

011319/DG01920   *PUB 117
Which form of navigation may be suspended without notice under defense planning?
⚓ A. electronic
B. celestial
C. piloting
D. None of the above

011320/DG02844   *PUB 117
Naval authorities would NOT give orders about which of the following, when the vessel is under control of the Naval Control of Shipping Organization?
A. Visual communication at sea
B. Rescue operations
C. Diversions
⚓ D. Schedules for loading cargo

011321/DG02763   *PUB 117
When a merchant vessel is under the Naval Control of Shipping Organization in wartime, naval authorities may give orders pertaining to _____.
A. minimum manning standards
⚓ B. regulations about darkening ship
C. the stowage of explosives
D. the types of cargoes permitted on board

011322/DG01881   *PUB 117
In time of war Naval Control of Shipping Authorities may give orders concerning the _____.
A. cargo to be loaded
B. final destination
⚓ C. ship's route
D. All of the above

011323/DG01647   *PUB 117
Under Naval Control of Shipping who is responsible for routing and diverting ships and convoys?
A. The Maritime Defense Zone Sector
⚓ B. The Operational Control Authority
C. The National Shipping Authority
D. Any Navy Command

011324/DG03085   *USCP; *PUB 117
Naval Control of Shipping (NCS) publications should be _____.
A. in the Master's custody
B. safely stowed
C. turned over to the relieving Master
⚓ D. All of the above

011325/DG01835   *PUB 117
Your vessel's operators send a message that your vessel has been consigned to Naval Control of Shipping. The message will refer you to _____.
⚓ A. Radio Aids to Navigation (PUB 117)
B. the Coast Pilot
C. the International Code of Signals (PUB 102)
D. the Light List

011326/DG01393   *PUB 117
Your vessel's operators send a message that your vessel has been consigned to Naval Control of Shipping. The message will refer you to _____.
A. the Light List
⚓ B. Radio Aids to Navigation (PUB 117)
C. the International Code of Signals (PUB 102)
D. the Coast Pilot

011327/DG01200   *PUB 117
Your vessel's operators send a message that your vessel has been consigned to Voluntary Naval Control of Shipping. The message will refer you to _____.
A. the Light List
B. the International Code of Signals (PUB 102)
⚓ C. Radio Aids to Navigation (PUB 117)
D. the Coast Pilot

011328/DG01611   *PUB 117
On a transpacific voyage, you receive a message from your vessel's operators saying that your vessel has been consigned to Naval Control of Shipping. Further information is contained in _____.
⚓ A. Radio Aids to Navigation (PUB 117)
B. the Coast Pilot
C. the International Code of Signals (PUB 102)
D. the Light List

011329/DG02593   *PUB 117
On a transpacific voyage, you receive a message from your vessel's operators saying that your vessel has been consigned to voluntary Naval Control of Shipping. Further information is contained in _____.
A. the Light List
⚓ B. Radio Aids to Navigation (PUB 117)
C. the International Code of Signals (PUB 102)
D. the Coast Pilot

011330/DG00193   *PUB 117
On a transpacific voyage, you receive a message from your vessel's operators saying that your vessel has been consigned to Naval Control of Shipping. Further information is contained in _____.
A. the Light List
B. the International Code of Signals (PUB 102)
⚓ C. Radio Navigational Aids (PUB 117)
D. the Coast Pilot

011331/DG01123   *PUB 117
On a transpacific voyage, you receive a message from your vessel's operators saying that your vessel has been consigned to Naval Control of Shipping. Further information is contained in _____.
A. the Light List
B. the Coast Pilot
C. the International Code of Signals (PUB 102)
⚓ D. Radio Aids to Navigation (PUB 117)

011332/DG03451   ***PUB 117**

After inventorying the Naval Control of Shipping publications you find there is no copy of ATP-2, Volume II "Allied Control of Shipping Manual - Bridge Supplement". You should ask for a replacement from the _____.

⚓ A.   Maritime Administration

B.   Coast Guard

C.   Chief of Naval Operations

D.   local Operational Control Authority

011333/DG02557   ***PUB 117**

Which Naval Control of Shipping publication should be aboard your vessel?

⚓ A.   ATP-2 Vol. II - Allied Control of Shipping Manual

B.   NWP-II - Underway Replenishment Guide

C.   Warship Recognition Cards

D.   ATP-1 - Allied Tactical Signals

011334/DG02813   ***PUB 117**

Which Naval Control of Shipping publication should be aboard your vessel?

⚓ A.   ATP-2, Volume II "Allied Control of Shipping Manual - Guide to Masters"

B.   ATP-1, Volume II "Allied Tactical Signals"

C.   NWP-14, "Amphibious Operations"

D.   PUB 102, "International Code of Signals"

011335/DG02804   ***PUB 117**

Which publication is NOT carried on board U.S. merchant vessels operating under Naval Control of Shipping?

A.   Allied Control of Shipping Manual - Guide to Masters

B.   Communications Supplement

⚓ C.   Tactical Control and Routing of Merchant Vessels

D.   All of the above are carried on board

ANCHORS & GROUND TACKLE

TYPES OF ANCHORS

011336/DG00564 **AMSM**
The anchors on the bow are known as _____.
A. bower anchors
B. kedge anchors
C. spare anchors
D. stream anchors

011337/DG02549 **AMSM; PETEX**
An example of a modern anchor which has a stock is a(n) _____.
A. articulated anchor
B. Flipper Delta anchor
C. Baldt anchor
D. Danforth anchor

011338/DG01750 **ENCY. NAUT. KNOW.**
A grapnel is a _____.
A. device for securing a chain topping lift
B. hook to prevent the anchor cable from slipping
C. device used to drag for a submerged cable or line
D. type of clam bucket used for discharging bulk cargo

011339/DG02344 **AMSM; SHEFFIELD; PETEX**
An example of an anchor which has a stock is a _____.
A. Bruce anchor
B. Dunn anchor
C. Hook anchor
D. Danforth anchor

PARTS OF ANCHORS

011340/DG00514 **AMSM**
The part of an anchor which takes hold on the bottom is the _____.
A. arm
B. base
C. fluke
D. stock

011341/DG02500 **CHAPMAN**
Which part of an anchor actually digs into the bottom?
A. Stock
B. Fluke
C. Shank
D. Crown

011342/DG00554 **AMSM**
Which part of the patent anchor performs the same function as the stock of an old fashioned anchor; that is, forces the flukes to dig in?
A. Bill or pea
B. Arm
C. Shank
D. Tripping Palm

011343/DG01486 **AMSM**
Which is NOT a part of an anchor?
A. Bill
B. Devil's claw
C. Palm
D. Crown

GROUND TACKLE

011344/DG00504 **AMSM**
Anchors are prevented from running out when secured by the _____.
A. brake
B. devil's claw
C. pawls
D. All of the above

011345/DG03612 **AMSM**
Buckler plates are _____.
A. triangular-shaped plates connecting the bull chain to the topping lift
B. metal plates secured over the tops of the hawsepipes
C. faired shell plates with curvature in two directions
D. sheets of dunnage used to prevent heavy cargo from buckling the deck plates

011346/DG03504 **AMSM**
Metal plates that cover the top of the hawsepipe are called _____.
A. footings
B. plugs
C. buckler plates
D. stop waters

011347/DG00003 **AMSM**
A stopper used in securing the ground tackle for sea that consists of a grab attached to a turnbuckle is a _____.
A. riding pawl
B. buckler
C. devil's claw
D. locking ring

011348/DG01496 AMSM
The purpose of a devil's claw is to _____.
A. act as a chain stopper
B. prevent the windlass from engaging
C. prevent the chain from fouling on deck
D. control the wildcat

011349/DG00534 AMSM
Which is part of the ground tackle?
A. Charlie noble
B. Devil's claw
C. Gooseneck
D. Rat's tail

011350/DG00544 AMSM
If the winch should fail while you are hauling in the anchor, what prevents the anchor cable from running out?
A. Chain stopper
B. Devil's claw
C. Hawse ratchet
D. Riding pawl

011351/DG03291 AMSM
The riding pawl is _____.
A. a safety interlock in a cargo winch that prevents the runner from overspeeding
B. a stopper that prevents the anchor cable from running free if the cable jumps the wildcat
C. the device that locks the deck lashings of the Peck and Hale system
D. the lug that rides on the eccentric rib and engages the locking ring on the windlass

011352/DG03565 AMSM
The safety stopper that prevents the anchor cable from running free if the cable jumps the wildcat is the _____.
A. riding pawl
B. devil's claw
C. buckler plate
D. spill pipe

011353/DG03487 AMSM
The opening in the deck that leads the anchor cable outside the hull is the _____.
A. hawsepipe
B. fall pipe
C. drop-pipe
D. spill pipe

011354/DG03347 AMSM
The opening in the deck beneath the anchor windlass that leads to the chain locker is the _____.
A. hawsepipe
B. fallpipe
C. drop-pipe
D. spill pipe

011355/DG03466 AMSM
What is a spill pipe?
A. A drainage pipe that carries rain or spray from an upper deck to a lower deck
B. A pipe under the anchor windlass leading to the chain locker
C. A chute, usually over the stern, to lead dumped garbage clear of the hull
D. An opening in the deck leading outside the hull

ANCHOR WINDLASS

011356/DG02261 PETEX
The machinery associated with heaving in and running out anchor chain is the _____.
A. winch
B. windlass
C. draw works
D. dynamic pay out system

011357/DG01375 MMOH
A chain stripper is used to _____.
A. prevent chain from clinging to the wildcat
B. clean the marine debris from the chain
C. flake chain from a boat's chain locker
D. clean chain prior to an x-ray inspection

011358/DG00524 MMOH
The purpose of the stripping bar on an anchor windlass is to _____.
A. clean off any mud that may have accumulated on the chain
B. engage or disengage the wildcat
C. fairlead the chain from the hawsepipe to the wildcat
D. prevent the chain from fouling the wildcat

011359/DG00022 INT. MARITIME DICTIONARY; AMSM
A wildcat is a _____.
A. deeply-grooved drum on the windlass with sprockets which engage the links of the anchor chain
B. winch that is running out of control due to a failure of the overspeed trips
C. line that has jumped off the gypsyhead while under strain
D. nylon line that parts under strain and whips back in a hazardous manner

011360/DG00474 AMSM
On an anchor windlass, the wheel over which the anchor chain passes is called a _____.
A. brake compressor wheel
B. devil's claw
C. wildcat
D. winchhead

011361/DG02192   **PETEX; AMSM**

The part of a windlass which physically engages the chain during hauling or paying out is the _____.

A. devil's claw
B. bull gear
C. wildcat
D. cat head

011362/DG01506   **AMSM**

The sprocket wheel in a windlass, used for heaving in the anchor, is called a _____.

A. capstan
B. dog wheel
C. fairlead
D. wildcat

011363/DG03511   **AMSM**

The wheel on the windlass with indentations for the anchor chain is the _____.

A. grabber
B. wildcat
C. locking ring
D. pawl

011364/DG03689   **AMSM**

The wildcat is linked to the central drive shaft on most windlasses by _____.

A. an electromagnetic brake
B. a hydraulic coupling
C. aligning the keyways on both and inserting a key
D. a mechanical coupling where lugs engage detents

011365/DG02352   **PETEX**

The recessed areas on a wildcat are called _____.

A. pawls
B. sockets
C. pockets
D. devil's claws

011366/DG02290   **PETEX**

The sprocket teeth on a wildcat are known as the _____.

A. pawls
B. devil's claws
C. whelps
D. pockets

DIAGRAM D038DG

011367/DG03514   **AMSM**

Which type of anchor is depicted? See Diagram D038DG

A. Stock
B. Danforth
C. Patent
D. Old-fashioned

011368/DG03465   **AMSM**

Which type of anchor is illustrated? See Diagram D038DG

A. Stockless
B. Danforth
C. Old-fashioned
D. Kedge

011369/DG03378   **AMSM**

The part of the anchor indicated by the letter F is the _____. See Diagram D038DG

A. shank
B. bar
C. stock
D. shot

011370/DG03244   **AMSM**

The shank is indicated by which letter? See Diagram D038DG

A. K
B. J
C. H
D. F

011371/DG03176   **AMSM**

The part of the anchor indicated by the letter G is the _____. See Diagram D038DG

A. fluke
B. shank
C. tripping palm
D. crown

011372/DG03584   **AMSM**

The tripping palm is indicated by which letter? See Diagram D038DG

A. F
B. G
C. H
D. J

011373/DG03148   **AMSM**

The part of the anchor indicated by the letter H is the _____. See Diagram D038DG

A. fluke
B. shank
C. tripping palm
D. crown

011374/DG03394   **AMSM**

The crown of the anchor shown is indicated by which letter? See Diagram D038DG

A. K
B. J
C. H
D. G

011375/DG03690   **AMSM**

The part of the anchor indicated by the letter I is the
_____. See Diagram D038DG

A. tripping palm
⚓ B. fluke
C. bill
D. stock

011376/DG03322   **AMSM**

The fluke is indicated by which letter? See Diagram
D038DG

A. F
B. G
C. H
⚓ D. I

011377/DG03442   **AMSM**

The part of the anchor indicated by the letter J is the
_____. See Diagram D038DG

A. crown
B. shank
⚓ C. bill
D. tip

011378/DG03459   **AMSM**

The pea is indicated by which letter? See Diagram
D038DG

⚓ A. J
B. H
C. G
D. F

011379/DG03076   **AMSM**

The part of the anchor indicated by the letter K is the
_____. See Diagram D038DG

A. crown
⚓ B. ring
C. shank
D. bending shot

011380/DG03604   **AMSM**

The jews' harp is indicated by which letter? See
Diagram D038DG

⚓ A. K
B. J
C. H
D. F

ANCHOR NOMENCLATURE

ANCHOR TERMINOLOGY

011381/DG00494   **ENCY. NAUT. KNOW.**

What best describes an anchor buoy?

A. A black ball that is hoisted when the ship anchors
⚓ B. A buoy attached to the anchor
C. A buoy attached to the scope of an anchor chain
D. A mark of the number of fathoms in an anchor
    chain

011382/DG02540   **CHAPMAN**

In small craft terminology, all of the anchor gear
between a boat and her anchor is called the

_____.

A. stock
B. chock
C. scope
⚓ D. rode

011383/DG03270   **INT. MARITIME DICTIONARY**

A vessel is tide rode when it is _____.

A. carrying extra rudder to compensate for the current
B. necessary to adjust the course steered to allow for
    the current
⚓ C. at anchor and stemming the current
D. being forced off of a pier by the hydraulic effect of
    the current

011384/DG03432   **INT. MARITIME DICTIONARY**

A vessel is wind rode when it is _____.

⚓ A. at anchor and heading into the wind
B. backing into the wind
C. carrying lee rudder
D. necessary to apply a leeway correction to the
    course

ANCHOR CHAIN

011385/DG02491   **AMSM**

Before being certified by the American Bureau of
Shipping, anchor chain must undergo _____.

A. USCG inspection
⚓ B. a breaking test
C. x-ray inspection
D. spectroanalysis

011386/DG00357   **PETEX V**

What does the proof test load of an anchor chain
demonstrate?

A. Breaking strength of the chain
⚓ B. Strength of the chain to a specified limit
C. Adequate holding power for new bottom
    conditions
D. Safe working load of the chain

011387/DG01855 API MOORING RECOMMENDATION
Which problem is virtually impossible to detect during an in-service inspection of used anchor chain?
A. Cracks
B. Elongation
C. Loose studs
⚓ D. Fatigue

011388/DG03262   AMSM
Fracture damage to the end links of the anchor cable, or to the jews' harp may be eliminated by _____.
A. using a small diameter connecting shackle
B. ensuring the swivel is well lubricated and free to turn
C. installing the connecting shackle with the bow towards the anchor
⚓ D. securing a piece of wood to the jews' harp

011389/DG03724   AMSM
What part of the ground tackle is the most likely to develop fractures due to extensive anchor use?
A. Anchor shank
B. Swivel
⚓ C. Jews' harp
D. Fluke

011390/DG03448   AMSM
When inspecting ground tackle, fractures are most frequently found in the _____.
A. anchor shank
⚓ B. end links
C. swivel
D. fluke

011391/DG02490   CHAPMAN
The best method of protecting that portion of a fiber anchor line nearest the anchor from chafing on the bottom is by _____.
A. using a small scope ratio
⚓ B. replacing that portion with a short length of chain
C. using a hockle to keep that portion of the anchor line off the bottom
D. using a synthetic line

011392/DG03790   SEATECH
The locking pin that joins the parts of a detachable link is held in position by _____.
A. a tack weld
B. the self-locking characteristics of its taper
C. a cotter pin
⚓ D. a lead plug

011393/DG00574   AMSM
Which type of link is generally used to connect shots of anchor chain?
⚓ A. Detachable
B. Open
C. Pear shaped
D. Stud link

011394/DG02179   AMSM; PETEX
A design modification of an anchor chain which prevents kinking is the _____.
A. detachable link
⚓ B. stud link
C. Kenter link
D. connecting link

011395/DG00484   AMSM
On stud-link anchor chain the addition of the stud increases the strength of the link by about _____.
A. 10%
⚓ B. 15%
C. 20%
D. 50%

011396/DG02798   AMSM; PETEX
The primary purpose of the stud is to prevent the anchor chain from _____.
⚓ A. kinking
B. distorting
C. elongating
D. breaking

ANCHOR CHAIN MEASUREMENTS

011397/DG01476   ENCY. NAUT. KNOW.
How is the size of chain determined?
A. Length of link in inches
⚓ B. Diameter of metal in link in inches
C. Links per fathom
D. Weight of stud cable in pounds

011398/DG01526   MMOH
One shot of anchor chain is equal to how many feet (meters)?
A. 6 (1.8 meters)
B. 15 (4.6 meters)
C. 45 (13.7 meters)
⚓ D. 90 (27.4 meters)

011399/DG01406   MMOH
How many fathoms are in a shot of anchor cable?
A. 6
⚓ B. 15
C. 20
D. 30

011400/DG01516   **MMOH**
The length of a standard "shot" of chain is _____.
A. 12 fathoms
B. 15 fathoms
C. 18 fathoms
D. 20 fathoms

011401/DG01436   **MMOH**
How many feet are there in 2 shots of anchor chain?
A. 50
B. 60
C. 180
D. 360

011402/DG02658   **TORMH**
A Kip is equal to _____.
A. 1000 lbs.
B. 1000 kgs.
C. 2000 lbs.
D. 2240 lbs.

011403/DG03098   **LADAGE**
A weight of 1,000 short tons is equivalent to
_____.
A. 1,500 foot-pounds
B. 2,240 long tons
C. 2,000 pounds
D. 2,000 kips

011404/DG02761   **LADAGE**
A short ton is a unit of weight consisting of
_____.
A. 1,000 pounds
B. 2,000 pounds
C. 2,205 pounds
D. 2,240 pounds

ANCHOR CHAIN MARKINGS

011405/DG01446   **MMOH**
The marking on an anchor chain for 30 fathoms is
_____.
A. two links on each side of the 30 fathom detachable
    link are painted white
B. one link on each side of the 30 fathom detachable
    link is painted white
C. three links on each side of the 30 fathom
    detachable link are painted white
D. only the detachable link is painted red

011406/DG01426   **AMSM**
Forty-five fathoms is marked on the anchor chain by
_____.
A. one turn of wire on the first stud from each side of
    the detachable link
B. two turns of wire on the second stud from each
    side of the detachable link
C. three turns of wire on the third stud from each side
    of the detachable link
D. four turns of wire on the fourth stud from each side
    of the detachable link

011407/DG01456   **MMOH**
How many turns of wire normally mark either side of
the detachable link 45 fathoms from the anchor?
A. 1
B. 2
C. 3
D. 4

011408/DG01746   **KNIGHTS**
Which would you NOT use to report the amount of
anchor chain out? "Three shots _____."
A. at the water's edge
B. on deck
C. on the bottom
D. well in the water

011409/DG03722   **AMSM**
The next-to-last shot of an anchor cable is usually
painted _____.
A. white
B. international orange
C. yellow
D. red

011410/DG03586   **AMSM**
The last shot of an anchor cable is usually painted
_____.
A. white
B. international orange
C. yellow
D. red

ANCHORING PROCEDURES

SCOPE OF ANCHOR CHAIN

011411/DG02284   **CHAPMAN**
In determining the scope of anchor line to pay out when
anchoring a small boat, one must consider the
_____.
A. charted depth of water only
B. depth of water, including tidal differences
C. type of line being used for the anchor rope
D. type of anchor being used

011412/DG01606   CHAPMAN

To safely anchor a vessel there must be sufficient "scope" in the anchor cable. Scope is the ratio of _____.

A. weight of cable to weight of vessel
B. weight of cable to weight of anchor
C. length of anchor to depth of water
⚓ D. length of cable to depth of water

011413/DG02808   PETEX

Under the forces of its own weight, the suspended length of line will fall into a shape known as a _____.

A. polygon
B. holding arc
⚓ C. catenary curve
D. parabolic curve

011414/DG02714   PETEX

The major components which determine the length of catenary in a deployed anchor cable are cable tension, cable weight, and _____.

A. water density
B. bottom conditions
C. environmental forces
⚓ D. water depth

011415/DG02494   PETEX

The major components which determine the length of a catenary in a deployed anchor cable are water depth, cable weight, and _____.

⚓ A. cable tension
B. water temperature
C. bottom conditions
D. water density

011416/DG02564   PETEX

The major components which determine the length of catenary in a deployed anchor cable are water depth, cable tension, and _____.

A. environmental forces
B. bottom conditions
⚓ C. cable weight
D. water density

011417/DG01616   AMSM

In moderate wind and current what should be the length of chain with a single anchor?

⚓ A. 5 times the depth of the water in good holding ground
B. 10 times the depth of the water in shallow water
C. 2 times the depth of the water in poor holding ground
D. 8 times the depth of the water in deep water

011418/DG01546   KNIGHTS

What is the best guide for determining the proper scope of anchor chain to use for anchoring in normal conditions?

A. One shot of chain for every ten feet of water
⚓ B. One shot of chain for every fifteen feet of water
C. One shot of chain for every thirty feet of water
D. One shot of chain for every ninety feet of water

011419/DG01646   CHAPMAN

What is the normal length of anchor cable used to anchor a vessel?

A. An amount equal to the depth of the water
B. Two times the depth of water
C. Three to four times the depth of water
⚓ D. Five to seven times the depth of water

011420/DG01636   AMSM

When anchoring a vessel under normal conditions, which scope of chain is recommended?

A. Four times the depth of water
B. Two and one-half times the depth of water
⚓ C. Five to seven times the depth of water
D. Fifteen times the depth of water

011421/DG01536   KNIGHTS

When anchoring, it is a common rule of thumb to use a length of chain _____.

⚓ A. five to seven times the depth of water
B. seven to ten times the depth of water
C. twice the depth of water
D. twice the depth of water plus the range of tide

011422/DG01556   AMSM

When anchoring, good practice requires 5 to 7 fathoms of chain for each fathom of depth. In deep water you should use _____.

A. the same ratio
B. more chain for each fathom of depth
⚓ C. less chain for each fathom of depth
D. two anchors with the same ratio of chain

011423/DG01566   AMSM

In bad weather, what length of chain should be used with a single anchor?

A. 3 times the depth of water
B. 6 times the depth of water
⚓ C. 10 times the depth of water
D. 15 times the depth of water

011424/DG02022   MMOH

In determining the scope of cable to be used when anchoring, what would NOT be considered?

A. Depth of the water
B. Character of the holding ground
⚓ C. maintenance cost for the chain
D. Type of anchor cable

HOLDING CAPACITY

011425/DG01416   **MMOH**
What is meant by veering the anchor chain?
A. Bringing the anchor to short stay
B. Heaving in all the chain
C. Locking the windlass to prevent more chain from running out
⚓ D. Paying out more chain

011426/DG02981   **DEEP DRILLER**
When the anchor is brought to and holding, the horizontal component of anchor cable tensions should equal the _____.
A. displacement tonnage
B. weight forces
C. buoyancy forces
⚓ D. environmental forces

011427/DG01961   **CHAPMAN**
A sufficient amount of chain must be veered when anchoring a vessel to ensure _____.
A. the vessel has enough room to swing while at anchor
⚓ B. the anchor flukes bite into the ocean bottom
C. there is a sufficient scope of chain to keep the anchor on the bottom
D. there is more chain out than there is in the chain locker

011428/DG03564   **PETEX**
The angle at which the fluke penetrates the soil is called the _____.
⚓ A. fluke angle
B. tripping angle
C. penetration angle
D. holding angle

011429/DG00232   **PETEX**
The angle at which the fluke penetrates the soil is called the _____.
A. tripping angle
⚓ B. fluke angle
C. penetration angle
D. holding angle

011430/DG02589   **PUECH; PETEX**
The angle at which the anchor flukes penetrate the soil is the _____.
A. burial angle
B. penetration angle
⚓ C. fluke angle
D. holding angle

011431/DG02029   **CHAPMAN**
When anchored, increasing the scope of the anchor chain normally serves to _____.
A. prevent fouling of the anchor
B. decrease swing of the vessel
⚓ C. prevent dragging of the anchor
D. reduce strain on the windlass

011432/DG01586   **CHAPMAN**
By paying out more anchor cable, you _____.
A. decrease the holding power of your anchor
B. decrease the swing of your vessel while at anchor
⚓ C. increase the holding power of your anchor
D. increase the possibility that your vessel will drag anchor

011433/DG01930   **ORMH**
The holding capabilities of an anchor are determined PRIMARILY by the _____.
A. design of the anchor
B. weight of the anchor
⚓ C. scope of the anchor chain
D. size of the vessel

011434/DG00217   **ORMH; CHAPMAN**
The holding capability of an anchor is primarily determined by the _____.
A. shape of the anchor
B. stowage of the anchor on board
⚓ C. anchor's ability to dig in
D. size of the vessel and its draft

011435/DG03395   **ORMH**
The holding power of an anchor at a given scope of cable increases when the _____.
⚓ A. amount of chain lying along the bottom increases
B. length of the catenary is reduced
C. mooring line tension is increased
D. amount of chain lying along the bottom decreases

011436/DG01969   **CHAPMAN**
If you shorten the scope of anchor cable, your anchor's holding power _____.
⚓ A. decreases
B. increases
C. remains the same
D. has no relation to the scope

011437/DG01275   **PUECH**
The tension on an anchor cable increases so that the angle of the catenary to the seabed at the anchor reaches 10°. How will this affect the anchor in sandy soil?
A. It will have no effect.
B. It will increase the holding power.
⚓ C. It will reduce the holding power.
D. It will cause the anchor to snag.

BOTTOM CHARACTERISTICS

011438/DG02149   **KNIGHTS**
When anchoring in a clay bottom, what is one hazard that may cause the anchor to drag?
A. The flukes may dig in unevenly and capsize the anchor when under stress.
B. The flukes may not dig in.
⚓ C. The anchor may get shod with clay and not develop full holding power.
D. The anchor will tend to dig in and come to rest near the vertical.

011439/DG02480   **CHAPMAN**
A Danforth lightweight anchor does NOT hold well in which type of bottom?
A. Mud
⚓ B. Grass
C. Sand
D. Clay

011440/DG01376   **CHAPMAN; ENCY. NAUT. KNOW.; INT. MARITIME DICTIONARY; CRENSHAW; SEATECH**
Generally speaking, the most favorable bottom for anchoring is _____.
A. very soft mud
B. rocky
⚓ C. a mixture of mud and clay
D. loose sand

011441/DG03320   **CHAPMAN**
Which type of bottom is best suited for holding an anchor of a small boat?
⚓ A. Mud and clay
B. Rocky
C. Sandy
D. Gravel

011442/DG04090   **TORMH; ENCY. NAUT. KNOW.; INT. MARITIME DICTIONARY; CRENSHAW; SEATECH; NICHOLLS**
The BEST holding ground for conventional anchors is _____.
A, very soft mud
⚓ B. hard mud
C. shale
D. rock

011443/DG03645ORMH; INT. MARITIME DICTIONARY; ENCY. NAUT. KNOW.; SEATECH
Conventional anchors are least likely to hold in a bottom consisting of _____.
A. soft clay
B. hard mud
⚓ C. very soft mud
D. sand

011444/DG02470   **CHAPMAN; ENCY. NAUT. KNOW.; INT. MARITIME DICTIONARY; CRENSHAW; SEATECH**
Which type of bottom provides most anchors with the best holding ability?
A. Clay and rocks
B. Soft mud
⚓ C. Sandy mud
D. Soft sand

011445/DG03588   **TORMH; ENCY. NAUT. KNOW.; INT. MARITIME DICTIONARY; CRENSHAW; SEATECH; NICHOLLS**
Conventional anchors are least likely to hold in a bottom consisting of _____.
A. soft clay
B. hard mud
C. sand
⚓ D. rock

011446/DG04018   **TORMH; ENCY. NAUT. KNOW.; INT. MARITIME DICTIONARY; CRENSHAW; SEATECH; NICHOLLS**
The BEST holding ground for conventional anchors is _____.
⚓ A, sand
B. very soft mud
C. shale
D. rock

011447/DG02459   **PUECH**
Tripping defects in anchors frequently occur in _____.
A. deep water
B. shallow water
C. stiff soils
⚓ D. soft soils

ANCHORING PROCEDURES

011448/DG01648   **CHAPMAN**
When steaming through an anchorage, a shipmaster should _____.
A. avoid crossing close astern of the anchored ships
⚓ B. avoid crossing close ahead of the anchored ships
C. keep the ship moving at a good speed to reduce set
D. transit only on a flood tide

011449/DG01858   **CHAPMAN**
The easiest way to anchor a vessel in a current is to _____.
A. stem the current and make very slow headway when the anchor is dropped
⚓ B. stem the current and be falling aft very slowly when the anchor is dropped
C. stem the current and endeavor to make neither headway nor sternway when the anchor is dropped
D. stop all headway through the water and keep the current astern when the anchor is dropped

011450/DG01766 MMOH

When anchoring in a current, you should _____.
A. drop the anchor with the bow headed downstream
B. back your vessel into the current
C. anchor while stemming the current
D. All of the above

011451/DG01726 AMSM

When attempting to free an anchor jammed in the hawsepipe, the simplest method of freeing it may be _____.
A. starting the disengaged windlass at high speed
B. rigging a bull rope to pull it out
C. to grease the hawsepipe
D. to pry it loose with a short piece of pipe

011452/DG01149 MMOH

You are on anchor watch. As an aid to preventing thievery on the vessel you should _____.
A. show running lights, anchor lights and deck lights
B. only show the required anchor lights and keep the rest of the vessel darkened
C. maintain water on deck with firehoses led out and all-purpose nozzles attached
D. show anchor lights, deck lights and cargo lights hung over the vessel's side

011453/DG01145 MMOH

You are on watch at night in clear visibility and the vessel has just been anchored. The first thing that you should do after the anchor has been let go is to _____.
A. stop the engines
B. take bearings to obtain ship's position
C. turn off the running lights and turn on the anchor lights
D. lower the accommodation ladder and illuminate it

011454/DG01736 AMSM

Before letting the anchor go, you should check that the _____.
A. chain is clear
B. anchor is clear of obstructions
C. wildcat is disengaged
D. All of the above

011455/DG01796 AMSM

Which safety check(s) should be made before letting go the anchor?
A. See that the anchor is clear of obstructions.
B. See that the chain is all clear.
C. See that the wildcat is disengaged.
D. All of the above

011456/DG01147 MMOH

You are on watch and the pilot has just anchored the vessel. The next thing that you should do after the anchor has been let go is to _____.
A. stop the engines
B. escort the pilot to the accommodation ladder
C. plot the vessel's position on the chart
D. make a round of the weather decks

011457/DG01466 AMSM

When dropping anchor, you are stationed at the windlass brake. The most important piece(s) of gear is(are) _____.
A. a hard hat
B. a long sleeve shirt
C. gloves
D. goggles

011458/DG01175 MACELREVEY

You have arrived at your anchorage location. You have put the engines astern prior to letting go the anchor. How will you know when the vessel has stopped making way?
A. The ship's Doppler log reads zero
B. The backwash of the propeller reaches amidships
C. An azimuth bearing on the beam remains steady
D. All of the above

011459/DG01176 MACELREVEY

You have arrived at your anchorage location. You have put the engines astern prior to letting go the anchor. How will you know when the vessel has stopped over the ground?
A. The ship's log reads zero
B. The backwash of the propeller reaches amidships
C. An azimuth bearing on the beam remains steady
D. All of the above

011460/DG01756 KNIGHTS

When anchoring a vessel, it is best to release the anchor when _____.
A. going full astern
B. going full ahead
C. going slow astern
D. dead in the water

011461/DG01776 CHAPMAN

When anchoring in calm water, it is best to _____.
A. maintain slight headway when letting go the anchor
B. wait until the vessel is dead in the water before letting go the anchor
C. have slight sternway on the vessel while letting go the anchor
D. let the anchor go from the stern with the anchor cable leading from the bow

011462/DG01666   **MMOH; KNIGHTS**

While anchoring your vessel, the best time to let go the anchor is when the vessel is _____.

A. dead in the water

⚓ B. moving slowly astern over the ground

C. moving fast ahead over the ground

D. moving fast astern over the ground

011463/DG04050   **BOWD**

You are on a 120,000 DWT loaded bulk carrier. When anchoring without the aid of tugs, your maximum speed should not exceed how many feet per second?

⚓ A. 0.5 (0.3 knot)

B. 1.0 (0.6 knot)

C. 1.3 (0.8 knot)

D. 1.75 (1.0 knot)

ANCHORING PROCEDURES (SHALLOW WATER)

011464/DG02119   **MMOH**

You are coming to anchor in 8 fathoms of water. In this case, the _____.

⚓ A. anchor may be dropped from the hawsepipe

B. anchor should be lowered to within 2 fathoms of the bottom before being dropped

C. anchor should be lowered to the bottom then the ship backed and the remainder of the cable veered

D. scope should be less than 3 times the depth of the water

ANCHORING PROCEDURES (DEEP WATER)

011465/DG02111   **MMOH**

You are anchoring in 16 fathoms of water. On a small to medium size vessel, the _____.

A. anchor may be dropped from the hawsepipe

⚓ B. anchor should be lowered to within 2 fathoms of the bottom before being dropped

C. scope should always be at least ten times the depth of the water

D. scope should always be less than 5 times the depth of the water

ANCHORING PROCEDURES (VERY DEEP WATER)

011466/DG01716   **KNIGHTS**

Which is the correct procedure for anchoring a small to medium size vessel in deep water?

A. Let the anchor fall free from the hawsepipe, but apply the brake at intervals to check the rate of fall.

B. Back the anchor slowly out of the hawsepipe a few feet, and then let it fall in the normal fashion.

C. Let the anchor fall off the brake right from the hawsepipe, but keep a slight strain on the brake.

⚓ D. Under power, back the anchor out until it is near, but clear, of the bottom before letting it fall.

ANCHOR RECOVERY

011467/DG01396   **ENCY. NAUT. KNOW.**

Lifting the anchor from the bottom is called _____.

A. broaching the anchor

B. shifting the anchor

C. walking the anchor

⚓ D. weighing the anchor

011468/DG01676   **AMSM**

When preparing to hoist the anchor, you should FIRST _____.

⚓ A. engage the wildcat

B. put the brake in the off position

C. take off the chain stopper

D. take the riding pawl off the chain

011469/DG01686   **MMOH**

When weighing anchor in a rough sea, how would you avoid risk of damaging the bow plating?

A. Heave it home as fast as you can.

B. Heave it home intermittently, between swells.

⚓ C. Leave the anchor under foot, until the vessel may be brought before the sea.

D. Wait for a calm spot between seas, then house it.

RECOVERING FOULED ANCHORS

011470/DG02550   **CHAPMAN**

When a small craft's anchor fouls in a rocky bottom, the first attempt to clear it should be made by _____.

A. hauling vertically on the line

B. making the line fast to the bitt and bringing the vessel further forward

⚓ C. reversing the angle and direction of pull, with moderate scope

D. increasing the scope and running slowly in a wide circle with the anchor line taut

011471/DG02906   **CHAPMAN**

You are planning to anchor in an area where several anchors have been lost due to fouling. As a precaution, you should _____.

A. anchor using both anchors

B. anchor with scope of 8 or more to 1

C. use a stern anchor

⚓ D. fit a crown strap and work wire to the anchor

DRAGGING ANCHOR

011472/DG03452   **KNIGHTS**

A drift lead indicates that the vessel is dragging anchor when the line is _____.

⚓ A. taut and leading forward

B. slack

C. leading out perpendicular to the centerline

D. leading under the hull

011473/DG01346   **KNIGHTS**

The best method of determining if a vessel is dragging anchor is to note _____.
- A. the amount of line paid out
- B. how much the vessel sheers while at anchor
- C. any change in the tautness of the anchor chain
- ⚓ D. changes in bearings of fixed objects onshore

011474/DG03269   **KNIGHTS**

What provides little or no indication that a vessel is dragging anchor?
- ⚓ A. Changing range to an object abeam
- B. Drift lead with the line tending forward
- C. The cable alternates between slack and heavy tension
- D. Changing bearing to a fixed distant object abeam

011475/DG03692   **KNIGHTS**

What provides little or no indication that a vessel is dragging anchor?
- A. Increasing radar range to a fixed object ahead
- ⚓ B. Drift lead with the line leading perpendicular to the centerline
- C. Vibrations felt by placing a hand on the anchor cable
- D. Changing bearings to distant fixed objects abeam

011476/DG01356   **CHAPMAN**

If your vessel is dragging her anchor in a strong wind, you should _____.
- A. shorten the scope of anchor cable
- ⚓ B. increase the scope of anchor cable
- C. put over the sea anchor
- D. put over a stern anchor

011477/DG01366   **CHAPMAN**

The best method to stop a vessel from dragging anchor in a sand bottom is to _____.
- A. reduce the length of the cable
- ⚓ B. pay out more anchor cable
- C. back the engines
- D. swing the rudder several times to work the anchor into the bottom

011478/DG01706   **MMOH**

Your vessel is anchored in an open roadstead with three shots of chain out on the port anchor. The wind freshens considerably and the anchor begins to drag. Which action should you take FIRST?
- A. Drop the starboard anchor short with about one shot of chain.
- B. Sheer out to starboard using the rudder, then drop the starboard anchor with about four shots of chain.
- C. Put the engines slow ahead to help the anchor.
- ⚓ D. Veer out more chain on the port anchor.

011479/DG02126   **KNIGHTS**

You have anchored in a mud and clay bottom. The anchor appears to be dragging in a storm. What action should you take?
- A. Shorten the scope of the cable.
- B. Veer cable to the anchor.
- C. Drop the other anchor underfoot.
- ⚓ D. Drop the second anchor, veer to a good scope, then weigh the first anchor.

MOORING PROCEDURES

MOORING WITH ANCHORS

011480/DG01696   **KNIGHTS**

Mooring with two bow anchors has which major advantage over anchoring with one bow anchor?
- A. The vessel will not reverse direction in a tidal current.
- ⚓ B. The radius of the vessel's swing will be shortened.
- C. A mooring approach may be made from any direction.
- D. The vessel will not swing with a change in wind.

011481/DG01786   **CHAPMAN**

You are anchoring in a river where the current is from one direction only. The best way to lay out two anchors is to have them _____.
- A. directly in line with the bow
- B. side by side, with their lines on the port and starboard side
- ⚓ C. so that their lines form an angle
- D. on top of one another

011482/DG02037   **NICHOLLS; CHAPMAN**

You are riding to a single anchor. The vessel is yawing excessively. Which action should be taken to reduce the yawing?
- A. Veer chain to the riding anchor
- B. Heave to a shorter scope of chain on the riding anchor
- C. Drop the second anchor at the extreme end of the yaw and veer the riding anchor
- ⚓ D. Drop the second anchor at the extreme end of the yaw, then adjust the cables until the scope is equal

MOORING TO BUOYS

011483/DG01336   **CHAPMAN; KNIGHTS**

When picking up your mooring at the buoy, the correct method is to _____.
- A. approach the buoy with the wind and current astern
- ⚓ B. approach the buoy with the wind and current ahead
- C. approach the buoy with wind and sea abeam
- D. stop upwind and up current and drift down on the buoy

011484/DG02988   **KNIGHTS**
You are mooring to a buoy. You should approach the buoy with the current from _____.

⚓ A. ahead
   B. broad on the bow
   C. abeam
   D. astern

011485/DG01326   **CHAPMAN**
After casting off moorings at a mooring buoy in calm weather, you should _____.

   A. go full ahead on the engine(s)
⚓ B. back away a few lengths to clear the buoy and then go ahead on the engines
   C. go half ahead on the engines and put the rudder hard right
   D. go half ahead on the engines and pass upstream of the buoy

MEDITERRANEAN MOOR PROCEDURES

011486/DG01177   **MACELVEREY**
A "Mediterranean moor" should be used when _____.

   A. when anchoring in the Mediterranean
⚓ B. when docking stern to a berth
   C. when docking bow to a berth
   D. when anchoring in a strong current

011487/DG02552   **KNIGHTS**
When using a Mediterranean Moor, the vessel is moored with her _____.

   A. bow to the pier
   B. anchors crossed
   C. anchor chains forward, side to the pier
⚓ D. stern to the pier

011488/DG01286   **KNIGHTS**
The anchors should be dropped well out from the pier while at a Mediterranean moor to _____.

   A. eliminate navigational hazards by allowing the chain to lie along the harbor bottom
   B. increase the anchor's reliability by providing a large catenary in the chain
⚓ C. permit the ship to maneuver in the stream while weighing anchors
   D. prevent damage to the stern caused by swinging against the pier in the approach

011489/DG01316   **KNIGHTS**
The anchor chain should be kept moderately taut during a Mediterranean moor to _____.

   A. facilitate speed of recovery during the weighing process
   B. indicate the anchor's location to passing or mooring ships
⚓ C. prevent damage to the stern in the event of a headwind
   D. provide a steady platform for the gangway between the fantail and pier

011490/DG01296   **KNIGHTS**
To ensure the best results during the Mediterranean moor, the chains should _____.

   A. be crossed around the bow
   B. tend out at right angles to the bow
   C. tend aft 60° from each bow
⚓ D. tend forward 30° on either bow

011491/DG01276   **KNIGHTS**
When moored with a Mediterranean moor, the ship should be secured to the pier by having _____.

⚓ A. a stern line and two quarter lines crossing under the stern
   B. a stern line, 2 bow lines, and 2 quarter lines leading aft to the pier
   C. all regular lines leading to the pier in opposition to the anchor
   D. two bow lines and two midship lines leading aft to the pier

011492/DG01306   **KNIGHTS; MMOH**
You are making mooring lines fast to bitts, stern to, as in some Mediterranean ports. A swell is liable to make the vessel surge. How should you tie up?

⚓ A. Use manila or synthetic fiber hawsers only.
   B. Use wires only from the stern and each quarter.
   C. Use synthetic fiber and/or manila hawsers as required.
   D. Use wires from each quarter and manila hawsers from the stern.

ANCHOR COMPUTATIONS

SCOPE OF ANCHOR CHAIN

011493/DG01949   **AMSM**
Using a scope of 5, determine how many feet of cable you should put out to anchor in 5 fathoms of water.

   A. 100 feet
⚓ B. 150 feet
   C. 200 feet
   D. 250 feet

011494/DG01576   **MMOH**

Using a scope of five, determine how many shots of chain you should put out to anchor in 5 fathoms of water?

A. 1
⚓ B. 2
C. 3
D. 5

011495/DG01596   **AMSM**

Using a scope of five, determine how many feet of chain you should put out to anchor in 12 fathoms of water.

A. 60 feet (18 meters)
B. 72 feet (22 meters)
⚓ C. 360 feet (110 meters)
D. 450 feet (137 meters)

011496/DG01626   **AMSM**

Using a scope of 6, determine how many feet of anchor cable you should put out to anchor in 12 feet (3.7 meters) of water.

A. 2 feet (0.6 meters)
B. 18 feet (5.5 meters)
C. 48 feet (14.6 meters)
⚓ D. 72 feet (21.9 meters)

011497/DG01607   **AMSM**

Using a scope of 6, how much cable would have to be used in order to anchor in 24 feet of water?

A. 4 feet
B. 18 feet
C. 30 feet
⚓ D. 144 feet

ANCHOR SWING DIAMETER

011498/DG04044   **DUTTON**

You are arriving in port and are assigned to anchor in anchorage circle B-4. It has a diameter of 500 yards and your vessel's LOA is 484 feet. If you anchor in 8 fathoms at the center of the circle, what is the maximum number of shots of chain you can use and still remain in the circle?

A, 6 shots
B. 5 shots
C. 4 shots
⚓ D. 3 shots

011499/DG04060   **DUTTON**

You are arriving in port and are assigned to anchor in anchorage circle B-4. It has a diameter of 550 yards and your vessel's LOA is 449 feet. If you anchor in 9 fathoms at the center of the circle, what is the maximum number of shots of chain you can use and still remain in the circle?

A, 6 shots
B. 5 shots
⚓ C. 4 shots
D. 3 shots

011500/DG04048   **DUTTON**

You are arriving in port and are assigned to anchor in anchorage circle B-4. It has a diameter of 600 yards and your vessel's LOA is 525 feet. If you anchor in 10 fathoms at the center of the circle, what is the maximum number of shots of chain you can use and still remain in the circle?

⚓ A, 4 shots
B. 5 shots
C. 6 shots
D. 7 shots

011501/DG04052   **DUTTON**

You are arriving in port and are assigned to anchor in anchorage circle B-4. It has a diameter of 700 yards and your vessel's LOA is 600 feet. If you anchor in 11 fathoms at the center of the circle, what is the maximum number of shots of chain you can use and still remain in the circle?

A, 4 shots
⚓ B. 5 shots
C. 6 shots
D. 7 shots

MANEUVERING DIAGRAM

TURNING CIRCLE

011502/DG01087 WATCHSTAND GUIDE; MODSHIPS; INTRO. NAVAL ARCH.; WILLERTON

The turning circle of a vessel is the path followed by the _____.

A. center of gravity
B. outermost part of the ship while making the circle
C. bow
D. tipping center

011503/DG00595 WATCHSTAND GUIDE; MODSHIPS; INTRO. NAVAL ARCH.; WILLERTON

The turning circle of a vessel is the path followed by the _____.

A. outermost part of the ship while making the circle
B. center of gravity
C. bow
D. tipping center

011504/DG02400 WATCHSTAND GUIDE; MODSHIPS; INTRO. NAVAL ARCH.; WILLERTON

The turning circle of a vessel is the path followed by the _____.

A. bow
B. outermost part of the ship while making the circle
C. center of gravity
D. tipping center

011505/DG00176 WATCHSTAND GUIDE; MODSHIPS; INTRO. NAVAL ARCH.; WILLERTON

The turning circle of a vessel is the path followed by the _____.

A. tipping center
B. bow
C. outermost part of the ship while making the circle
D. center of gravity

011506/DG04091 WATCHSTAND GUIDE; MODSHIPS; INTRO. NAVAL ARCH.; WILLERTON

The turning circle of a vessel making a turn of over 360 degrees is the path followed by the _____.

A. bow
B. center of gravity
C. centerline
D. bridge

011507/DG01966 WATCHSTAND GUIDE; MODSHIPS; INTRO. NAVAL ARCH.; WILLERTON

The turning circle of a vessel making a turn of over 360 degrees is the path followed by the _____.

A. bow
B. bridge
C. center of gravity
D. centerline

011508/DG00086 WATCHSTAND GUIDE; MODSHIPS; INTRO. NAVAL ARCH.; WILLERTON

The turning circle of a vessel making a turn of over 360 degrees is the path followed by the _____.

A. bow
B. bridge
C. centerline
D. center of gravity

011509/DG00025 WATCHSTAND GUIDE; MODSHIPS; INTRO. NAVAL ARCH.; WILLERTON

The turning circle of a vessel making a turn over 360 degrees is the path followed by the _____.

A. center of gravity
B. bow
C. bridge
D. centerline

ADVANCE

011510/DG02950 KNIGHTS

In relation to the turning circle of a ship, the term "advance" means the distance _____.

A. gained at right angles to the original course
B. gained in the direction of the original course
C. moved sidewise from the original course when the rudder is first put over
D. around the circumference of the turning circle

011511/DG00126 MODSHIPS

The distance a vessel moves parallel to the original course from the point where the rudder is put over to any point on the turning circle is called the _____.

A. advance
B. drift angle
C. pivoting point
D. transfer

011512/DG00166 KNIGHTS

The distance gained in the direction of the original course when you are making a turn is known as _____.

A. advance
B. drift
C. tactical diameter
D. transfer

011513/DG00156 KNIGHTS

When heading on a course, you put your rudder hard over. The distance traveled parallel to the direction of the original course from where you put your rudder over to any point on the turning circle is known as _____.

A. advance
B. head reach
C. tactical diameter
D. transfer

TRANSFER

011514/DG00116 **KNIGHTS**
In relation to the turning circle of a ship, the term "transfer" means the distance _____.
A. gained in the direction of the original course
B. gained at right angles to the original course
C. the ship moves sidewise from the original course away from the direction of the turn after the rudder is first put over
D. around the circumference of the turning circle

011515/DG00296 **KNIGHTS**
You are on a course of 000° T and put the rudder right 30°. In which direction will the transfer be measured?
A. 000° T
B. 090° T
C. 180° T
D. 270° T

KICK

011516/DG00106 **KNIGHTS**
In relation to the turning circle of a ship, the term "kick" means the distance _____.
A. around the circumference of the turning circle
B. gained at right angles to the original course
C. gained in the direction of the original course
D. or throw of a vessel's stern from her line of advance upon putting the helm hard over

TACTICAL DIAMETER

011517/DG00096 **MODSHIPS**
The distance a vessel moves at right angles to the original course, when a turn of 180° has been completed, is called the _____.
A. advance
B. pivoting point
C. tactical diameter
D. kick

HEAD REACH

011518/DG00206 **DUTTON**
In stopping distances of vessels, "head reach" can best be described as the _____.
A. difference between the vessel's speed through the water at any instant and the new speed ordered on the telegraph
B. distance the vessel has actually run through the water since a change of speed was ordered
C. distance the vessel will run between taking action to stop her and being stationary in the water
D. speed at which a vessel should proceed to ensure that she will run a predetermined distance, once her engines have been stopped

011519/DG00036 **MMOH**
The distance that a vessel travels from the time that the order to put engines full astern until the vessel is dead in the water is known as _____.
A. advance
B. head reach
C. surge
D. transfer

PIVOT POINT

011520/DG00026 **KNIGHTS**
The pivoting point of a fully loaded vessel with normal trim proceeding ahead at sea speed is _____.
A. right at the bow
B. one-third the length of the vessel from the bow
C. one-half the length of the vessel from the bow
D. two-thirds the length of the vessel from the bow

011521/DG01125 **CHAPMAN; KNIGHTS**
The pivoting point of a vessel going ahead is _____.
A. about one-third of the vessel's length from the bow
B. about two-thirds of the vessel's length from the bow
C. at the hawsepipe
D. near the stern

011522/DG00186 **CHAPMAN**
The pivoting point of a vessel going ahead is _____.
A. at the hawsepipe
B. about one-third of the vessel's length from the bow
C. about two-thirds of the vessel's length from the bow
D. near the stern

011523/DG01139 **CHAPMAN**
The pivoting point of a vessel going ahead is _____.
A. near the stern
B. at the hawsepipe
C. about one-third of the vessel's length from the bow
D. about two-thirds of the vessel's length from the bow

011524/DG01605 **CHAPMAN; KNIGHTS**
The pivoting point of a vessel going ahead is _____.
A. near the stern
B. about two-thirds of the vessel's length from the bow
C. at the hawsepipe
D. about one-third of the vessel's length from the bow

011525/DG00016   **CRENSHAW**

When underway and proceeding ahead, as the speed increases, the pivot point tends to _____.

A. move aft

⚓ B. move forward

C. move lower

D. remain stationary

011526/DG03047   **HOOYER; CHAPMAN**

When backing down with sternway, the pivot point of a vessel is _____.

⚓ A. about one-quarter of the vessel's length from the stern

B. at the bow

C. about one-third of the vessel's length from the bow

D. aft of the propellers

011527/DG04043   **HOOYER; CHAPMAN**

When backing down with sternway, the pivot point of a vessel is _____.

A, aft of the propellers

⚓ B. about one-quarter of the vessel's length from the stern

C. about one-third of the vessel's length from the bow

D. at the bow

011528/DG00366   **HOOYER; CHAPMAN**

When backing down with sternway, the pivot point of a vessel is _____.

A. at the bow

B. about one-third of the vessel's length from the bow

⚓ C. about one-quarter of the vessel's length from the stern

D. aft of the propellers

011529/DG00612   **HOOYER; CHAPMAN**

When backing down with sternway, the pivot point of a vessel is _____.

A. at the bow

B. about one-third of the vessel's length from the bow

C. aft of the propellers

⚓ D. about one-quarter of the vessel's length from the stern

MANEUVERING CHARACTERISTICS
DIAGRAM D034DG

011530/DG02280   **KNIGHTS**

You are conducting trials to determine the maneuvering characteristics of your vessel. While making a turn, you take ranges and bearings of an isolated light with the results as shown. Based on this information, what is the advance for a turn of 45°? See Diagram D034DG

A. 590 yards

B. 635 yards

⚓ C. 690 yards

D. 740 yards

011531/DG02265   **KNIGHTS**

You are conducting trials to determine the maneuvering characteristics of your vessel. While making a turn, you take ranges and bearings of an isolated light with the results shown. Based on this information, what is the transfer for a turn of 45°? See Diagram D034DG

⚓ A. 130 yards

B. 165 yards

C. 195 yards

D. 230 yards

011532/DG02235   **KNIGHTS**

You are conducting trials to determine the maneuvering characteristics of your vessel. While making a turn, you take ranges and bearings of an isolated light with the results as shown. Based on this information, what is the advance for a turn of 75°? See Diagram D034DG

⚓ A. 825 yards (754 meters)

B. 860 yards (774 meters)

C. 910 yards (819 meters)

D. 955 yards (860 meters)

011533/DG02189   **KNIGHTS**

You are conducting trials to determine the maneuvering characteristics of your vessel. While making a turn you take the ranges and bearings of an isolated light with the results shown. Based on this information, what is the transfer for a turn of 75°? See Diagram D034DG

A. 340 yards (306 meters)

⚓ B. 300 yards (274 meters)

C. 230 yards (207 meters)

D. 190 yards (171 meters)

011534/DG02214   **KNIGHTS**

You are conducting trials to determine the maneuvering characteristics of your vessel. While making a turn, you take ranges and bearings of an isolated light with the results as shown. Based on this information, what is the advance for a turn of 90°? See Diagram D034DG

A. 820 yards

⚓ B. 870 yards

C. 930 yards

D. 975 yards

011535/DG02198   **KNIGHTS**

You are conducting trials to determine the maneuvering characteristics of your vessel. While making a turn, you take ranges and bearings of an isolated light with the results as shown. Based on this information, what is the transfer for a turn of 90°? See Diagram D034DG

A. 355 yards

⚓ B. 380 yards

C. 410 yards

D. 455 yards

011536/DG02256 KNIGHTS

You are conducting trials to determine the maneuvering characteristics of your vessel. While making a turn, you take ranges and bearings of an isolated light with the results as shown. Based on this information, what is the transfer for a turn of 180°? See Diagram D034DG

- A. 875 yards
- ⚓ B. 910 yards
- C. 975 yards
- D. 1015 yards

MANEUVERING CHARACTERISTICS
DIAGRAM D035DG

011537/DG02212 KNIGHTS

You have determined the maneuvering characteristics of your vessel by taking the radar ranges and bearings of an isolated light while making a turn. The results are listed in illustration D035DG. Based on this data what is the advance for a turn of 30°? See Diagram D035DG

- A. 380 yards
- B. 420 yards
- ⚓ C. 470 yards
- D. 525 yards

011538/DG00171 KNIGHTS

You have determined the maneuvering characteristics of your vessel by taking the radar ranges and bearings of an isolated light while making a turn. The results are as listed. Based on this data what is the transfer for a turn of 30°? See Diagram D035DG

- ⚓ A. 40 yards
- B. 140 yards
- C. 190 yards
- D. 230 yards

011539/DG02276 KNIGHTS

You have determined the maneuvering characteristics of your vessel by taking radar ranges and bearings of an isolated light while making a turn. The results are as shown. Based on this data what is the advance for a turn of 60°? See Diagram D035DG

- ⚓ A. 665 yards
- B. 710 yards
- C. 745 yards
- D. 780 yards

011540/DG01911 KNIGHTS

You have determined the maneuvering characteristics of your vessel by taking the radar ranges and bearings of an isolated light while making a turn. The results are listed. Based on this data what is the transfer for a turn of 60°? See Diagram D035DG

- ⚓ A. 105 yards
- B. 155 yards
- C. 205 yards
- D. 255 yards

011541/DG02228 KNIGHTS

You have determined the maneuvering characteristics of your vessel by taking the radar ranges and bearings of an isolated light while making a turn. The results are listed. Based on this data what is the transfer for a turn of 60°? See Diagram D035DG

- ⚓ A. 140 yards (126 meters)
- B. 180 yards (162 meters)
- C. 225 yards (203 meters)
- D. 270 yards (243 meters)

011542/DG02259 KNIGHTS

You have determined the maneuvering characteristics of your vessel by taking radar ranges and bearings of an isolated light while making a turn. The results are as shown. Based on this data what is the advance for a turn of 90°? See Diagram D035DG

- A. 490 yards
- B. 350 yards
- ⚓ C. 790 yards
- D. 885 yards

011543/DG02250 KNIGHTS

You have determined the maneuvering characteristics of your vessel by taking radar ranges and bearings of an isolated light while making a turn. The results are as shown. Based on this data what is the transfer for a turn of 90°? See Diagram D035DG

- ⚓ A. 400 yards
- B. 430 yards
- C. 485 yards
- D. 525 yards

011544/DG02195 KNIGHTS

You have determined the maneuvering characteristics of your vessel by taking the radar ranges and bearings of an isolated light while making a turn. The results are as listed. Based on this data what is the transfer for a turn of 180°? See Diagram D035DG

- A. 745 yards
- B. 770 yards
- ⚓ C. 850 yards
- D. 890 yards

011545/DG02193 KNIGHTS

You have determined the maneuvering characteristics of your vessel by taking the radar ranges and bearings of an isolated light while making a turn. The results are listed in illustration D035DG. Based on this data what is the tactical diameter of the turning circle? See Diagram D035DG

- A. 755 yards
- B. 780 yards
- C. 820 yards
- ⚓ D. 880 yards

APPROACHING PILOT STATION & MANEUVERING UNDER PILOT

PILOT DUTIES & RESPONSIBILITIES

011546/DG03073   **MMOH**

You are on a large merchant vessel entering a U.S. port. There is a Pilot on board and he has the conn. Which statement is TRUE?

A. The Pilot becomes solely responsible for the safe navigation of the vessel only if the Master relinquishes the conn.

B. The Pilot is solely responsible for the safe maneuvering of the ship only if he is required to be on board by law.

⚓ C. The Master is responsible for the safe navigation of the ship and the Pilot is employed for his local knowledge.

D. The Pilot is solely responsible for the internal working of the ship.

011547/DG00775   **MMOH**

You are on a large merchant vessel entering a U.S. port. There is a Pilot onboard and he has the conn. Which statement is TRUE?

A. The Pilot becomes solely responsible for the safe navigation of the vessel only if the Master relinquishes the conn.

B. The Pilot is solely responsible for the internal working of the ship.

C. The Pilot is solely responsible for the safe maneuvering of the ship only if he is required to be on board by law.

⚓ D. The Master is responsible for the safe navigation of the ship and the Pilot is employed for his local knowledge.

011548/DG00572   **SHIPHAND**

A vessel is entering port "A" for the first time and has a Pilot conning the vessel. The Master is unsure that the Pilot is taking sufficient action to prevent a collision. What should the Master do?

A. Nothing; The Pilot is required by law and is solely responsible for the safety of the vessel.

B. State his concerns to the Pilot but do not interfere with the handling of the vessel.

C. Direct the Pilot to stop the vessel and anchor if necessary until the situation clears.

⚓ D. Recommend an alternative action and if not followed relieve the Pilot.

011549/DG01677   **SHIPHAND**

A vessel is entering port and has a Pilot conning the vessel. The Master is unsure that the Pilot is taking sufficient action to prevent a collision. What should the master do?

⚓ A. Recommend an alternative action and if not followed relieve the Pilot.

B. Nothing; the Pilot is required by law and is solely responsible for the safety of the vessel.

C. Direct the Pilot to stop the vessel and anchor if necessary until the situation clears.

D. State his concerns to the Pilot but do not interfere with the handling of the vessel.

011550/DG02861   **SHIPHAND**

A vessel is entering port and has a Pilot conning the vessel. The Master is unsure that the Pilot is taking sufficient action to prevent a collision. What should the Master do?

A. Direct the Pilot to stop the vessel and anchor if necessary until the situation clears.

⚓ B. Recommend an alternative action and if not followed relieve the pilot.

C. State his concerns to the Pilot but do not interfere with the handling of the vessel.

D. Nothing; the Pilot is required by law and is solely responsible for the safety of the vessel.

011551/DG00050   **SHIPHAND**

A vessel is entering port and has a Pilot conning the vessel. The Master is unsure that the Pilot is taking sufficient action to prevent a collision. What should the Master do?

A. Nothing; the Pilot is required by law and is solely responsible for the safety of the vessel.

B. State his concerns to the Pilot but do not interfere with the handling of the vessel.

⚓ C. Recommend an alternative action and if not followed relieve the Pilot.

D. Direct the Pilot to stop the vessel and anchor if necessary until the situation clears.

011552/DG00185   **SHIPHAND; MMOH**

Before a Master relieves a Pilot of the conn, the _____.

⚓ A. Master should foresee any danger to the vessel on the present course

B. vessel must be in extremis

C. Master should agree to sign a release of liability form

D. Master must first request the Pilot to take corrective action

011553/DG00777 SHIPHAND; MMOH
Before a Master relieves a Pilot of the conn, the
_____.

A. Master must always request the Pilot to take corrective action
⚓ B. Master should foresee any danger to the vessel on the present course
C. Master should agree to sign a release of liability form
D. vessel must be in extremis

011554/DG02291 SHIPHAND; MMOH
Before a Master relieves a Pilot of the conn, the
_____.

A. Master must first request the Pilot to take corrective action
B. Master should agree to sign a release of liability form
⚓ C. Master should foresee any danger to the vessel on the present course
D. vessel must be in extremis

011555/DG03031 SHIPHAND; MMOH
Before a Master relieves a Pilot of the conn, the
_____.

A. vessel must be in extremis
B. Master must request the Pilot to take corrective action
C. Master should release the Pilot from all liability
⚓ D. Master should foresee any danger to the vessel on the present course

011556/DG03693MMOH; INT. MARITIME DICTIONARY
When the Pilot is embarked he or she _____.
A. relieves the Master of his duties
B. is solely responsible for the safe navigation of the vessel
⚓ C. is a specialist hired for his or her local navigational knowledge
D. relieves the officer of the watch

011557/DG00565MMOH; INT. MARITIME DICTIONARY
When the pilot is embarked he or she _____.
A. relieves the officer of the watch
B. relieves the Master of his duties
C. is solely responsible for the safe navigation of the vessel
⚓ D. is a specialist hired for his or her local navigational knowledge

011558/DG01992MMOH; INT. MARITIME DICTIONARY
While the Pilot is embarked he or she _____.
A. is solely responsible for the safe navigation of the vessel
⚓ B. is a specialist hired for his or her local navigational knowledge
C. relieves the officer of the watch
D. relieves the Master of his duties

011559/DG03111 MMOH
While the Pilot is maneuvering the vessel to a dock, what is the PRIMARY responsibility of the watch officer?
⚓ A. Insure that helm and throttle orders given by the Pilot are correctly executed.
B. Judge the appropriateness of the Pilot's orders and countermand them if necessary.
C. Supervise the signaling and flag etiquette.
D. Record the bells and their times in the bell book.

011560/DG00563 MMOH
While the Pilot is maneuvering the vessel to a dock, what is the PRIMARY responsibility of the watch officer?
A. Supervise the signaling and flag etiquette.
B. Record the bells and their times in the bell book.
⚓ C. Insure that helm and throttle orders given by the Pilot are correctly executed.
D. Judge the appropriateness of the Pilot's orders and countermand them if necessary.

011561/DG02049 MMOH
While the Pilot is maneuvering the vessel to a dock, what is the PRIMARY responsibility of the watch officer?
A. Supervise the signaling and flag etiquette.
B. Record the bells and their times in the bell book.
C. Judge the appropriateness of the Pilot's orders and countermand them if necessary.
⚓ D. Insure that helm and throttle orders given by the Pilot are correctly executed.

011562/DG01896 AMSM; MMOH
You are on a large merchant vessel entering a U.S. port. There is a Pilot on board and he has the conn. Which statement is TRUE?
⚓ A. The Master is responsible for the safe navigation of the ship and the Pilot is employed for his local knowledge.
B. The Pilot is solely responsible for the safe maneuvering of the ship only if he is required to be on board by law.
C. The Pilot is solely responsible for the internal working of the ship.
D. The Pilot becomes solely responsible for the safe navigation of the vessel only if the Master relinquishes the conn.

011563/DG00167   **MMOH**
You are on a large merchant vessel entering a U.S. port. There is a Pilot on board and he has the conn. Which statement is TRUE?
A. The Pilot is solely responsible for the safe maneuvering of the ship only if he is required to be on board by law.
⚓ B. The Master is responsible for the safe navigation of the ship and the Pilot is employed for his local knowledge.
C. The Pilot is solely responsible for the internal working of the ship.
D. The Pilot becomes solely responsible for the safe navigation of the vessel only if the Master relinquishes the conn.

011564/DG00175   **MMOH**
While the Pilot is maneuvering the vessel to a dock, what is the primary responsibility of the watch officer?
A. Judge the appropriateness of the Pilot's orders and countermand them if necessary
⚓ B. Insure that helm and throttle orders given by the Pilot are correctly executed
C. Record the bells and their times in the bell book
D. Supervise the signaling and flag etiquette

011565/DG02136   ***46 USC 8502**
Your enrolled vessel is bound from Baltimore, MD, to Norfolk, VA, via Chesapeake Bay. Which statement about the required pilot is TRUE?
⚓ A. The pilot need only be licensed by the Coast Guard.
B. The Pilot must be licensed by either Virginia or Maryland.
C. The Pilot must be licensed by Virginia and Maryland.
D. The Pilot must be licensed by Virginia, Maryland and the Coast Guard.

011566/DG00037   ***46 USC 8502**
Your enrolled vessel is bound from Baltimore, MD, to Norfolk, VA, via Chesapeake Bay. Which statement about the required Pilot is TRUE?
A. The Pilot must be licensed by either Virginia or Maryland.
⚓ B. The Pilot need only be licensed by the Coast Guard.
C. The Pilot must be licensed by Virginia and Maryland.
D. The Pilot must be licensed by Virginia, Maryland and the Coast Guard.

011567/DG00567   ***46 USC 8502**
Your enrolled vessel is bound from Baltimore, MD, to Norfolk, VA, via Chesapeake Bay. Which statement about the required Pilot is TRUE?
A. The Pilot must be licensed by Virginia and Maryland.
B. The Pilot must be licensed by either Virginia or Maryland.
⚓ C. The Pilot need only be licensed by the Coast Guard.
D. The Pilot must be licensed by Virginia, Maryland and the Coast Guard.

011568/DG03694   ***46 USC 8502**
Your enrolled vessel is bound from Baltimore, MD, to Norfolk, VA, via Chesapeake Bay. Which statement about the required pilot is TRUE?
A. The pilot must be licensed by Virginia or Maryland.
B. The Pilot must be licensed by either Virginia or Maryland.
C. The Pilot must be licensed by Virginia, Maryland and the Coast Guard.
⚓ D. The Pilot need only by licensed by the Coast Guard.

MANEUVERING TO THE PILOT STATION
011569/DG01086   **WILLERTON**
When taking a Pilot from a pilot vessel in a seaway, which way should you head your vessel if the ladder is on the leeward side?
A. Bow to the sea and no way on your vessel
B. Sea on the lee quarter with ship moving ahead slowly
⚓ C. Sea on the weather bow and ship moving ahead slowly
D. Sea on the quarter with sternway on the ship

011570/DG02606   **SHIPHAND**
You are approaching the pilot station with the wind fine on the starboard bow and making about 3 knots. You can help to calm the seas by taking what action just before the pilot boat comes along on the port side?
A. Backing full
B. Stopping the engines
C. Giving right full rudder
⚓ D. A short burst of ahead full with left full rudder

011571/DG00426   **KNIGHTS**

You are stopped with no way upon your vessel at the pilot station. Your vessel is a large twin-screw ship. You must come around 180° to board your Pilot. How should you use the engines and rudder to turn the ship fastest in the least amount of space?

- A. Full ahead on the engines and hard over rudder
- B. Full ahead on one engine, full astern on the other
- ⚓ C. Half ahead with hard over rudder, then full astern on inboard engine
- D. Slow ahead with hard over rudder

SHALLOW WATER EFFECTS

MANEUVERING CHARACTERISTICS

011572/DG00726   **CHAPMAN**

A common occurrence when a vessel is running into shallow water is that _____.

- A. the wake is less pronounced
- B. the vessel is more responsive to the rudder
- ⚓ C. squat will cause a decrease in bottom clearance and an increase in draft
- D. All of the above

011573/DG00656   **BAPTIST**

A deep draft VLCC (100,000 DWT+) navigating in a narrow channel or canal _____.

- ⚓ A. draws more water than when underway in deep water
- B. draws less water with an increase in speed
- C. requires less power for a given speed
- D. steers better under full power

011574/DG01167   **MACELREVEY**

A vessel will "squat" when it proceeds underway _____.

- A. only in deep water
- B. only in shallow water
- ⚓ C. in all depths of water
- D. only in narrow channels

011575/DG00776   **SHIPHAND**

In most cases, when a large merchant vessel enters shallow water at high speed the _____.

- A. maneuverability will increase
- B. speed will increase
- ⚓ C. bow will squat farther than the stern
- D. vessel will rise slightly, on a level plane

011576/DG02608   **WILLERTON**

Most very large ocean going vessels, such as bulk carriers and large tankers, tend to squat _____.

- ⚓ A. by the bow
- B. by the stern
- C. at the end nearest the bottom
- D. evenly fore and aft

011577/DG00045   **CRENSHAW**

Which shallow water effect will increase dramatically if you increase your ship's speed past its "critical speed"?

- ⚓ A. Squatting
- B. Smelling the bottom
- C. Sinkage
- D. Bank cushion

011578/DG00806   **CHAPMAN**

Which will most likely occur when entering shallow water?

- A. Rudder action will become more effective.
- B. The vessel's list will change.
- ⚓ C. The vessel's trim will change.
- D. An increase in speed will occur.

011579/DG00103   **CRENSHAW**

Your ship is in shallow water and the bow rides up on its bow wave while the stern sinks into a depression of its transverse wave system. What is this called?

- A. Broaching
- B. Fish tailing
- ⚓ C. Squatting
- D. Parallel sinkage

011580/DG01155   **MACELVEREY**

In the context of shiphandling, what would be the definition of shallow water?

- ⚓ A. Water depth of less than twice a vessel's draft
- B. Water depth of less than 1-1/2 times a vessel's draft
- C. Under keel clearance of twice a vessel's draft
- D. Under keel clearance of less than 10 feet

011581/DG00766   **KNIGHTS**

Insufficient space between the hull and bottom in shallow water will prevent normal screw currents resulting in _____.

- A. waste of power
- B. sudden sheering to either side
- C. sluggish rudder response
- ⚓ D. All of the above

011582/DG00816   **KNIGHTS**

Water may boil up around the stern of a vessel in a channel due to _____.

- A. slack water when upbound
- ⚓ B. shallow water
- C. a cross current
- D. a head current

011583/DG00796   **CHAPMAN**

When you enter shallow water, you would expect your rudder response to _____.

- ⚓ A. be sluggish and your speed to decrease
- B. be sluggish and your speed to increase
- C. improve and your speed to decrease
- D. improve and your speed to increase

011584/DG00786   **CHAPMAN**

You are on a single-screw vessel with a right-handed propeller, and you are making headway. When you enter shallow water, _____.

A. you will have better rudder response

B. your speed will increase without a change in your throttle

⚓ C. your rudder response will become sluggish

D. your vessel will tend to ride higher

011585/DG00746   **CHAPMAN**

Which effect does speed through the water have on a vessel which is underway in shallow water?

A. A decrease in the speed results in a decrease in steering response and maneuverability.

⚓ B. An increase in speed results in the stern sucking down lower than the bow.

C. An increase in speed results in the vessel rising on an even plane.

D. A decrease in speed results in the vessel sucking down on an even plane.

011586/DG00736   **CHAPMAN; KNIGHTS**

You notice that your speed has decreased, the stern of your vessel has settled into the water, and your rudder is sluggish in responding. The MOST likely cause is _____.

A. mechanical problems with the steering gear

⚓ B. shallow water

C. loss of lubricating oil in the engine

D. current

011587/DG01162   **MACELVEREY**

How does a vessel's rate of turn change when entering shallow water?

A. It is faster.

B. It is slower.

⚓ C. There is no change.

D. It remains constant for varying propeller revolutions.

011588/DG01163   **MACELREVEY**

When piloting a vessel, how are visual references used to establish a constant rate of turn?

⚓ A. Fixed objects that stay on the same relative bearing when the ship is turning indicate a constant rate of turn.

B. Visual references cannot be used to maintain a constant rate of turn.

C. Begin the turn when the fixed object is on the beam.

D. Keep the fixed object's relative bearing opening, for a constant rate of turn.

011589/DG01172   **MACELREVEY**

You are making a sharp turn in a channel and using a buoy four points on the bow to gauge your rate of turn. If you observe the buoy moving aft relative to you, what should you do?

⚓ A. Increase the rate of turn

B. Decrease the rate of turn

C. Maintain a constant rate of turn

D. Decrease speed

011590/DG01173   **MACELREVEY**

You are making a sharp turn in a channel and using a buoy four points on the bow to gauge your rate of turn. If you observe the buoy moving forward relative to you, what should you do?

A. Increase the rate of turn

⚓ B. Decrease the rate of turn

C. Maintain a constant rate of turn

D. Increase speed

011591/DG01153   **MACELREVEY**

What affect does shallow water have on a vessel's stopping distance?

A. The stopping distance is shorter.

⚓ B. The stopping distance is longer.

C. There is no difference in the stopping distance.

D. The propeller is more effective when going astern in shallow water.

011592/DG03018   **SHIPHAND**

When turning a vessel in shallow water, which statement is TRUE?

A. The rate of turn is increased.

B. The rate of turn is decreased.

⚓ C. The turning diameter increases.

D. The turning diameter remains the same.

BANK EFFECTS & PASSING SHIPS

BANK CUSHION

011593/DG00846   **KNIGHTS**

A vessel proceeding along the bank of a river or channel has the tendency to _____.

A. continue in line with the bank

B. hug the bank

⚓ C. sheer away from the bank

D. increase speed

011594/DG00696   **KNIGHTS**

A vessel traveling down a narrow channel, especially if the draft is nearly equal to the depth of the water, may set off the nearer side. This effect is known as _____.

A. smelling the bottom

B. squatting

C. bank suction

⚓ D. bank cushion

011595/DG00856   **KNIGHTS**
A wedge of water building up between the bow and nearer bank which forces the bow out and away describes _____.
⚓ A. bank cushion
B. bank suction
C. combined effect
D. bend effect

011596/DG00686   **KNIGHTS**
The effect known as "bank cushion" acts in which of the following ways on a single-screw vessel proceeding along a narrow channel?
⚓ A. It forces the bow away from the bank.
B. It forces the stern away from the bank.
C. It forces the entire vessel away from the bank.
D. It heels the vessel toward the bank.

011597/DG00716   **KNIGHTS**
Your vessel is proceeding along a narrow channel. The effect called bank cushion has which effect on the vessel?
⚓ A. Forces the bow away from the bank
B. Forces the stern away from the bank
C. Forces the entire vessel bodily away from the bank
D. Decreases the draft at the bow

BANK SUCTION

011598/DG02581   **KNIGHTS; SHIPHAND**
How does the effect known as "bank suction" act on a single-screw vessel proceeding along a narrow channel?
⚓ A. It pulls the stern toward the bank.
B. It heels the vessel toward the bank.
C. It pushes the entire vessel away from the bank.
D. It pulls the bow toward the bank.

011599/DG00706   **KNIGHTS**
How does the effect known as "bank suction" act on a single-screw vessel proceeding along a narrow channel?
A. It pulls the bow toward the bank.
⚓ B. It pulls the stern toward the bank.
C. It pushes the entire vessel away from the bank.
D. It heels the vessel toward the bank.

011600/DG00623   **BRADY**
When hugging a bank in a narrow channel, you should take precautions against _____.
A. bank suction, squat and the effects of vessels passing close aboard
B. clogged sea chests, plugged sea strainers and overheated machinery
C. striking underwater obstructions close to the bank
⚓ D. All of the above

011601/DG00203   **KNIGHTS**
How does the effect known as "bank suction" act on a single-screw vessel proceeding along a narrow channel?
A. It pulls the bow toward the bank.
B. It pushes the entire vessel away from the bank.
⚓ C. It pulls the stern toward the bank.
D. It heels the vessel toward the bank.

011602/DG00615   **BRADY**
When a wedge of water builds up between the head of the barge and the bank it is referred to as _____.
⚓ A. bank cushion
B. bank suction
C. bow wave
D. veering cushion

011603/DG00622   **BRADY**
A predictable result of a vessel nearing a bank or edge of a channel is that the _____.
⚓ A. stern is drawn to the bank as the bow sheers off
B. bow sheers toward the bank
C. vessel continues in a straight line, but with greatly reduced maneuverability
D. vessel will be drawn bodily into the bank unless the engines are stopped

011604/DG00215   **KNIGHTS**
How does the effect known as "bank suction" act on a single-screw vessel proceeding along a narrow channel?
A. It pulls the bow toward the bank.
B. It heels the vessel toward the bank.
C. It pushes the entire vessel away from the bank.
⚓ D. It pulls the stern toward the bank.

011605/DG00633   **BRADY**
A tug is best positioned for towing and maneuvering on rivers and other restricted waters where wave action is limited when _____.
⚓ A. directly astern and pushing the tow
B. towing on a hawser
C. towing alongside and parallel to the vessel it is towing
D. towing on the hip

011606/DG00625   **BRADY**
Which statement is FALSE?
A. Your stern is sucked down and your draft increases when going from deep to shallow water.
B. Excessive speed while passing moored vessels may cause them to surge and break their moorings.
C. Excessive speed while passing a tow being pushed ahead or pushing a tow into an eddy too fast may break up the tow.
⚓ D. None of the above

ENCOUNTERING BANK EFFECTS

011607/DG02568   **SHIPHAND; HOOYER**
You are proceeding along the right bank of a narrow channel aboard a right-handed single-screw vessel. The vessel starts to sheer due to bank suction/cushion effect. You should _____.
A. stop engines and put the rudder left full
B. back full with rudder amidships
C. decrease speed and put the rudder right full
⚓ D. increase speed and put the rudder right full

011608/DG00666   **KNIGHTS**
You are proceeding at a slow speed with your starboard side near the right bank of a channel. If your vessel suddenly sheers toward the opposite bank, the best maneuver would be _____.
A. full ahead, hard left rudder
⚓ B. full ahead, hard right rudder
C. full astern, hard left rudder
D. full astern, hard right rudder

011609/DG00912   **KNIGHTS; CRENSHAW**
You are aboard vessel "A" in a narrow channel and the pilot is approaching vessel "B" as shown. The reason he has not previously changed course to the starboard side of the channel is _____. See Diagram 37
A. to avoid vessel squat in the shallower water near the bank
⚓ B. to avoid the effects of bank cushion and bank suction
C. because there is less chance of striking submerged objects in mid-channel
D. because the current has less eddies in mid-channel

PASSING SHIP MANEUVERS

011610/DG00886   **KNIGHTS**
Two vessels are abreast of each other and passing port to port in a confined waterway. What should you expect as your bow approaches the screws of the other vessel?
A. Your speed will significantly increase.
B. Your draft will significantly decrease.
⚓ C. Your bow will sheer towards the other vessel.
D. Your bow will sheer away from the other vessel.

011611/DG00876   **KNIGHTS; BSW**
You intend to overtake a vessel in a narrow channel. As you approach the other vessel's stern _____.
A. you will gain speed
B. both vessels will gain speed
⚓ C. the vessels will drift together
D. the vessels will drift apart

BERTHING & UNBERTHING

APPROACH TECHNIQUES

011612/DG01156   **KNIGHTS**
The best time to work a boat into a slip is _____.
A. when the wind is against you
B. with the current setting against you
⚓ C. at slack water
D. with a cross current

011613/DG01838   **CHAPMAN**
You are docking a vessel. If possible, you should _____.
A. go in with the current
⚓ B. go in against the current
C. approach the dock at a 90° angle and swing to
D. pass a mooring line to the dock with a heaving line and let the crew pull the vessel in

011614/DG01848   **CHAPMAN**
You are docking a vessel. Wind and current are most favorable when they are _____.
A. crossing your course in the same direction
B. crossing your course in opposite directions
⚓ C. parallel to the pier from ahead
D. setting you on the pier

011615/DG01116   **KNIGHTS**
On a single-screw vessel, when coming port side to a pier and being set off the pier, you should _____.
A. swing wide and approach the pier so as to land starboard side to
B. approach the pier on a parallel course at reduced speed
⚓ C. make your approach at a greater angle than in calm weather
D. point the vessel's head well up into the slip and decrease your speed

011616/DG01216   **CHAPMAN; KNIGHTS**
It is easier to dock a right-hand, single-screw vessel _____.
A. starboard side to the wharf
B. either side to the wharf
⚓ C. port side to the wharf
D. stern to the wharf

011617/DG02910   **KNIGHTS**
Your vessel is a single-screw ship with a right-hand propeller. There is no current. The easiest way to make a landing is _____.
⚓ A. port side to
B. starboard side to
C. dropping anchor and swinging the ship in to the pier
D. either port or starboard side to, with no difference in degree of difficulty

011618/DG04042   **BOWD**

You are on a 120,000 DWT loaded bulk carrier. What is the maximum safe docking speed when coming alongside?

A, 0.1 foot per second (0.06 knot)

⚓ B. 0.2 foot per second (0.12 knot)

C. 0.5 foot per second (0.30 knot)

D. 0.75 foot per second (0.44 knot)

UTILIZING ENGINES & RUDDER

011619/DG01433   **KNIGHTS**

You are 15 feet off a pier and docking a vessel using only a bow breast line and stern breast line. Once the slack is out of both lines you begin to haul in on the bow breast line. What is the effect on the vessel?

A. The bow will come in and the stern will go out.

B. The bow and stern come in equally closer toward the pier.

⚓ C. The bow will come in and the stern will remain the same distance off the pier.

D. The stern will come in and the bow will remain the same distance off the pier.

011620/DG01206   **CHAPMAN**

You are landing a single-screw vessel with a left-handed propeller, starboard side to the dock. As you approach the dock you back your engine with your rudder amidships. You would expect the vessel to _____.

A. lose headway without swinging

B. turn its bow towards the dock

⚓ C. turn its stern towards the dock

D. drift away from the dock

011621/DG01778   **CHAPMAN**

You are landing a single-screw vessel with a right-handed propeller port side to a dock. As you approach the dock, you back down on your engine with rudder amidships. You would expect the vessel to _____.

A. drift away from the dock

B. lose headway without swinging

⚓ C. swing its stern towards the dock

D. swing its stern away from the dock

011622/DG01196   **CHAPMAN**

You are landing a single-screw vessel, with a right-hand propeller, starboard side to the dock. When you have approached the berth and back the engine, you would expect the vessel to _____.

A. lose headway without swinging

⚓ B. turn her bow toward the dock

C. turn her bow away from the dock

D. head into the wind, regardless of the side the wind is on

UTILIZING MOORING LINES

011623/DG00993   **KNIGHTS**

Your vessel is docking, but not yet alongside. Which line will be the most useful when maneuvering the vessel alongside the pier?

A. Bow breast line

⚓ B. Bow spring line

C. Inshore head line

D. Offshore head line

011624/DG01720   **CHAPMAN; KNIGHTS**

Your vessel is to dock bow first at a pier. Which line will be the most useful when maneuvering the vessel alongside the pier?

⚓ A. Bow spring line

B. Bow breast line

C. Stern breast line

D. Inshore head line

011625/DG02933   **CHAPMAN; KNIGHTS**

Your vessel is to dock bow first at a pier. Which line will be the most useful when maneuvering the vessel alongside the pier?

A. Stern breast line

⚓ B. Bow spring line

C. Bow breast line

D. Inshore head line

011626/DG04057   **CHAPMAN; KNIGHTS**

Your vessel is to dock bow in at a pier without the assistance of tugboats. Which line will be the most useful when maneuvering the vessel alongside the pier?

⚓ A, Bow spring line

B. Inshore head line

C. Stern breast line

D. Bow breast line

011627/DG03294   **CHAPMAN; KNIGHTS**

Your vessel is to dock bow in at a pier without the assistance of tugboats. Which line will be the most useful when maneuvering the vessel alongside the pier?

A. Bow breast line

B. Stern breast line

⚓ C. Bow spring line

D. Inshore head line

011628/DG02957   **CHAPMAN; KNIGHTS**

Your vessel is to dock bow in at a pier without the assistance of tugboats. Which line will be the most useful when maneuvering the vessel alongside the pier?

A. Bow breast line

B. Inshore head line

C. Stern breast line

⚓ D. Bow spring line

011629/DG04047   **CHAPMAN; KNIGHTS**

Your vessel is to dock bow in at a pier. Which line will be the most useful when maneuvering the vessel alongside the pier?

A, Inshore head line

⚓ B. Bow spring line

C. Stern breast line

D. Bow breast line

011630/DG00212   **KNIGHTS**

Your vessel is port side to a pier with a spring line led aft from the bow. In calm weather, putting the engines ahead with the rudder hard left should bring _____.

⚓ A. the bow in and the stern out

B. both the bow and stern in

C. the bow out and the stern in

D. both the bow and stern out

011631/DG00446   **CHAPMAN; KNIGHTS**

A twin-screw vessel can clear the inboard propeller and maneuver off a pier best by holding a(n) _____.

A. forward spring line and going slow ahead on the inboard engine

B. after spring line and going slow astern on the outboard engine

C. forward spring line and going slow ahead on both engines

⚓ D. forward spring line and going slow ahead on the outboard engine

011632/DG01136   **KNIGHTS**

Your vessel is to dock bow first at a pier without the assistance of tugboats. Which line will be the most useful when maneuvering the vessel alongside the pier?

A. Bow breast line

⚓ B. Bow spring line

C. Inshore head line

D. Stern breast line

UTILIZING ANCHORS

011633/DG00636   **KNIGHTS**

The use of an anchor to assist in turning in restricted waters is _____.

A. a last resort

⚓ B. good seamanship

C. the sign of a novice shiphandler

D. to be used only with a single-screw vessel

011634/DG02454   **SHIPHAND**

You are going astern (single-screw, right-handed propeller) with the anchor down at a scope of twice the depth of the water. As the anchor dredges, you should expect the _____.

A. stern to walk to the same side as the anchor being used

B. vessel to back in a straight line

⚓ C. stern to walk to port but at a reduced rate

D. stern to walk to port at a faster rate than normal

011635/DG02574   **SHIPHAND**

You are proceeding down a channel and lose the engine(s). You must use the anchors to stop the ship. Which statement is true?

A. Pay out all of the cable before setting up on the brake to insure the anchors dig in and hold.

B. For a mud, mud and clay, or sandy bottom pay out a scope of 5 to 7 times the depth before setting up on the brake.

⚓ C. Use one or both anchors with a scope of twice the depth before setting the brake.

D. Drop the anchor to short stay and hold that scope.

011636/DG02612   **SHIPHAND**

When using the anchor to steady the bow while approaching a dock you must be aware of the fact that _____.

A. the vessel will tend to take a large sheer towards the side where the anchor is down

B. steering control is ineffective in trying to turn to the side opposite to that of the anchor being used

C. the anchor cable must never lead under the hull

⚓ D. using an offshore anchor decreases the chances of the anchor holding

011637/DG00213   **HOOYER**

You are the Master of a single-screw vessel. You are docking at a port which has no tugs available. You decide to drop the offshore anchor to help in docking. The amount of chain you should pay out is _____.

A. 5 to 7 times the depth of the water

⚓ B. 1-1/2 to 2 times the depth of the water

C. equal to the depth of the water

D. you should NEVER use the anchor to help in docking

011638/DG02652   **SHIPHAND**

You are using the anchor to steady the bow while maneuvering. You have the proper scope of anchor cable when the _____.

⚓ A. bow is held in position with the engines coming slowly ahead

B. anchor is just touching the bottom

C. scope is not more than 5 times the depth of the water

D. cable enters the water at an angle between 60° and 85° from the horizontal

011639/DG01126   **SHIPHAND**

You are approaching a pier and intend to use the port anchor to assist in docking port side to. You would NOT use the anchor if _____.

A. the current was setting you on the pier

B. another vessel is berthed ahead of your position

C. the wind was blowing from the starboard side

⚓ D. there is shallow water enroute to the berth

011640/DG01146   **MMOH**

While your vessel is docked port side to a wharf, a sudden gale force wind causes the vessel's bow lines to part. The bow begins to fall away from the dock, and no tugs are immediately available. Which measure(s) should you take FIRST?

A. Call the Master and the deck gang.

B. Slip the stern lines, let the vessel drift into the river, and then anchor.

⚓ C. Let go the starboard anchor.

D. Obtain assistance and attempt to put some new bow lines out.

011641/DG01258   **MMOH**

While your vessel is docked port side to a wharf, a sudden gale force wind causes the vessel's stern lines to part. The stern begins to fall away from the dock, and no tugs are immediately available. Which measure(s) should you take FIRST?

A. Notify the engineroom of the need for propulsion.

⚓ B. Shut down any cargo transfer that's in progress.

C. Let go the port anchor and veer to a short scope of chain.

D. Obtain assistance from the terminal to put new stern lines out.

UTILIZING TUGS

011642/DG02492   **SWIT**

When a tug makes up to a large vessel, the spring line should lead from the forwardmost part of the tug so that _____.

A. friction on the spring line is minimized

B. the length of the spring line is minimized

C. the head line and spring line can be worked simultaneously

⚓ D. the tug can pivot freely

011643/DG01236   **SWIT**

You are docking a ship with a single-screw tug assisting on your starboard bow. How should the tug be tied up if you are anticipating that she will have to hold your bow off while you stem the current?

A. One head line would be sufficient.

B. The tug would need at least two head lines.

C. The tug should put a spring line up, leading astern on the ship.

⚓ D. The tug should put a stern line up, leading ahead on the ship.

011644/DG02572   **SWIT**

A tug would NOT assist a ship to steer if the tug is made up to the large vessel _____.

A. by a tow line ahead of the vessel

B. forward on either bow of the vessel

⚓ C. approximately amidships of the vessel

D. on the vessel's quarter

011645/DG03134   **SWIT**

When using two tugs to assist in mooring a large, deeply laden ship, the most powerful tug is usually placed _____.

⚓ A. forward to control the bow

B. amidships to move the entire vessel evenly

C. aft to assist the ship's rudder and propeller

D. anywhere, since the maneuverability of the tug governs the placement not the power

011646/DG01266   **KNIGHTS**

You are docking a vessel in a slip which has its entrance athwart the tide. You land the ship across the end of the pier, stemming the tide, preparatory to breaking the ship around the corner. You have one tug to assist. Where would you generally tie up the tug?

A. Have her on a hawser from the stern.

B. Tie her up on the inshore bow to hold the ship off the end.

⚓ C. Tie her up on the offshore bow.

D. Tie her up on the inshore quarter to lift the stern.

011647/DG01256   **BRADY**

You are docking an oceangoing single-screw vessel under normal circumstances with a single tug. The tug is usually used to _____.

⚓ A. control the bow and is tied to the offshore bow

B. control the stern and is tied to the stern on the offshore side

C. pull the vessel into the slip and is tied to the bow

D. push the ship bodily alongside and is tied to the offshore side amidships

011648/DG01246   **WILLERTON**

When a tug is pulling on a hawser at right angles to the ship, and the pilot wants to come ahead or astern on the ship's engine, care must be taken that the pilot _____.

- A. does not break the towline
- ⚓ B. does not get too much way on the vessel
- C. keeps a steady course so the towline will remain tight
- D. turns the ship toward the direction of pull

011649/DG01226   **PLUMMER**

You are docking a vessel starboard side to with the assistance of two tugs. You are attempting to hold the vessel off by operating both tugs at right angles to the vessel and at full power. You must ensure that _____.

- A. steerageway is not taken off
- B. the bow doesn't close the dock first
- C. the bow closes the dock first
- ⚓ D. the ship has no headway at the time

011650/DG01187   **SWIT**

You are taking the bow line from the port bow of a large vessel that is underway when the stern of your tug comes in contact with the vessel. The forward motion of both vessels causes your tug to be turned toward the other vessel and contact the stem thereby being "stemmed". You should immediately _____.

- A. stop engines and the vessel's wake will push you clear of the bow
- ⚓ B. go full astern with rudder amidships
- C. go full ahead with the rudder hard over to starboard
- D. go full ahead with the rudder amidships

011651/DG01182   **BRADY**

Your vessel must moor port side to a berth limited by vessels ahead and astern using a single tug. You are stemming a slight current and there is a light breeze of the dock. Your tug should be made up to the vessel's _____.

- A. stern on a hawser
- B. quarter
- C. waist
- ⚓ D. bow

ENGINE CONTROL & MANEUVERING
CHARACTERISTICS

CONTROLLABLE-PITCH PROPELLER

011652/DG00355   **CHAPMAN**

Generally, you can best keep a vessel under steering control when the vessel has _____.

- ⚓ A. headway
- B. sternway
- C. no way on, with engines stopped
- D. no way on, with engines full ahead

011653/DG02858   **SWIT**

Which characteristic is a disadvantage of a controllable- pitch propeller as compared to a fixed-pitch propeller?
- A. Slightly higher fuel consumption
- B. Lack of directional control when backing
- C. Inefficient at high shaft RPM
- ⚓ D. Some unusual handling characteristics

011654/DG02924   **WILLERTON**

You are on a large vessel fitted with a right-handed controllable-pitch propeller set at maximum forward pitch. Which statement about reversing is TRUE?
- A. When the pitch is reversed, the stern will slew to port even with headway.
- B. The vessel will respond to the rudder until sternway is developed, then the stern will slew to starboard.
- ⚓ C. There will probably be a loss of steering control.
- D. The vessel will have full rudder control throughout the speed change from ahead to astern.

011655/DG02920   **WILLERTON**

You are on a large vessel fitted with a right-handed controllable-pitch propeller. When making large speed changes while decreasing pitch, which statement is TRUE?
- A. You will probably have full directional control throughout the speed change.
- ⚓ B. You may lose rudder control until the ship's speed has dropped to correspond to propeller speed.
- C. The stern will immediately slew to starboard due to unbalanced forces acting on the propeller.
- D. The stern will immediately slew to port due to unbalanced forces acting on the propeller.

011656/DG02930 WILLERTON

A large vessel is equipped with a controllable pitch propeller. Which statement is TRUE?

⚓ A. When dead in the water, it is often difficult to find the neutral position and slight headway or sternway may result.

B. When going directly from full ahead to full astern, there is complete steering control.

C. When the vessel has headway and the propeller is in neutral, there is no effect on rudder control.

D. When maneuvering in port, full ahead or astern power can usually be obtained without changing shaft RPM.

SINGLE SCREW VESSELS (AHEAD)

011657/DG01798 CHAPMAN

You are on a single-screw vessel with a left-handed propeller making no way in the water. How will your vessel react when you apply right rudder?

A. Bow will kick to starboard

B. Bow will kick to port

⚓ C. Rudder alone has no effect on the vessel

D. Stern will kick to port, then slowly swing to starboard

011658/DG00376 CHAPMAN; KNIGHTS

You are aboard a right-handed single-screw vessel with headway on. The engine is put full astern and the rudder hard left. What will the bow do?

A. It will swing to the left, and will swing left faster as the vessel loses way.

⚓ B. It will swing to the left, straighten out and then swing to the right as the vessel loses way.

C. It will swing to the left without increasing or decreasing its swing.

D. The bow will swing to the right.

011659/DG01588 MMOH

You are aboard a single-screw vessel (right-hand propeller) going full ahead with good headway. The engine is put astern and the rudder is placed hard left. The stern of the vessel will swing to _____.

⚓ A. starboard until headway is lost and then to port

B. port

C. port until headway is lost and then may possibly swing to starboard

D. port slowly at first and then quickly to port

011660/DG01608 KNIGHTS

Your ship is dead in the water with the rudder amidships. As the right-handed screw starts to turn ahead, the bow will tend to go _____.

A. to starboard

⚓ B. to port

C. straight ahead

D. as influenced by the tide and sea

SINGLE SCREW VESSELS (ASTERN)

011661/DG00346 CHAPMAN

A vessel is equipped with a single right-handed screw. With rudder amidships and calm wind, the vessel will most likely back _____.

A. straight astern

⚓ B. to port

C. to starboard

D. in no particular direction

011662/DG00326 CHAPMAN

In order to back a right-handed, single-screw vessel in a straight line, you will probably need to use _____.

A. very little rudder

B. some left rudder

⚓ C. some right rudder

D. full left rudder

011663/DG00336 CHAPMAN

When a vessel with a single right-hand propeller backs to port the _____.

⚓ A. bow falls off to starboard

B. vessel moves to port without changing heading

C. bow swings to port

D. vessel moves to starboard without changing heading

011664/DG00386 CHAPMAN

You are maneuvering a vessel with a right-hand propeller. The rudder is amidships. The vessel will generally back _____.

⚓ A. to port

B. to starboard

C. in a straight line directly astern

D. downstream, the stern going in the direction of the current

011665/DG02146 MMOH

You are on a single-screw vessel with a right-handed propeller. The vessel is going full speed astern with full right rudder. The bow will swing _____.

A. quickly to port, then more slowly to port

⚓ B. probably to port

C. slowly to port, then quickly to starboard

D. probably to starboard

011666/DG00306 CHAPMAN

You are aboard a single-screw vessel with a right-handed propeller. The vessel is dead in the water and the rudder is amidships. If you reverse your engine you would expect your vessel to _____.

⚓ A. kick its stern to port

B. kick its stern to starboard

C. move astern without swinging

D. swing its stern to starboard, then to port

TWIN SCREW VESSELS (AHEAD)

011667/DG01618   **CHAPMAN**

A twin-screw vessel is easier to maneuver than a single-screw vessel because the twin-screw vessel _____.

- A. permits the rudder to move faster
- B. generates more power
- C. can turn without using her rudder
- D. can suck the water away from the rudder

011668/DG00396   **KNIGHTS**

A vessel is equipped with twin propellers, both turning outboard with the engines half ahead. If there is no wind or current and the rudders are amidships, what will happen?
- A. The bow will swing to starboard.
- B. The bow will swing to port.
- C. The vessel will steer a zigzag course.
- D. The vessel will steer a fairly straight course.

011669/DG00456   **CHAPMAN**

You are conning a twin-screw vessel going ahead with rudders amidships. If the port screw stops turning the bow will _____.
- A. go to port
- B. go to starboard
- C. not veer to either side
- D. go first to port and then to starboard

011670/DG01628   **CHAPMAN**

You are going ahead on twin engines when you want to make a quick turn to port. Which actions will turn your boat the fastest?
- A. Reverse port engine; apply left rudder
- B. Reverse port engine; rudder amidships
- C. Reverse starboard engine; apply left rudder
- D. Reverse starboard engine; rudder amidships

011671/DG00526   **CHAPMAN; KNIGHTS**

You are going ahead on twin engines with rudders amidships. Your port engine stalls. To continue your course you should _____.
- A. apply right rudder
- B. apply left rudder
- C. keep your rudder amidships
- D. increase engine speed

011672/DG02460   **CHAPMAN**

You are operating a twin-screw vessel and lose your port engine. You continue to operate on your starboard engine only. Which action would you take to move your vessel ahead in a straight line?
- A. Compensate with right rudder.
- B. Compensate with left rudder.
- C. Surge the starboard engine.
- D. Rudder amidships - no compensation is necessary on a twin-screw vessel.

011673/DG00406   **KNIGHTS**

A twin-screw vessel with a single rudder is making headway. The engines are full speed ahead. There is no wind or current. Which statement is FALSE?
- A. If one screw is stopped, the ship will turn toward the side of the stopped screw.
- B. The principal force which turns the ship is set up by the wake against the forward side of the rudder.
- C. Turning response by use of the rudder only is greater than on a single-screw vessel.
- D. With the rudder amidships, the ship will steer a fairly steady course.

011674/DG00546   **CHAPMAN**

A twin-screw ship going ahead on the starboard screw only tends to move _____.
- A. in a straight line
- B. to port
- C. from side to side
- D. to starboard

011675/DG00436   **CHAPMAN; MMOH**

The rudders are amidships and both screws are going ahead. What will happen if the starboard screw is stopped?
- A. The bow will go to port.
- B. The bow will go to starboard.
- C. The bow will remain steady.
- D. The stern will go to starboard.

011676/DG00516   **CHAPMAN; KNIGHTS**

You are going ahead on twin engines with rudder amidships. Your starboard engine stalls. To continue on course, you should _____.
- A. apply left rudder
- B. apply right rudder
- C. increase engine speed
- D. keep your rudder amidships

011677/DG00466   **CHAPMAN; KNIGHTS**

A twin screw vessel, making headway with both engines turning ahead, will turn more readily to starboard if you _____.
- A. reverse port engine, apply right rudder
- B. reverse port engine, rudder amidships
- C. reverse starboard engine, apply right rudder
- D. reverse starboard engine, rudder amidships

011678/DG01638   **CHAPMAN**

On a twin-screw, twin-rudder vessel, the most effective way to turn in your own water, with no way on, is to put _____.
- A. one engine ahead and one engine astern, with full rudder
- B. one engine ahead and one engine astern, with rudders amidships
- C. both engines ahead, with full rudder
- D. both engines astern, with full rudder

011679/DG00566   **CHAPMAN**

The BEST way to steer a twin-screw vessel if you lose your rudder is by using _____.

A. one engine and a steering oar
B. both engines at the same speed
C. one engine at a time
⚓ D. one engine running at reduced speed and controlling the vessel with the other

TWIN SCREW VESSELS (ASTERN)

011680/DG00506   **CHAPMAN**

With rudders amidships and negligible wind, a twin-screw vessel moving astern with both engines backing will back _____.

A. to port
B. to starboard
⚓ C. in a fairly straight line
D. in a circular motion

011681/DG00476   **CHAPMAN**

You are backing on twin engines with rudders amidships, when your port engine stalls. To continue backing on course, you should _____.

A. apply left rudder
⚓ B. apply right rudder
C. increase engine speed
D. keep your rudder amidships

011682/DG00496   **CHAPMAN**

Your twin-screw vessel is moving ASTERN with rudders amidships. The starboard screw suddenly stops turning. Your vessel's head will _____.

⚓ A. go to port
B. go to starboard
C. remain stationary
D. suddenly drop down

011683/DG00486   **CHAPMAN**

You are backing on twin engines with rudders amidships. Your starboard engine stalls. To continue backing on course, you should _____.

⚓ A. apply left rudder
B. apply right rudder
C. increase your engine speed
D. keep your rudder amidships

011684/DG00785   **CHAPMAN**

With rudders amidships and negligible wind, a twin-screw vessel moving ahead on the port screw and backing on the starboard screw will _____.

A. move in a straight line
⚓ B. pivot to starboard
C. pivot to port
D. walk sideways to starboard

011685/DG00556   **CHAPMAN**

You may BEST turn a twin-screw vessel about, to the right, in a narrow channel by using _____.

A. both engines ahead and helm
B. one engine only
⚓ C. port engine ahead and the starboard engine astern
D. both engines astern and use helm

011686/DG00536   **CHAPMAN**

Your vessel is backing on the starboard screw, and going ahead on the port screw. The bow will _____.

A. back on a straight line
B. move ahead on a straight line
C. swing to port
⚓ D. swing to starboard

RUDDER CONTROL

011687/DG02732   **SWIT**

Flanking rudders effect a vessel's heading because of the _____.

⚓ A. effect of the propeller flow on the rudders
B. water flow due to the vessel's movement through the water
C. tunnel affect of the water flow past opposing rudders
D. discharge current being channeled to impinge on the vessel's deadwood

011688/DG02812   **SWIT**

If a tug equipped with flanking rudders is to be turned in a confined circle, when going astern, the stern will move to port the quickest if _____.

⚓ A. the rudder is hard to port and the flanking rudders are hard to port
B. the rudder is amidships and the flanking rudders are hard to port
C. the rudder is hard to port and the flanking rudders are hard to starboard
D. all rudders are hard to starboard

011689/DG02932   **SHIPHAND**

Which type of rudder may lose its effectiveness at angles of 10 or more degrees?

A. Contra-guide
⚓ B. Balanced spade
C. Unbalanced
D. Flat plate

DISPLACEMENT EFFECTS

011690/DG02940   **SHIPHAND**

A vessel reduces speed without backing. The rate that her speed through the water decreases depends primarily on the _____.
- A. vessel's horsepower
- B. sea state
- C. number of propellers
- ⚓ D. vessel's displacement

011691/DG02822   **BOWD**

Which statement about stopping a vessel is TRUE?
- A. A lightly laden vessel requires as much stopping distance as a fully laden vessel when the current is from astern.
- B. A vessel is dead in the water when the back wash from astern operation reaches the bow.
- C. A tunnel bow thruster can be used in an emergency to reduce the stopping distance.
- ⚓ D. When a vessel is dead in the water any speed displayed by Doppler log reflects the current.

011692/DG00046   **PLUMMER**

Which statement concerning the handling characteristics of a fully loaded vessel as compared with those of a light vessel is FALSE?
- A. A fully loaded vessel will be slower to respond to the engines.
- B. A fully loaded vessel will maintain her headway further.
- C. A light vessel will be more affected by the wind.
- ⚓ D. A light vessel loses more rudder effect in shallow water.

WIND EFFECTS

011693/DG00076   **ENCY. NAUT. KNOW.**

Leeway is the _____.
- A. difference between the true course and the compass course
- B. momentum of a vessel after her engines have been stopped
- ⚓ C. lateral movement of a vessel downwind of her intended course
- D. displacement of a vessel multiplied by her speed

011694/DG00056   **KNIGHTS**

The effect of wind on exposed areas of the vessel is most noticeable when _____.
- ⚓ A. backing
- B. going slow ahead
- C. going full ahead
- D. turning

011695/DG00146   **KNIGHTS**

When turning a ship in restricted space with a strong wind, it is normally best to _____.
- A. go ahead on both engines with the rudder hard to one side, if on a twin-screw vessel
- B. back down with the rudder hard to one side, if on a single-screw vessel
- C. take advantage of the tendency to back to port, if on a twin-screw vessel
- ⚓ D. turn so that the tendency to back into the wind can be used, if on a single-screw vessel

011696/DG01768   **SHIPHAND**

As a rule, ships of most configurations, when drifting in calm water with negligible current, will lie _____.
- A. bow to the wind
- ⚓ B. beam to the wind
- C. stern to the wind
- D. with the wind on the quarter

011697/DG00066   **CHAPMAN**

Most of your vessel's superstructure is forward. How will the vessel lie when drifting with no way on?
- A. With the wind from ahead
- B. With the wind off the port beam
- C. With the wind off the starboard beam
- ⚓ D. With the wind from abaft the beam

011698/DG03644   **ARMSTRONG**

You are drifting in a locale where there is no current. As a rule, your vessel will lie _____.
- A. bow to the wind
- ⚓ B. beam to the wind
- C. stern to the wind
- D. with the wind on the quarter

HEAVY WEATHER OPERATIONS

HEAVING TO

011699/DG00926   **CRENSHAW**

Usually the most gentle way of riding out a severe storm on a larger vessel is _____.
- A. head on at slow speeds
- B. hove to
- ⚓ C. running before the seas
- D. to rig a sea anchor

011700/DG00335 MMOH; NICHOLS

You are steaming in a heavy gale and find it necessary to heave to. Under most circumstances, this is best done by _____.

A. stopping the engines and drifting beam to the seas

B. going slow astern and taking the seas on the quarter

⚓ C. taking the sea fine on the bow and reducing the speed to the minimum to hold that position

D. maintaining speed and taking the sea broad on the bow

011701/DG01016 CHAPMAN

Your vessel is off a lee shore in heavy weather and laboring. Which action should you take?

⚓ A. Put the sea and wind about two points on either bow and reduce speed.

B. Heave to in the trough of the sea.

C. Put the sea and wind on either quarter and proceed at increased speed.

D. Put the bow directly into the sea and proceed at full speed.

POUNDING

011702/DG00676 TIDE TABLES

Conditions for crossing a rough bar are usually best at _____.

A. low water slack

⚓ B. high water slack

C. high water ebb

D. high water flood

011703/DG01076 CHAPMAN

You are underway in heavy weather and your bow is into the seas. To prevent pounding, you should _____.

A. change course, in order to take the seas at an 85 degree angle from the bow

⚓ B. decrease speed

C. increase speed

D. secure all loose gear

011704/DG03300 CHAPMAN

You are heading into the sea during rough weather. Having too much weight forward can cause your small boat to _____.

A. broach

⚓ B. plunge into the wave

C. rise rapidly over the wave

D. list

011705/DG00946 MMOH

Which measure should NOT be taken to reduce the pounding of a vessel in a head sea?

⚓ A. Add ballast in the after peak.

B. Add ballast forward.

C. Alter course.

D. Reduce speed.

BROACHING

011706/DG01056 CHAPMAN

In which situation could a vessel most easily capsize?

A. Running into head seas

⚓ B. Running in the trough

C. Running with following seas

D. Anchored with your bow into the seas

011707/DG01036 CHAPMAN

What is meant by the term "broaching to"?

A. Having the vessel head toward the sea

B. Running before a sea

⚓ C. Being turned broadside to the sea

D. Having the vessel filled with water

011708/DG00966 CHAPMAN

When a boat turns broadside to heavy seas and winds, thus exposing the boat to the danger of capsizing, the boat has _____.

⚓ A. broached

B. pitchpoled

C. trimmed

D. yawed

011709/DG01828 CHAPMAN; KNIGHTS

Your vessel is broken down and rolling in heavy seas. You can reduce the danger of capsizing by _____.

A. constantly shifting the rudder

B. moving all passengers to one side of the boat

⚓ C. rigging a sea anchor

D. moving all passengers to the stern

HULL STRESSES

011710/DG00034 WILLERTON

Your vessel has been loaded in a sagging condition. Enroute you encounter heavy weather and notice buckling in the midships deck plating of your vessel. To relieve the strain you could _____.

A. pump fuel oil from midships to the ends of the vessel

B. reduce speed

C. take a course which most eases the vessel

⚓ D. All of the above

SYNCHRONOUS ROLLING

011711/DG02521   **MMOH**
The period of roll is the time difference between

_____.
A. zero inclination to full inclination on one side
B. full inclination on one side to full inclination on the other side
⚓ C. full inclination on one side to the next full inclination on the same side
D. zero inclination to the next zero inclination

011712/DG00976   **KNIGHTS**
When the period of beam seas equals the natural rolling period of a vessel, what will most likely occur?
A. Excessive pitching
B. Excessive yawing
⚓ C. Excessive rolling
D. No change should be evident

011713/DG02760   **LADAGE**
When the wave period and the apparent rolling period are the same _____.
⚓ A. synchronous rolling occurs
B. roll period decreases
C. roll period increases
D. roll amplitude is dampened

011714/DG01066   **CHAPMAN**
If your propeller is racing in rough weather, you should

_____.
⚓ A. decrease your engine speed
B. ignore it
C. increase your engine speed
D. stop your engine until the rough weather passes

011715/DG01026   **CHAPMAN**
When making way in heavy seas you notice that your vessel's screw is being lifted clear of the water and racing. One way to correct this would be to

_____.
A. increase speed
⚓ B. decrease speed
C. move more weight forward
D. shift the rudder back and forth several times

011716/DG00956   **CHAPMAN**
When a vessel is swinging from side to side off course due to quartering seas, the vessel is _____.
A. broaching
B. pitchpoling
C. rolling
⚓ D. yawing

011717/DG00996   **CHAPMAN**
With a following sea, a vessel will tend to _____.
A. heave to
B. pound
C. reduce speed
⚓ D. yaw

011718/DG01046   **CHAPMAN**
In a following sea, a wave has overtaken your vessel and thrown the stern to starboard. To continue along your original course, you should _____.
⚓ A. use more right rudder
B. use more left rudder
C. increase speed
D. decrease speed

011719/DG00986   **CHAPMAN**
When running before a heavy sea, moving weights aft will affect the handling of a vessel by _____.
A. reducing rolling
B. increasing rolling
⚓ C. reducing yawing
D. increasing yawing

011720/DG01006   **CHAPMAN; KNIGHTS**
Which action reduces the yawing of a vessel in a following sea?
A. Increasing GM
B. Pumping out tanks aft
C. Shifting weights to the bow
⚓ D. Shifting weights to the stern

RECEIVING SURVIVORS
FROM LIFEBOATS & LIFERAFTS

APPROACH MANEUVERS

011721/DG01985   **CHAPMAN**
You are on a 165 foot (50.3 meters) long vessel with a draft of 9 feet (2.7 meters) and twin screws. Which statement about rescuing a survivor in the water with ship pickup is TRUE?
A. You should stop to windward of the man and drift down on him.
B. You should stop with the man on your weather beam and twist the ship up to him.
⚓ C. A pickup off the weather bow gives maximum maneuverability with the least possibility of injury to the man.
D. Ship pick up should never be used with a shallow draft vessel.

011722/DG01728   **MFPFFS**

You are trying to rescue survivors from a wrecked vessel on fire. You should approach _____.

A. to leeward of the wrecked vessel

B. at a speed of at most one-half that of the wrecked vessel

C. at a speed of at least that of the wrecked vessel

⚓ D. to windward of the wrecked vessel

011723/DG01487   **MMOH**

You are approaching a disabled vessel in order to remove survivors from it. If your vessel drifts faster than the disabled vessel, how should you make your approach?

⚓ A. To windward of the disabled vessel

B. To leeward of the disabled vessel

C. Directly astern of the disabled vessel

D. At three times the drifting speed of the disabled vessel

011724/DG01950   **MERSAR**

You are proceeding to a distress site and expect large numbers of people in the water. Which statement is TRUE?

A. You should stop to windward of the survivors in the water and only use the ship's boats to recover the survivors.

B. If the survivors are in inflatable rafts you should approach from windward to create a lee for the survivors.

⚓ C. An inflatable liferaft secured alongside can be an effective boarding station for transfer of survivors from the boats.

D. Survivors in the water should never be permitted alongside due to the possibility of injury from the vessel.

011725/DG01347   **MERSAR 4 Ed.; USCP**

You are proceeding to a distress site where the survivors are in liferafts. Which action will assist in making your vessel more visible to the survivors?

A. Steering a zigzag course with 5 to 10 minutes on each leg

⚓ B. Making smoke in daylight

C. Dumping debris over the side to make a trail to your vessel

D. Continuous ringing of the general alarm

011726/DG02104   **MERSAR; *USCP**

You are proceeding to a distress site where the survivors are in liferafts. Which action will assist in making your vessel more visible to the survivors?

A. Steering a zigzag course with 5 to 10 minutes on each leg

B. Steering a sinuous course

C. Dumping debris over the side to make a trail to your vessel

⚓ D. Making smoke in daylight

011727/DG02074   **MERSAR; *USCP**

You are proceeding to a distress site. The survivors are in liferafts. What will make your ship more visible to the survivors?

A. Steering a sinuous course

B. Steering a zig-zag course

⚓ C. Turning on all available deck lights at night

D. Dumping debris over the side to make a trail to your vessel

---

WAKE REDUCTION & PROPULSION

PROPULSION SYSTEMS

011728/DG00196   **BAPTIST**

A VLCC (100,000 DWT+) with a 30,000 Shaft Horsepower Steam Turbine is slow to respond to engine movements and has less stopping power than normal ships because it has a _____.

A. bigger propeller

⚓ B. smaller power to weight ratio

C. smaller propeller

D. larger power to weight ratio

011729/DG01818   **BRADY**

When comparing twin screw tug to single-screw tugs, which statement about a twin-screw tug is FALSE?

A. If one engine fails, you do not lose control of the tow.

B. It is more maneuverable.

⚓ C. It develops more bollard pull for the same horsepower.

D. It is generally subject to more propeller damage from debris in the water.

PROPELLER FORCES

011730/DG02870   **KNIGHTS**

A single-screw vessel going ahead tends to turn more rapidly to port because of propeller _____.

A. discharge current

B. suction current

⚓ C. sidewise force

D. thrust

011731/DG00576   **CHAPMAN**

In twin-screw engine installations while going ahead, maneuvering qualities are most effective when the tops of the propeller blades both turn _____.

A. to starboard

⚓ B. outboard from the center

C. to port

D. inboard toward the center

011732/DG01598   **MMOH**

On a vessel with a single propeller, transverse force has the most effect on the vessel when the engine is put _____.

A. full ahead
⚓ B. full astern
C. half ahead
D. slow astern

011733/DG00286   **KNIGHTS; CRENSHAW**

Sidewise force of the propeller tends to throw a vessel's stern to the right or left, depending on rotation. This force is caused by _____.

A. back current from the rudder
B. greater pressure on the right or left side of the propeller, depending on rotation
C. lower pressure on the right or left side of the propeller, depending on rotation
⚓ D. torque from the velocity and angle at which the surrounding water impinges upon the propeller blades

011734/DG00246   **KNIGHTS**

The force exerted by a propeller which tends to throw the stern right or left is called _____.

A. slip
⚓ B. sidewise force
C. rotational force
D. thrust

011735/DG00416   **KNIGHTS**

While moving ahead, a twin-screw ship has an advantage over a single-screw ship because _____.

A. correct trim will be obtained more easily
B. drag effect will be canceled out
⚓ C. side forces will be eliminated
D. speed will be increased

WAKE CURRENTS

011736/DG00276   **KNIGHTS**

As a ship moves through the water, it causes a wake, which is also moving forward relative to the sea. In addition to a fore and aft motion, this wake also has a(n) _____.

A. downward and inward flow
B. downward and outward flow
⚓ C. upward and inward flow
D. upward and outward flow

011737/DG01578   **MODSHIPS**

A stream of water immediately surrounding a moving vessel's hull, flowing in the same direction as the vessel is known as _____.

A. directional current
B. forward current
C. propeller current
⚓ D. wake current

011738/DG00226   **MODSHIPS**

Which statement is TRUE concerning the vessel's slipstream?

A. It has no effect on the steering of the vessel.
B. It has no effect on the rudder when the helm is amidships.
C. Its velocity is the same as that of the wake.
⚓ D. The propeller gives it a helical motion.

011739/DG00216   **KNIGHTS**

As a ship moves through the water, it drags with it a body of water called the wake. The ratio of the wake speed to the ship's speed is called _____.

A. propeller velocity
B. speed of advance
C. wake distribution
⚓ D. wake fraction

WAKE REDUCTION

011740/DG00826   **CHAPMAN**

In order to reduce your wake in a narrow channel you should _____.

A. apply enough rudder to counter the effect of the current
B. change your course to a zigzag course
⚓ C. reduce your speed
D. shift the weight to the stern

ICE OPERATIONS

ICE MEASUREMENT

011741/DG01652   **BOWD**

Ice concentration is measured in tenths. What concentration range of ice corresponds to 1 - 3 tenths?

⚓ A. Very Open Pack
B. Open Pack
C. Close Pack
D. Very Close Pack

011742/DG01621   **BOWD**

Ice concentration is measured in tenths. What concentration range of ice corresponds to "Open Pack"?

A. less than 1 tenth
B. 1 - 3 tenths
⚓ C. 4 - 6 tenths
D. 7 - 8 tenths

011743/DG01658   **BOWD**

Ice concentration is measured in tenths. What concentration range of ice corresponds to "Close Pack"?

- A. 9-10 tenths
- B. 7-8 tenths
- C. 4-6 tenths
- D. 1-3 tenths

ICE NOMENCLATURE & CHARACTERISTICS

011744/DG00616   **BOWD**

Ice blink is _____.

- A. the dark appearance of the underside of a cloud layer due to reflection of a surface of open water
- B. the soft light appearance on the underside of a cloud layer due to reflection from a surface of open water
- C. the yellowish-white glare on the underside of a cloud layer
- D. water sky

011745/DG01402   **BOWD**

What form of ice is of land origin?

- A. Shuga
- B. Floe
- C. Spicule
- D. Bergy bit

011746/DG01307   **BOWD**

Which type of ice is a hazard to navigation?

- A. Ice rind
- B. Pancake ice
- C. Frazil ice
- D. Growlers

011747/DG02031   **BOWD**

Multi-year ice is the hardest sea ice and should be avoided if possible. It is recognizable because of what tone to its surface color?

- A. Greenish
- B. Bluish
- C. Grey
- D. Grey-white

011748/DG04070   **BOWD**

Small floes of rough, hummocky sea ice capable of damaging a vessel _____.

- A, can usually be detected by radar in a smooth sea at a range of 4 to 6 kilometers
- B. are indistinguishable from sea return on the PPI
- C. are invisible to radar when covered with a thick layer of snow
- D. are usually seen at night before they are close enough to provide a radar echo

011749/DG03048   **BOWD**

The proximity of pack ice may be indicated by _____.

- A. changes in seawater salinity
- B. glare on clouds on the horizon
- C. changes in air temperature
- D. icebergs

011750/DG01622   **BOWD**

What is NOT an indication that pack ice may be nearby?

- A. The presence of icebergs
- B. Ice blink
- C. Absence of wave motion
- D. Sighting a walrus in the Arctic

011751/DG00626   **BOWD**

What should NOT be used as an indicator that ice may be nearby?

- A. A dark appearance of the sky
- B. A gradual drop in sea water temperature to below 32° F
- C. A yellowish glare in the sky
- D. The presence of seals or certain type birds

011752/DG02098   **BOWD**

Snow has obliterated surface features and the sky is covered with uniform, altostratus clouds. There are no shadows and the horizon has disappeared. What is this condition called?

- A. Ice blink
- B. Whiteout
- C. Water sky
- D. Aurora reflection

STABILITY & TRIM FOR ICE OPERATIONS

011753/DG00596   **KNIGHTS; WATCH GUIDE**

Before entering an ice area, the ship should be _____.

- A. either trimmed by the head or the stern
- B. on an even keel
- C. trimmed down by the head
- D. trimmed down by the stern

011754/DG00606   **BOWD**

For operations in pack ice, a vessel should _____.

- A. be on an even keel
- B. be trimmed slightly by the head
- C. have a drag of not more than 2 to 3 feet
- D. be ballasted so the forefoot is near the surface

ICE MANEUVERING

011755/DG01710   **BOWD**
In general, a reinforced vessel can safely navigate in ice provided the concentration does not exceed how many tenths?
A. 1 - 2 tenths
B. 3 - 4 tenths
⚓ C. 5 - 7 tenths
D. 8 - 9 tenths with ice breaker assistance

011756/DG01656   **BOWD**
In general, an un-reinforced vessel can safely navigate in ice provided the concentration does not exceed how many tenths?
A. 9 - 10 tenths
B. 6 - 8 tenths
C. 4 - 6 tenths
⚓ D. 1 - 3 tenths

011757/DG02015   **BOWD**
During a period of "whiteout", you should expect which of the following?
A. Snowfall or blowing snow
⚓ B. Lack of ability to estimate distance
C. Harsh contrast between sun-illuminated snow cover and the background
D. Hazy horizons with extensive mirage effects

011758/DG02091   **BOWD**
When operating in an area where sea ice and icebergs are present, which statement is TRUE?
⚓ A. Icebergs may travel in a direction many degrees different from the sea ice.
B. Both icebergs and sea ice will move in approximately the same direction and at the same speed.
C. Icebergs and sea ice will move in the same direction, but at different speeds due to the sail effect of the berg.
D. Icebergs and sea ice will move in the same direction, but the iceberg will move slower because of its underwater bulk.

011759/DG01442   **BOWD**
You are on an ice-reinforced vessel about to enter pack ice. You should _____.
A. enter the pack on the windward side where there is a well defined ice edge
B. trim to an even keel or slightly down by the bow to take maximum benefit of the ice reinforcement
C. take maximum advantage of coastal leads caused by offshore winds
⚓ D. look for areas of rotten ice and enter perpendicular to the ice edge

011760/DG02060   **BOWD**
In polar regions you should NOT expect to see _____.
A. mirage effects
B. sea smoke
⚓ C. extensive snowfall
D. false horizons

011761/DG01537   **BOWD**
Which is NOT a potential hazard of approaching close to an iceberg?
⚓ A. The brash ice in the vicinity may clog sea intakes.
B. The berg may calve with the bergy bit hitting the vessel.
C. There may be underwater rams extending out from the berg.
D. The berg may suddenly tilt or capsize due to uneven melting and hit the vessel.

MANEUVERING IN SHALLOW & INLAND WATER

MANEUVERING IN RIVERS

011762/DG00866   **CHAPMAN**
For the deepest water when rounding a bend in a river, you should navigate your vessel _____.
A. toward the inside of the bend
⚓ B. toward the outside of the bend
C. toward the center of the river just before the bend, then change course for the river's center after the bend
D. in the river's center

011763/DG00836   **CHAPMAN**
River currents tend to _____.
A. pick up speed where the channel widens
B. run slower in the center of the channel
C. hug the inside of a bend
⚓ D. cause the greatest depth of water to be along the outside of a bend

011764/DG00916   **CHAPMAN**
A condition where two currents meet at the downstream end of a middle bar can be determined by a _____.
A. small whirlpool
B. smooth patch of water
⚓ C. V-shaped ripple with the point of the V pointing downstream
D. V-shaped ripple with the point of the V pointing upstream

011765/DG00906   **CHAPMAN**
A snag or other underwater obstruction may form a
_____ .

⚓ A. V-shaped ripple with the point of the V pointing
     upstream
   B. V-shaped ripple with the point of the V pointing
     downstream
   C. small patch of smooth water on a windy day
   D. smoothing out of the vessel's wake

011766/DG00896   **CHAPMAN**
A V-shaped ripple with the point of the V pointing
upstream in a river may indicate a _____ .
   A. submerged rock, not dangerous to navigation
   B. sunken wreck, not dangerous to navigation
⚓ C. towed-under buoy
   D. All of the above

TOWING ASTERN/TOWING ALONGSIDE

TOWING HAWSERS & SEAMANSHIP

011767/DG02301   **BRADY**
In towing, chocks are used to _____.
A. protect the towline from chafing
B. secure the end of the towline on the tug
C. stop off the towline while retrieving it
D. absorb shock loading on the towline

011768/DG03372   **BRADY**
The lead of a tow bridle is usually redirected with a
_____.
A. bollard
B. chock
C. pad eye
D. devil's claw

011769/DG01866   **BRADY**
Chafing gear is used to _____.
A. increase mechanical advantage on a towing
   recovery wheel
B. eliminate yawing of disabled tow
C. protect towlines from wearing down against edges
   of vessel
D. connects towline to trailer eye of disabled tow

011770/DG03330   **BRADY**
When towing astern, chafing gear should NOT be used
on a hawser which is _____.
A. attached to an "H" bitt
B. attached to an automatic towing engine
C. held amidships by a gob rope
D. connected to a swivel

011771/DG03982   **BRADY**
Fairleads perform the same function as _____.
A. deadeyes
B. bollards
C. bitts
D. chocks

011772/DG01548   **BRADY**
What could be used as fairleads on a towed vessel?
A. Chocks
B. Double bitts
C. Roller chocks
D. All of the above

011773/DG01878   **BRADY**
When being towed, a fairlead is a _____.
A. fabricated shape used to change the direction of a
   flexible member of the tow hookup
B. fabricated shape used to secure the tow hookup to
   the towed vessel
C. line connecting the fishplate to the bridle legs
D. line connecting the tow bridle to the towed vessel

011774/DG00527   **BRADY**
What equipment is NOT used to protect a towing
hawser?
A. Hawser boards and chafing gear
B. Halyards and snaphooks
C. Seizing wire, rope yarn and marline
D. Norman pins and tow spans

011775/DG03390   **BRADY**
When towing, a tow hook is used to _____.
A. provide quick release of the hawser
B. pull a tow alongside
C. attach a hawser to a tow which has no bitts or pad
   eyes
D. join two hawsers for lengthening a tow

011776/DG03360   **BRADY**
On a light tow, what could you substitute for a
fishplate?
A. heart-shaped shackle
B. pelican hook
C. swivel
D. ring

011777/DG01558   **BRADY**
When making up a tow connection, you should use
_____.
A. safety hooks
B. plain eye hooks
C. round pin shackles
D. screw pin shackles

011778/DG03370   **REID; BLANK; BRADY**
In astern towing, a tow span, also called the "tow bar"
or "towing arch", is used to _____.
A. insure that the hawser leads directly aft as it passes
   over the stern of the towing vessel
B. increase the stability of the towing vessel by
   raising the hawser off the deck
C. reduce chafing of the towing hawser
D. prevent fouling of the hawser on deck gear located
   on the stern of the towing vessel

011779/DG00553   **BRADY**
A bridle for an ocean tow consists of _____.
A. two chains of equal length
B. a single nylon pendant rove through a heavy ring
   free to move on the pendant
C. two long legs of wire rope shackled to a fishplate
D. a single length of heavy chain with both ends
   secured on deck to welded pad eyes

011780/DG00573   **BRADY**

An ocean towing bridle whose legs are of equal length, but too short, may _____.

A. put excessive strain on each leg

B. cause unequal distribution of the load to one leg

C. cause the bridle legs to jump clear of the chocks or fairleads

D. None of the above

011781/DG01888   **BRADY**

How many legs does the bridle for an ocean tow have?

A. One

B. Two

C. Three

D. Four

011782/DG01868   **BRADY**

When being towed by one tug, the towing bridle should be connected to towing _____.

A. bitts with figure eights

B. pad eyes with pelican hooks

C. pad eyes with safety hooks

D. All of the above

011783/DG00583   **BRADY**

Which factor(s) must you consider when making up a towing bridle?

A. The horsepower of the tug

B. The beam of the barge

C. The weight of the tow

D. All of the above

011784/DG00552   **BRADY**

Which type of bridle is the most effective for a heavy ocean tow?

A. Nylon because of its strength

B. Polypropylene because it floats and is easier to handle

C. Stud link anchor chain for chafe resistance and strength

D. Wire rope for flexibility and strength

011785/DG00570   **BRADY**

A chain bridle is preferable to a wire rope towing bridle on a long ocean tow because chain _____.

A. is more flexible and has the ability to absorb shock because of its weight

B. is less subject to wear and damage from abrasion

C. requires little maintenance

D. All of the above

011786/DG00555   **BRADY**

A chain bridle is used when towing astern because it _____.

A. is easy to connect

B. provides an effective catenary and absorbs shock due to its weight

C. makes rigging a swivel unnecessary

D. prevents the tow from yawing by the drag of the chains in a seaway

011787/DG00547   **BRADY**

Where is a surge line placed in the towing hookup?

A. Connected between the main towing hawser and the towing bridle

B. Connected between the "H" towing bitts and the main towing hawser

C. End of line fastened directly to the drum of the towing winch

D. As both legs of the towing bridle

011788/DG00580   **BRADY**

Which statement is FALSE about using a wire bridle on an ocean tow?

A. The inboard end of each bridle leg should have a large eye splice to fit over the bitts.

B. The strength of each leg should be at least one-half that of the main towing hawser.

C. Each leg should be at least 60 to 90 feet long.

D. None of the above

011789/DG01806   **BRADY**

If the situation arose where it became necessary to tow a disabled vessel, which statement is TRUE concerning the towing line?

A. The towing line between the two vessels should be clear of the water.

B. The towing line should be taut at all times between the vessels.

C. There should be a catenary so the line dips into the water.

D. None of the above

011790/DG00525   **BRADY**

To lay out a towing hawser in a fore-and-aft direction so each bight is clear and can run out freely without snagging describes _____.

A. flemishing

B. faking

C. spooling

D. worming, parceling and serving

011791/DG00593   **BRADY**

To lead the towing hawser over the center of the stern when not under a strain you could _____.

A. fairlead it through a stern roller chock

B. lead it through the Norman pins

C. hold it in the median position by a gob rope

D. All of the above when so equipped

011792/DG01867   **BRADY**

To overcome the effects of static forces between two vessels of vastly different tonnages that may potentially part a line, you should _____.

A. rig a bridle at both the bow of the disabled vessel and stern of the towing vessel

⚓ B. commence tow at a slow bell and increase speed incrementally

C. pay out extra towline and increase speed rapidly to "jump start" disabled vessel

D. at slow bell alter course 30 degrees to both side of disabled tow

011793/DG00772   **BRADY**

To reduce stress on the towing hawser when towing astern (ocean tow), the hawser should be _____.

A. secured to the aftermost fitting on the towing vessel

B. just touching the water

⚓ C. underwater

D. as short as possible

011794/DG00603   **BRADY**

To reduce the amount of catenary you may _____.

⚓ A. shorten the hawser or increase the tug's speed

B. lengthen the hawser or reduce the tug's speed

C. place your tug in irons

D. make a sharp turn

011795/DG00493   **BRADY**

What does "end for end" mean in regard to a towing hawser?

A. To take the kinks out of the hawser

B. To fake it down in figure eights

C. To increase the catenary

⚓ D. To swap ends of the hawser to minimize wear

011796/DG00512   **BRADY**

When paying out nylon line from around the bitts _____.

⚓ A. stand clear of the bits and use two or more round turns under your figure eights

B. you can surge the line even with a single turn

C. no extra turns are necessary since nylon has a high coefficient of friction

D. stand in the bight of the line

011797/DG01528   **BRADY**

You are being towed by one tug. As you lengthen the bridle legs you _____.

A. increase your chances of breaking the towing hawser

⚓ B. reduce the yawing of your vessel

C. reduce the spring effect of the tow connection

D. increase your chances of breaking the bridle legs

011798/DG01837   **AMSM**

A "skiff hook" is a device used to _____

A. shorten the length of catenary in the towline

⚓ B. attach a towline to the eye bolt to the bow of a trailer-able boat

C. to create a temporary fairlead

D. join a towline to a pair of towing bridles

011799/DG01538   **BRADY**

Your vessel is being towed and you are using a tripping rope. A tripping rope of fiber or wire is used to _____.

A. give added strength to the main tow hawser

B. retrieve the main tow hawser

⚓ C. retrieve the outboard legs of the bridle where they are connected to the fishplate

D. open the pelican hook at the fishplate

011800/DG01898   **BRADY**

Back-up wires on a towed vessel provide _____.

A. a factor of safety

B. additional strength

C. a distribution of the towing load

⚓ D. All of the above

011801/DG01518   **BRADY**

Your vessel is being towed and back-up wires have been installed. Back-up wires carry the towing load in the event that the _____.

A. bridle legs part

⚓ B. towing bitt or pad eye fails

C. bight ring fails

D. main towing hawser parts

011802/DG00550   ***33 CFR 164.74 (b) (1); BRADY**

If the towing bridle legs are not of equal length _____.

A. excessive strain is placed on the shorter leg

B. the shorter leg may fail

C. the longer leg is slack

⚓ D. All of the above

011803/DG00467   ***33 CFR 164.74 (b) (1); BRADY**

Of which type of material may a towing hawser be constructed?

A. Wire rope

B. Nylon

C. Polyester

⚓ D. All of the above

011804/DG00483   **BRADY**

A towing hawser is readied for service by _____.

A. spooling it on a winch cathead

B. coiling it in a counterclockwise direction on the fantail

⚓ C. faking it on deck in a fore and aft direction

D. spooling it on a reel lying on its side to prevent rolling

011805/DG03684   **BRADY**
In towing, heaving lines are used for _____.
A. passing a tow bridle to the tug
B. passing a messenger line
C. heaving in the tow bridle
D. service lines with rocket line throwers

011806/DG03340   **BRADY**
It is NOT advisable to use nylon for alongside towing because it _____.
A. stretches too much
B. is too difficult to make fast
C. parts too readily
D. is too susceptible to mildew

011807/DG03350   **BRADY**
It is not advisable to use nylon for alongside towing because it _____.
A. stretches too much
B. is too expensive for everyday towing usage
C. binds on the cleats
D. parts too readily

011808/DG01448   **BRADY**
Nylon line is better suited than manila for _____.
A. towing alongside
B. towing astern
C. holding knots and splices
D. resisting damage from chemicals

011809/DG03494   **TUGS, TOWBOATS & TOWING**
Nylon rope is often used in the makeup of a towline because it _____.
A. floats
B. stretches
C. handles easily
D. resists rot

011810/DG01919   **CHAPMAN**
The disadvantage of using three strand nylon line for towing is its _____.
A. inherent weakness
B. tendency to rot if left damp
C. danger to crew if it parts
D. strength and shock absorbing abilities

011811/DG03960   **BRADY**
The line with the most stretch is _____.
A. manila
B. nylon
C. polypropylene
D. dacron

011812/DG03248   **BRADY**
The rope which is the lightest is _____.
A. manila
B. nylon
C. polypropylene
D. dacron

011813/DG00503   **BRADY**
Which statement is FALSE?
A. Nylon can stretch approximately 40% and still recover.
B. Only nylon stoppers should be used on nylon hawsers.
C. Nylon is most practical for use on hip towing.
D. With proper care nylon hawsers will greatly outlast manila and other natural fibers.

011814/DG00497   **BRADY**
Which type of towing hawser is preferred for towing astern?
A. Manila
B. Polypropylene
C. Nylon
D. Polyester

011815/DG00470   **BRADY**
A towing hawser should be stowed _____.
A. in a sealed locker with adequate air circulation
B. by spooling it on the winch
C. by faking on a rack
D. by hanging it in the engineroom

011816/DG00462   **BRADY**
The safe working load (SWL) of wire rope with a safety factor of 6 is what percent of its strength?
A. 10%
B. 17%
C. 50%
D. 80%

011817/DG00515   **BRADY**
What is NOT an advantage of a wire towing hawser?
A. Easy to handle when properly spooled on the drum of a towing winch.
B. Has more spring and shock resistance than synthetic.
C. Can be used to tow heavier loads because of its smaller diameter and more manageable size.
D. Subject to less deterioration than synthetic if properly maintained.

011818/DG00513   **BRADY**
Wire rope is used in the towing industry _____.
A. for back up wires and main towing hawsers
B. for face wires or jockeys when pushing ahead
C. as stern wires when pushing ahead
D. All of the above

PRINCIPLES OF TOWING

011819/DG01882   **BRADY**
Which effects listed below does NOT influence stability of a towing vessel?
A. Free surface
B. Load heights
C. Towline length
D. Ice

011820/DG00472   **BRADY**
On a long ocean tow, the bridle should be made up of two equal lengths of _____.
A. chain
B. wire
C. nylon
D. polyester

011821/DG01988   **BRADY**
When towing, what is the main reason for using a chain bridle on a wire hawser?
A. It makes for an easy connection.
B. It gives a spring effect to cushion the shock.
C. It eliminates the necessity of a swivel.
D. It does not chafe.

011822/DG01978   **BRADY**
When towing, the least amount of tension will be on each bridle leg when the two legs _____.
A. form a large angle with each other
B. form a small angle with each other
C. are of unequal length
D. are joined by a fishplate

011823/DG00465   **BRADY**
Which structural members improve a towing vessel's chance of surviving punctured shell plating?
A. Stringers
B. Longitudinals
C. Transverse watertight bulkheads
D. The rake

011824/DG00637   **BRADY**
A tow bridle is attached to the main tow hawser at the _____.
A. bight ring
B. tow hook
C. fishplate
D. swivel

011825/DG00540   **BRADY**
As seen from the tow, what should connect the leading ends of both towing bridle legs to the main towing hawser?
A. A cable clamp
B. A fishplate, flounder, or towing plate
C. A pad eye
D. The towing bitts

011826/DG03400   **BRADY; BLANK; REID**
In a tow made up astern, the fishplate _____.
A. connects the hawser to the bridle
B. connects the bridle to the tow
C. keeps the hawser amidships on the tug
D. is the capping piece on the "H" bitt

011827/DG00542   **BRADY**
Which best describes a "fishplate" used in towing?
A. A triangular-shaped heavy steel plate with a round hole inset from each corner
B. A steel plate in the shape of a flat fish
C. A rectangular-shaped piece of heavy steel plate with four holes
D. A circular piece of heavy steel with three holes forming an equilateral triangle

011828/DG00543   **BRADY**
You would be most likely to use a fishplate _____.
A. when towing alongside
B. on a hawser tow
C. when pushing ahead or in the notch
D. when running "light boat"

011829/DG03091   **CHAPMAN**
Towlines should be inspected for chafing where the towline _____.
A. passes over the stern of the towing vessel
B. passes through chocks
C. is attached to the disabled vessel
D. All of the above

011830/DG04049   **BRADY**
Tugs sometimes shackle a length of chain in the towline in order to _____.
A, take the wear should the towline drag bottom
B. assure that if the towline is overstressed it will part close to the bridle
C. prevent the towline from whipping should it part
D. put spring in the towline

011831/DG01488   **KNIGHTS**
What does the term "end-for-end" refer to in regard to a wire towing hawser?
A. Cutting off the bitter and towing ends of the wire rope
B. Splicing two wire ropes together
C. Removing the wire rope from the drum and reversing it so that the towing end becomes the bitter end
D. Removing the wire rope from the drum and turning it over so that the wire bends in the opposite direction when rolled on a drum

011832/DG00453   **BRADY**
What purpose does a tow hook serve?
⚓ A. To quickly connect or release the towing hawser
B. To help pick up the towing hawser from the water
C. To prevent the towing hawser from fouling the propeller
D. To recover the towing hawser from a barge

011833/DG00461   **BRADY**
Where is the best location to install a towing hook?
A. Forward of the towing bitts
B. On the fantail
C. Near the Norman Pins
⚓ D. Just aft of amidships

011834/DG04378   **BRADY**
Which statement concerning an automatic towing engine is FALSE?
A, It automatically maintains tow line tension.
B. It prolongs the life of the hawser by distributing chafing as the hawser is paid out and taken in.
⚓ C. As tension on the hawser increases, more line is taken in by the automatic towing engine.
D. As tension on the hawser decreases, more line is taken in by the automatic towing engine.

011835/DG00207   **BRADY**
A towing vessel's capability is BEST measured by horsepower, maneuverability, displacement, and _____.
A. stability
B. propeller design
⚓ C. bollard pull
D. towing winch horsepower

011836/DG00435   **BRADY**
The amount of force a tug can exert on a stationary pull is called its _____.
A. brake horsepower
B. indicated horsepower
C. shaft horsepower
⚓ D. bollard pull

011837/DG00177   **BRADY**
The measurement of the amount of force a towing vessel is capable of applying to a motionless tow is called _____.
A. shaft horsepower
B. delivered horsepower
⚓ C. bollard pull
D. towrope pull

011838/DG00464   **BRADY**
The static bollard pull of a tug is measured in tons and consists of the brake horsepower of the tug's engine divided by 100 and multiplied by a factor of _____.
A. 0.5
⚓ B. 1.3
C. 3.0
D. 10

011839/DG03218   **BRADY**
The term "bollard pull" refers to a towing vessel's _____.
A. propulsion horsepower available
B. pulling ability at cruise power
C. towing winch capability
⚓ D. pulling ability under static conditions

011840/DG01052   **REID**
A term used to describe the dip in a towline that acts as a shock absorber is _____.
⚓ A. catenary
B. step
C. shock dip
D. bight

011841/DG01615   **CHAPMAN**
A towing vessel should be on the crest of a wave at the same time as its tow and in the trough at the same time. The term used to describe this is _____.
A. tow strain
B. catenary length
⚓ C. being in step
D. Williamson's Tow

011842/DG03309   **BRADY**
Catenary as applied to tow lines denotes the _____.
⚓ A. dip of the line
B. stretch of the line
C. strain on the line
D. length of the line

011843/DG01805   **BRADY**
In towing it is desirable for the tug and the tow to ride wave crests simultaneously because _____.
⚓ A. shock loading on the tow line is reduced
B. towing speed is improved
C. the tow is more visible from the tug
D. the catenary of the towline is reduced

011844/DG03742   **BRADY**
It is good practice to use long towlines for ocean tows because the _____.
A. wear on the towline is equalized
B. weight of the towline increases the towing force
⚓ C. dip in the towline absorbs shock loads
D. danger of overriding is reduced

011845/DG00892   **BRADY**
On a shallow water tow, the catenary of the towline should be _____.
A. large
⚓ B. small
C. eliminated
D. adjusted frequently

011846/DG00665   **BRADY**
The catenary _____.
A. acts as a reserve length of towing hawser when the tug applies more power, and it dampens the surge effect of the tow
B. gives an approximation of the amount of strain on the towing hawser
C. is the dip in the towing hawser between the tug and the tow
⚓ D. All of the above

011847/DG01458   **BRADY**
The catenary in a towline is _____.
A. a short bridle
⚓ B. the downward curvature of the hawser
C. another name for a pelican hook
D. used to hold it amidships

011848/DG00693   **BRADY**
The effect of excessive catenary in shallow water may be _____.
A. dragging the towing hawser along the bottom and chafing it
B. snagging sunken or submerged objects
C. slowing, stopping or endangering the towing operation by placing the tug in irons
⚓ D. All of the above

011849/DG01948   **TUGS, TOWBOATS & TOWING**
The Honolulu (Christmas tree) tow was devised to _____.
⚓ A. keep the catenary to a minimum
B. allow easy removal of a center tow
C. reduce hawser length
D. increase the catenary

011850/DG03728   **BRADY**
The main reason a long towline is used during an ocean tow is that _____.
A. a margin of safety is provided should the line part
B. the towline will wear more evenly
⚓ C. there will be less stress on the towline
D. a slight increase in speed will be realized

011851/DG00692   **BRADY**
The tow makeup that is designed to keep the catenary of the tow hawser to a minimum is called the _____.
⚓ A. Christmas tree tow
B. tandem tow
C. British tow
D. tandem tug tow

011852/DG01478   **CHAPMAN; MMOH**
What does "in step" refer to in regards to towing?
A. The towed vessel follows exactly in the wake of the towing vessel.
B. There is no catenary in the towing hawser.
C. When turning, both the towed and towing vessels turn at the same time.
⚓ D. Both the towed and towing vessels reach a wave crest or trough at the same time.

011853/DG04040   **KNIGHTS**
When towing another vessel astern, the length of the towline should be _____.
A. as long as possible
B. such that one vessel will be on a crest while the other is in a trough
⚓ C. such that the vessels will be "in step"
D. not over two wave lengths in seas up to 10 feet

011854/DG02008   **KNIGHTS**
When towing another vessel, the length of the towing line should be _____.
A. as long as possible
B. as short as possible under the circumstances and not over two wave lengths
C. such that one vessel will be on a crest while the other is in a trough
⚓ D. such that the vessels will be in step

011855/DG01908   **BRADY**
When towing astern, increased catenary will _____.
A. increase control of the tow
B. prevent the towing vessel from going in irons
C. make the towing vessel less maneuverable
⚓ D. reduce shock stress on the towing hawser

011856/DG01998   **KNIGHTS**
When towing in an open seaway, it is important to use a towing line _____.
A. made only of wire rope, due to possible weather conditions
B. that will have the tow on a crest while your vessel is in a trough
⚓ C. that will have the tow on a crest while your vessel is on a crest
D. with little dip to gain maximum control of the tow

011857/DG01918　　　　　　　　**BRADY**
Which statement is TRUE concerning hawser towing?
A.　The catenary in a hawser should be sufficient so that the hawser just touches the bottom.
B.　The hawser is of sufficient length for towing when taut between tug and tow.
C.　Increasing speed usually increases the catenary in the hawser.
⚓ D.　Shortening the tow hawser generally decreases the maneuverability of the tug.

011858/DG00533　　　　　　　　**BRADY**
A towing hook may be released from the _____.
A.　tug's engineroom or the bow
⚓ B.　pilot house or aft steering station
C.　forecastle
D.　towing bitts by reaching over and releasing a lever

011859/DG03016　　　　　　　　**BRADY**
To obtain better steering control when you are towing alongside, your vessel should be positioned with its _____.
A.　bow extending forward of the tow
B.　stern amidships of the tow
⚓ C.　stern extending aft of the tow
D.　bow even with the bow of the tow

011860/DG03109　　　　　　　　**BRADY**
When hip towing, a line led from the bow of the towing vessel aft to the vessel being towed would be a _____.
A.　backing line
⚓ B.　towing line
C.　stern line
D.　breast line

011861/DG03102　　　　　　　　**BRADY**
When hip towing, a line led from the stern of the towboat forward to the barge provides the towing pull when _____.
A.　going ahead
B.　dead in the water
C.　in a following current
⚓ D.　backing

011862/DG03074　　　　　　　　**BRADY**
In securing a towing cable, consideration must be given to letting go in an emergency. The possible whip of towlines when released can be overcome by _____.
A.　increasing the shaft RPM prior to release
B.　using a pelican hook for quick release
⚓ C.　using preventers
D.　using a short chain for the lead through the stern chock

011863/DG00539　　　　　　　　**BRADY**
Which type of shackle is used for most towing connections?
⚓ A.　Safety shackles
B.　Round pin anchor shackles
C.　Screw pin shackles
D.　Heart shaped shackles

011864/DG01938　　　　　　　　**BRADY**
Towing a structure using two tugs approximately side by side, each using one hawser, is referred to as a _____.
A.　tandem tow
B.　Honolulu tow
⚓ C.　breasted tug tow
D.　tandem tug tow

011865/DG01958　　　　　　　　**BRADY**
When tandem tug towing, the more powerful of the two tugs should be _____.
A.　the lead tug
⚓ B.　behind the lead tug
C.　towing at a right angle to the smaller tug
D.　towing at a faster speed than the smaller tug

011866/DG01215　　　　　　　　**BRADY**
What is an advantage in the use of a towing hook?
A.　To prevent the tug from becoming tripped
B.　To quickly connect or release a tow, especially a sinking tow
C.　To facilitate berthing maneuvers
⚓ D.　All of the above

011867/DG00683　　　　　　　　**BRADY**
Barges and vessels are ballasted before departure to _____.
⚓ A.　improve their stability
B.　avoid polluting waters where liquid ballast may not be discharged
C.　prevent free surface effects
D.　allow movement of liquids within the barge for tank cleaning

011868/DG01468　　　　　　　　**BRADY**
What will NOT reduce yawing of a tow?
A.　Increasing the length of the towing hawser
B.　Trimming the tow by the stern
⚓ C.　Stowing deck loads forward
D.　Drogues put over the stern

011869/DG00433　　　　　　　　**BRADY**
When a tow is trimmed by the stern it is said to _____.
A.　hog
B.　sag
⚓ C.　drag
D.　list

011870/DG00685   **BRADY**
Which type of ballast is most commonly used in barges and ships?
⚓ A. Water
B. Oil
C. Concrete and barite
D. Sand, rock and gravel

011871/DG03013   **BRADY**
Which will NOT reduce yawing of a tow?
A. Increasing the length of the towing hawser
⚓ B. Trimming the tow by the bow
C. Trimming the tow by the stern
D. Drogues put over the stern

011872/DG02783   **KNIGHTS**
The effect of ocean current is usually more evident on a tug and tow than on a tug navigating independently because the _____.
⚓ A. speed of the tug and tow is less
B. towline catches the current
C. current causes yawing
D. current will offset the tow

011873/DG00667   **BRADY**
While towing in shallow water you should consider _____.
A. using a short towing hawser
B. using a floating hawser
C. the catenary and the effect it may have on the tow
⚓ D. All of the above

011874/DG03142   **BRADY**
Why are stern towing bitts placed well forward of the rudder when hawser towing?
A. To keep the hawser from fouling the rudder
B. To keep the towing bitts as far away as possible from the tugs pivoting point
⚓ C. To allow the stern to swing more freely when using rudder
D. To have as much of the towing hawser in use as possible

011875/DG03518   **BRADY**
A tug's horsepower available at the shaft is _____.
A. indicated horsepower
⚓ B. brake horsepower
C. dynamic horsepower
D. net horsepower

011876/DG03583   **BRADY**
Indicated horsepower refers to a towing vessel's power which is _____.
⚓ A. theoretically available
B. measured on a test bed
C. developed at the shaft
D. measured by dynamometer

011877/DG03104   **BRADY**
When maneuvering a heavy barge up a wide channel with a tug, the tow may be most closely controlled by making up to the barge _____.
A. with a short tow astern
B. nearly bow to bow, at a small angle
C. amidships, parallel to the barge
⚓ D. nearly stern to stern, at a small angle to the barge

011878/DG03044   **BRADY**
When you have a tow alongside, your stern should extend aft of the tow in order to _____.
A. avoid obscuring your stern light
B. provide a better lead for your lines
⚓ C. obtain better steering control
D. let the barge deflect floating objects from your propeller

011879/DG01313   **BRADY**
Where should a vessel being towed alongside be positioned for increased maneuverability?
A. Stern of the towed vessel aft of the stern of the towing vessel
B. Stern of the towed vessel even with the stern of the towing vessel
⚓ C. Stern of the towed vessel forward of the stern of the towing vessel
D. Bow of the towed vessel even with the bow of the towing vessel

011880/DG01928   **BRADY**
Which towing method maintains the most control over the tow?
A. Tandem towing
B. Honolulu towing
C. Tandem tug towing
⚓ D. Breasted tug towing

011881/DG00647   **BRADY**
Synchronous towing means that the _____.
A. tug is on the crest of a wave while the tow is in the trough
B. tug is in the trough while the tow is riding on the crest of a wave
⚓ C. tug and tow are both in the same relative position on different waves at the same time
D. port and starboard engines on the tug are turning at the same RPM

011882/DG02954   **BRADY**
An intermediate spring is _____.
A. fitted in each leg of the towing bridle
⚓ B. generally located between the "fishplate" and the main towing hawser
C. secured at the "H" bitts
D. usually made of manila hawser

011883/DG03112   **BRADY**

A tug is to assist in docking an oceangoing vessel on a hawser. The greatest danger to the tug is _____.
A. from the ship's propeller when making up aft
B. from being overrun if making up forward
C. hull damage while alongside passing a hawser
⚓ D. getting in a tripping position

011884/DG00737   **BRADY**

A heavy steel curved arch constructed athwartships and above the after deck on a towing vessel is sometimes called a _____.
A. chafing bar
⚓ B. Dutch tow bar
C. carling
D. None of the above

011885/DG00447   **BRADY**

One reason a tug's towing bitts are located forward of the rudders is because _____.
A. it makes it easier to hook up the towing hawser
B. this is where the towhook is located
⚓ C. this allows more responsive steering
D. it is traditional

011886/DG00445   **BRADY**

Where are the towing bitts best placed for towing purposes?
A. Near the centerline and over the rudders
B. On each side of the vessel near the stern
⚓ C. Forward of the rudder post and close to the tug's center of pivot
D. As far aft as possible

011887/DG00452   **BRADY**

Where should the foundation supports for towing bitts terminate?
A. Forward of the towing winch
⚓ B. In the frames or other substantial structural members below decks
C. On the deck plates in the engineroom
D. On deck, aft of the towing winch

011888/DG00735   **BRADY**

A heavy steel curved arch constructed athwartships and above the after deck on a towing vessel is sometimes called a _____.
A. main brace
⚓ B. texas bar
C. jockey bar
D. None of the above

011889/DG00463   **BRADY**

A texas bar _____.
A. prevents the towing hawser from snagging any equipment or gear on deck
B. may be equipped with a greased, free sliding spool to fairlead the towing hawser
C. allows the crew access to the fantail
⚓ D. All of the above

TOWING SAFETY

011890/DG00233   **CHAPMAN**

A vessel brought alongside should be fended off the towing vessel by _____.
A. crew members using their arms
B. a boat hook
⚓ C. fenders
D. No fending is necessary due to the rugged construction of most towing vessels.

011891/DG01395   **CHAPMAN**

A vessel brought alongside should be fended off the towing vessel by _____.
A. crew members using their arms
B. a boat hook
⚓ C. fenders
D. No fending is necessary due to the rugged construction of most towing vessels.

011892/DG01191   **BRADY**

Which statement is TRUE about the use of a "gob rope"?
A. The gob rope is a mooring line for tying up lighters for working cargo alongside a vessel anchored in an open roadstead.
⚓ B. The gob rope is used to secure the towline aft over the centerline of a tug..
C. The gob rope is a line hung over a vessel's side to assist in boarding.
D. The gob rope is a rope used in mooring a vessel to a buoy.

011893/DG01183   **BRADY**

Which towing equipment can be used to prevent the tripping of a tug?
A. Bridles
B. Chafing boards
⚓ C. Gob ropes
D. Drogues

011894/DG00227   **BRADY**

An ocean towing bridle should _____.
⚓ A. have equal legs of sufficient length
B. have a large angle between the legs
C. be formed on a bight of cable through a ring
D. never be made up of chain

011895/DG02292   **BRADY**
The biggest problem encountered when towing bridle legs are too short is _____.
A. retrieval
B. adjusting tension
⚓ C. excessive strain
D. hookup to main towline

011896/DG03556   **BRADY**
The choice of length of tow bridle legs is governed by the _____.
A. expected towing forces
B. capability of retrieving gear
C. freeboard of the unit being towed
⚓ D. need to reduce yaw

011897/DG02704   **BRADY**
The legs of a tow bridle are joined together with a _____.
A. bridle plate
B. shackle
⚓ C. fishplate
D. tri-link

011898/DG02048   **BRADY**
The MINIMUM acceptable size for a towing bridle would be that size in which the safe working load (SWL) of each leg of the bridle is equal to _____.
A. one-half the SWL of the main towing hawser
B. three-fourths the SWL of the main towing hawser
⚓ C. that of the main towing hawser
D. twice that of the main towing hawser

011999/DG02058   **BRADY**
What is NOT suitable for use in making up the towing rig for a heavy, long ocean tow?
A. Chain
⚓ B. Ring
C. Solid thimble
D. A fishplate

011900/DG04009   **BRADY**
What is used to prevent twisting of a towing bridle?
A, A bitt
B. A bulkhead
C. A V-spring
⚓ D. A fishplate

011901/DG03338   **BRADY**
What is used to prevent wear on towlines that bear on hard surfaces?
⚓ A. Chafing gear
B. Chocks
C. Grease
D. Boots

011902/DG02078   **BRADY**
While towing, bridle legs of unequal lengths may cause _____.
A. the bridle to foul
⚓ B. the shorter leg to fail
C. chafing on the fairlead or bitts
D. a bent swivel

011903/DG03521   **NICHOLLS; CHAPMAN**
Once a towline is connected between the towing vessel and the disabled vessel, the towing vessel should _____.
A. not exceed bare steerageway during the transit
B. take a strain as soon as you can to control the tow
⚓ C. come up to speed very slowly and maintain a "safe speed"
D. come up to speed quickly, then cut back power considerably to ease the strain

011904/DG03447   **KNIGHTS**
The best method to secure a tow line to a cleat is to _____.
⚓ A. take a turn around the cleat, then figure-eights, and a half-hitch
B. make figure-eights, followed by a half-hitch, then a figure-eight knot
C. take a turn, a half turn, and a figure-eight
D. take several turns around the cleat only

011905/DG03162   **BRADY**
When maneuvering from pull towing to breasted (alongside) towing, a twin-screw vessel is more likely than a single-screw vessel of equal horsepower to _____.
A. trip or capsize
⚓ B. foul the towline
C. go into irons
D. part the towing strap

011906/DG00689   **BRADY**
When your tug reduces speed to shorten tow, the _____.
A. length of the tow gets shorter as the strain is reduced
B. tow may continue its momentum and overtake the tug
C. towing hawser may drag the bottom and put the tug in irons
⚓ D. All of the above

011907/DG01508   **BRADY**
While towing, sudden shock-loading caused during heavy weather can be reduced by _____.
A. using a short tow hawser
B. using a nonelastic type hawser
⚓ C. using a heavier hawser
D. decreasing the catenary in the hawser

011908/DG02088   **BRADY**
You have been towing astern and have just let go the tow. Your deckhands are pulling in and faking the towline by hand on the stern. The most dangerous action to take is to _____.
A. continue ahead at slow speed
B. continue ahead at half speed
C. stop your engines
⚓ D. back down on your engines

011909/DG02533   **AMSM**
You should attach a towline to a trailer eye bolt using a(n) _____.
A. eye splice
⚓ B. bowline
C. towing hitch
D. square knot

011910/DG02028   **BRADY**
When making up a long, large coastwise tow, which of the following procedures is INCORRECT?
A. A chain towing bridle is generally preferred
B. Safety shackles should be used when connecting to the fishplate
C. Rig tripping ropes (retrieving lines)
⚓ D. Back-up wires are left slack

011911/DG00675   **BRADY**
An advantage of the modified Christmas Tree towing method is to _____.
A. increase the towing hawser's catenary and provide more spring
⚓ B. reduce catenary, allow operation in shallower water, and to release one barge without breaking up the entire tow
C. enable one tug and its crew without any outside assistance to make up or break down the tow
D. provide rapid delivery of logs from the northwestern United States to Hawaiian sawmills

011912/DG00847   **BRADY**
When towing astern what equipment should be stowed ready for use near the towline?
A. First aid kit
⚓ B. Axe or cutting torch
C. Fire extinguisher
D. Chafing gear

011913/DG00723   **BRADY**
What safety precautions must you take when maneuvering on a towing hook?
A. The engines must be operated on the slow bell.
⚓ B. Clear the afterdeck and fantail of personnel.
C. Lash the hook closed so it does not open accidentally.
D. The towing winch engine must be running.

011914/DG00733   **BRADY**
Before leaving port on an ocean tow, a tug captain should assure himself of all the following EXCEPT _____.
A. the towing hawser can be released quickly in an emergency
B. the correct navigation lights are rigged and operable on the tug and tow
⚓ C. an insurance underwriter has prepared a pre-sailing survey
D. a pick-up wire has been rigged on the tow in case of a breakaway.

011915/DG00655   **BRADY**
Good seamanship while towing in heavy weather requires all of the following EXCEPT _____.
A. reducing speed to reduce surging on the towline
B. lashing down or stowing all loose gear
C. dogging all hatches and watertight doors
⚓ D. streaming all of your towing hawser

011916/DG00937   **BRADY**
When towing astern, you notice that another vessel is about to pass between the towing vessel and the tow. You should immediately _____.
A. turn away from the approaching vessel
B. shine a spotlight in the direction of the approaching vessel
C. sever the towline
⚓ D. slow down and pay out the main tow hawser

011917/DG02038   **BRADY**
With a large ocean tow in heavy weather, you should NOT _____.
A. keep the stern of the tug well down in the water
⚓ B. adjust the towline so the tug is on the crest when the tow is in the trough
C. keep the low point of the catenary in the water
D. use a long towing hawser

011918/DG02591   **BRADY**
A tow astern is veering from side to side on its towline. The best way of controlling the action is to _____.
A. trim the tow by the bow
⚓ B. trim the tow by the stern
C. list the tow to windward
D. adjust the length of the towing bridle

011919/DG00722   **BRADY**
A tow can override its tug as a result of _____.
A. a mechanical breakdown on the tug
B. adverse tidal current conditions
C. the tug reducing its speed
⚓ D. All of the above

011920/DG03616   BRADY; ENCY. NAUT. KNOW.
A tug in irons is _____.
A. rudder bound
B. being tripped by the towline
C. unable to maneuver
D. broached

011921/DG00695   BRADY
A tug is "in irons" when held in a fixed position by _____.
A. the weight of its tow, its being anchored, or grounded
B. the towing hawser snagged on the bottom
C. an adverse current
D. lack of power or an engine breakdown

011922/DG00715   BRADY
The term "overriding" or "overrunning" when applied to towing, implies that _____.
A. there is more crew on board than required
B. the tow has overtaken its tug
C. the towing hawser comes out of the water
D. the Norman pins are not effective

011923/DG00427   BRADY
What is the greatest danger of an overriding tow?
A. Fouling of the towing hawser
B. Loss of steering
C. Tripping
D. Collision between the tow and the stern of the towing vessel

011924/DG03122   BRADY
When a tug is "in irons", she _____.
A. is made fast to the dock with engines secured
B. is in dry dock
C. may be in danger of being overrun by her tow
D. should pay out more towline

011925/DG01717   BRADY
With a large tow astern, there is immediate danger to the tug in the event of the _____.
A. tug losing power
B. tow line parting
C. bridle twisting
D. tow broaching

011926/DG01811   BRADY
You are towing a large barge on a hawser. Your main engine suddenly fails. What is the greatest danger?
A. The tug and the tow will go aground.
B. The tow will endanger other traffic.
C. The tow will overrun tug.
D. The tow will block the channel.

011927/DG01831   BRADY
A "loose" tow may cause all of the following EXCEPT _____.
A. loss of maneuverability
B. lines to part
C. damage to the towing vessel and tow
D. a saving in the transit time

011928/DG00362   BRADY
A towing vessel is tripped when _____.
A. it is overtaken by the tow
B. it is pulled sideways by the tow
C. the weight of the towing hawser causes loss of maneuverability
D. the propeller is fouled by the towing hawser

011929/DG00705   BRADY
A tug may be in danger of tripping when _____.
A. towed sideways by an overwhelming force on the towline
B. her tow moves parallel to and forward on either side of the tug
C. the tow is no longer directly astern but moves up on her quarter
D. All of the above

011930/DG00713   BRADY
How do the height and location of a tug's towing bitts relate to the danger of tripping?
A. The further forward and closer to amidships the more readily the tug will trip.
B. Placement further aft permits more effective pulling, better steering and eliminates the danger of tripping.
C. Installing the bitts down low lowers the center of gravity.
D. The height and position of towing bitts has no significance.

011931/DG00707   BRADY
Is tripping limited to harbor and coastal towing?
A. No. Forces tending to capsize a tug are as dangerous on the high seas as they are in harbor and coastal work.
B. Yes. The long towing hawser used in ocean towing eliminates the danger of tripping.
C. No. Tripping is common in ocean towing because of more frequent maneuvering
D. Yes. Because of increased water depths, forces required to capsize a tug are not usually found in ocean towing

011932/DG03152   **BRADY**

The danger of a towing vessel tripping is increased the closer the towline is secured to _____.
A. the stern
B. amidships
C. the bow
D. the quarter

011933/DG00699   **BRADY**

Under which condition is a tug likely to be tripped?
A. When the tow "jumps" on the line
B. While making up to tow a large oil rig
C. When the towing hawser leads forward of the quarter
D. When the tug exerts maximum bollard pull with the tow close astern

011934/DG00712   **BRADY**

What is the effect of releasing the towline in a tripping situation?
A. It disconnects the capsizing force and allows the tug to recover from its list.
B. It frees the tug from its towing responsibilities.
C. There is no effect other than relief.
D. Yawing

011935/DG01822   **SHIPHAND W/TUGS**

What is the principal danger in attempting to swing a barge on a hawser in order to slow the barge's speed?
A. Dangerous wakes may result from the swinging barge and capsize the tug.
B. The barge may swing too quickly and run over the tug.
C. Free surface effect of liquid inside the barge may rupture the barge bulkheads if the turn is too quick.
D. The barge may pass under the hawser and capsize the tug.

011936/DG03132   **BRADY**

What may prevent a tug from tripping or capsizing when towing a large vessel?
A. Surge lines
B. Norman Pins
C. Under riders
D. Safety shackles

011937/DG01836   **BRADY**

While towing, what is the principal danger in attempting to swing a barge on a hawser in order to slow the barge's speed?
A. The barge may swing too quickly and run over the tug.
B. The barge may pass under the hawser and capsize the tug.
C. Free surface affect of liquid inside the barge may rupture the barge bulkheads when turning too quickly.
D. Dangerous wakes may result from the swinging barge and capsize the tug.

011938/DG01821   **BRADY**

While towing, what is the principal danger in attempting to swing a barge on a short hawser in order to slow the barge's speed?
A. The barge may capsize from the sharp turn.
B. The barge may swing too quickly and run over the tug.
C. Free surface effect of liquid inside the barge may rupture the barge bulkheads when turning too quickly.
D. Dangerous wakes may result from the swinging barge and capsize the tug.

011939/DG03396   **BRADY**

A tow that veers to the side on the end of the towline is said to _____.
A. yaw
B. surge
C. sway
D. swing

011940/DG01498   **BRADY**

The biggest problem you generally encounter while towing a single tow astern is _____.
A. the catenary dragging on the bottom
B. swamping of the tow
C. the tow tending to dive
D. yaw

011941/DG02018   **CHAPMAN**

When towing astern, one way to reduce yawing of the tow is to _____.
A. trim the tow by the stern
B. trim the tow by the head
C. have the tow on an even keel
D. list the tow on the side it is yawing

011942/DG00669 **BRADY**
Which statement describes the motion of a yawing tow?
A. The tow twists, sometimes violently, astern of the tug
B. The tow sheers to one side behind the tug and maintains a position in a line diagonal to the tug's forward movement
C. The tow snakes behind the tug
⚓ D. All of the above

011943/DG02595 **BRADY**
Yawing can be described as _____.
A. jumping on the towline as the tow pitches
B. jumping on the towline as the tow slams into waves
⚓ C. veering from side to side on the end of the towline
D. corkscrew motion of the tow due to wave action

011944/DG02068 **BRADY**
You intend to tow a barge with one tug and expect continuous high winds from the north. To reduce the yaw of your tow, you should _____.
A. reduce the draft of the barge
⚓ B. shorten one leg of the bridle
C. place bulky deck loads as far aft as possible
D. trim the barge down by the bow

011945/DG00895 ***33 CFR 164.74 (a)**
Which factor would NOT lead to removing a towline from service?
A. An excessive number of miles of towing service.
B. Failing a tensile strength test that proved the towline was no longer appropriate for expected sea conditions.
⚓ C. When heavy grease on the towline saturates the core of the wire rope.
D. Its surface condition is noted, including its corrosion and discoloration.

011946/DG00883 ***33 CFR 164.74 (a) (1) (i) (ii) (iv)**
The size and material used for towline(s) must meet all of the following requirements, EXCEPT _____.
A. be appropriate to the vessel's horsepower or bollard pull
B. be strong enough to handle any static or dynamic loads expected during its service life
⚓ C. fit any spare wire clips carried on board the vessel for repair purposes
D. be suitable for exposure to the marine environment

011947/DG00885 ***33 CFR 164.74 (a) (2) (iii)**
How many wire clips must be used to make a temporary repair to a tow wire?
A. 3
B. 4
⚓ C. 5
D. Wire clips are never, under any circumstances, permitted

011948/DG00884 ***33 CFR 164.74 (a) (2) (iii) (ii) (i)**
When towing astern, each towline must meet all of these requirements, EXCEPT _____.
⚓ A. being suitable for use as soon as it is removed from its normal stowage location
B. having wire clips for other than a temporary repair
C. having the end either spliced with a thimble or fitted with a poured socket
D. being free of knots

011949/DG00887 ***33 CFR 164.74 (a) (3) (i) (ii) (iii)**
The condition of a towline must be monitored by _____.
A. keeping record of the towline's initial minimum breaking strength
B. keeping record of each retest of the towline's minimum breaking strength
C. conducting routine visual inspections of the towline
⚓ D. All of the above

011950/DG00882 ***33 CFR 164.74 (a) (3) (i), (a), (c)**
The owner or Master of a towing vessel that tows astern must keep records of the towline(s) that include all of the following information EXCEPT _____.
A. the towline's initial minimum breaking strength as determined by the manufacturer
⚓ B. an invoice showing the cost of the towline
C. the towline's nautical miles of use or time in service
D. the history of loading of the towline

011951/DG00899 ***33 CFR 164.74 (a) (3) (v)**
When must the owner or Master of a towing vessel retest a towline or remove it from service?
⚓ A. When the record of its material condition lapses for 3 months or more.
B. After it jams on the towing winch.
C. After it drags on the bottom.
D. When it has not been used for over 60 days.

011952/DG00905 ***33 CFR 164.74 (a) (3) (iii)**
When should you conduct a visual inspection of your towline?
A. Whenever its serviceability is in doubt.
B. In accordance with the manufacturer's recommendation.
C. At least once a month.
⚓ D. All of the above

011953/DG00889   *33 CFR 164.74 (a) (vi)
The owner or Master of a towing vessel must evaluate whether the entire towline, or a part of it, is no longer serviceable. The towline should be removed from service in all cases EXCEPT _____.
- A. when recommended by the manufacturer or an authorized classification society
- B. in accordance with a replacement schedule
- C. when the vessel is underway
- D. depending on the mileage or time that the towline has been in service

011954/DG00762 CHAPMAN; *33 CFR 164.74 (b) (6) (7)
A towing winch, that handles a wire towline, must have all of the following EXCEPT a _____.
- A. device that evenly spools and tightly winds the towline
- B. brake with holding power appropriate for the vessel's horsepower or bollard pull
- C. brake that can be operated when there is no power available to drive the winch
- D. source of emergency power to operate the winch

011955/DG00759   *33 CFR 164.74 (b)
The equipment used to control, protect and connect a towline is called _____.
- A. cat head
- B. terminal gear
- C. level wind
- D. poured socket

011956/DG00760   *33 CFR 164.74 (b) (2)
The connection to the towline must be secured with a _____.
- A. galvanized screw-pin shackle
- B. hardened steel thimble
- C. shackle secured a nut and cotter pin
- D. shackle fitted with a swivel piece

011957/DG00763   *33 CFR 164.74 (b) (4)
A vessel that tows astern must have a/an _____.
- A. towing winch
- B. method to easily release the towline
- C. oxy-acetylene cutting torch
- D. ax or knife mounted near the towing bitts

011958/DG00897   *33 CFR 164.74 (e), (f), (d)
Which factor(s) might indicate that a towline should be removed from service?
- A. Visible damage to the towline, including fishhooks.
- B. Measurements showing a decrease in diameter.
- C. A surface condition of corrosion and discoloration.
- D. All of the above

011959/DG00765   *33 CFR 164.76
The owner or Master of a vessel pushing ahead or towing alongside must ensure that each of the following is appropriate for the vessel's horsepower and tow arrangement EXCEPT _____.
- A. hydraulic couplings
- B. face wires
- C. push gear
- D. spring lines

011960/DG01876   BRADY
Which of the following responsibilities should you assume once you have agreed to assist a disabled vessel?
- A. All personnel on the disabled vessel don life jackets
- B. All passengers move to the highest point on the disabled vessel to remain clear of towing gear
- C. Operator of disabled vessel on the bow with a lifejacket and emergency tow disconnect equipment
- D. Operator of disabled vessel to dump fuel and ballast to improve disabled vessel's towing movement

011961/DG01860   CHAPMAN
A towline should be fastened to _____.
- A. the chocks at the bow of a towed vessel
- B. the most forward, centermost point of a towed vessel such as a sturdy bow rail
- C. the mast of a towed sailboat
- D. a secure fitting near the bow of the towed vessel

011962/DG02322   BRADY
Fittings used for towing must be _____.
- A. Coast Guard approved
- B. stamped with maximum working loads
- C. securely fastened
- D. positioned exactly at the bow of the towed vessel

011963/DG01909   BRADY
What imminent danger results from tripping?
- A. The barge(s) collide with the stern
- B. Capsizing your tug
- C. Your tug being pulled backwards by your tow
- D. The stern of the tug submerges causing flooding into engine room

011964/DG01912   BRADY
A towing vessel becomes tripped while towing on a hawser astern. What factor is LEAST important when assessing the risk of capsizing?
- A. Length of the towline
- B. Height of the towline connection
- C. Length of the barge
- D. Direction of opposing force

SINKING OF THE TOW

011965/DG00977   **BRADY**
An ocean tow is sinking in deep water. Attempts to sever the towing hawser are unsuccessful. Which action should now be taken?
A. Abandon the towing vessel.
B. Radio for emergency assistance.
⚓ C. Slip the towline and allow it to run off the drum.
D. Secure all watertight openings on the towing vessel.

011966/DG01841   **BRADY**
If a tow sinks in shallow water, you should _____.
A. release it immediately
B. attempt to beach it before it goes under
⚓ C. pay out cable until it's on the bottom and place a buoy on the upper end
D. shorten cable to keep it off the bottom

011967/DG00732   **BRADY**
Which action should be taken FIRST if your tow is sinking in shallow water?
⚓ A. Pay out the towline until the sunken tow reaches bottom.
B. Sever the towline.
C. Immediately head for the nearest shoreline.
D. Contact the Coast Guard.

PARTING OF THE TOW LINE

011968/DG03438   **BRADY**
One advantage of chain over wire rope for a tow bridle is that chain _____.
A. is better suited for inland towing
⚓ B. resists damage from chafing
C. handles more easily
D. equalizes towing forces better

011969/DG04092   **BRADY**
To reconnect a broken tow line, it is better to use a polypropylene messenger line because it _____.
A, has great strength
B. is very supple
⚓ C. floats
D. absorbs shock by stretching

011970/DG03686   **REID**
If the towline parts, you should _____.
A. start pushing ahead
B. abandon the towing vessel
⚓ C. retrieve the tow bridle
D. relieve strain on the retrieving line

011971/DG03346   **BRADY**
When connecting the tow bridle to a tug, the end of the bridle is passed with a _____.
A. heaving line
B. shot line
C. high line
⚓ D. messenger line

TOWING PUSHING AHEAD

TOW MAKEUP

011972/DG00646   **BRADY**
What shape barge offers the least resistance in river towing?
A. A square ended barge
⚓ B. Barges with raked shaped bows
C. Ship-shaped barges
D. Hopper barges

011973/DG02506   **DECKHAND MANUAL**
A tow of 9 barges is made up three abreast and three long. The towboat is faced up to the center string which is known as the _____.
A. main string
⚓ B. push string
C. power string
D. face string

011974/DG02502   **DECKHAND MANUAL**
A tow of 9 barges is made up three abreast by three long. The towboat is faced up to the last barge of the center string. The outer two strings of barges are the _____.
A. port and starboard strings
B. outer strings
⚓ C. drag strings
D. side strings

011975/DG03144   **DECKHAND MANUAL**
A tow consists of 8 barges: 6 jumbo barges made up 3 abreast and 2 long, with 2 standard barges abreast as lead barges. How long is this tow?
A. 525 feet
B. 545 feet
⚓ C. 565 feet
D. 595 feet

TOW RIGGING

011976/DG01865   **AMSM**
When towing a small trailer-able boat, the sturdiest fitting available to attach a tow rig is the _____.
A. towing cleat on the bow
B. most forward handrail stanchion
⚓ C. trailer eye
D. chock

011977/DG03088   DECKHAND MANUAL

A "check" line is _____.

A. a safety line attached to a man working over the side
B. used to measure water depth
C. used to slow the headway of a barge
D. used to measure the overhead height of a bridge

011978/DG03410   DECKHAND MANUAL

When "checking down" a barge using a check line you should use _____.

A. one round turn and at least two figure-eights around the timber heads
B. at least three figure-eights around the timber heads
C. a clove hitch around one timber head
D. at least three round turns around one timber head

011979/DG03022   DECKHAND MANUAL

You are in the process of adding a barge to your tow. A line run from your power capstan and around timber heads on your tow is made fast on the new barge so that it can be pulled into position. This line is called a _____.

A. scissors wire
B. capstan line
C. spring line
D. fore and aft line

011980/DG03420   DECKHAND MANUAL

A face line is used to _____.

A. prevent barge movement in a lock
B. secure two barges end-to-end
C. secure barges to the towboat
D. secure barges side-by-side

011981/DG03124   DECKHAND MANUAL

You attach a line to a stationary barge lying off your starboard beam in order to maneuver it into position to make up tow. The line used to do this is a _____.

A. jockey line
B. fore and aft line
C. check line
D. swing line

011982/DG00607   DECKHAND MANUAL

A lashing used to secure three or four barges at a common corner, lashed in an "X" fashion, is called a _____.

A. scissor wire
B. towing wire
C. breast wire
D. cross wire

DIAGRAM D024DG

011983/DG03092   REID

Item A is the _____. See Diagram D024DG

A. lashing
B. drag wire
C. scissor wire
D. tandem wire

011984/DG03168   DECKHAND MANUAL

Which item is rigged to transmit the thrust from one barge to another when backing down? See Diagram D024DG

A. I
B. H
C. C
D. B

011985/DG03114   DECKHAND MANUAL

Which item is rigged to transmit the thrust from one barge to another barge when going ahead? See Diagram D024DG

A. I
B. H
C. E
D. B

011986/DG04012   DECKHAND MANUAL

The purpose of item G is to _____. See Diagram D024DG

A, distribute the vessel's thrust over a wider area
B. prevent the towboat from capsizing if item I should part
C. prevent the knee from shifting when the rudder is put hard over
D. keep the barges from shifting fore and aft

011987/DG04026   REID

One of the greatest hazards of pushing ahead is parting which item shown? See Diagram D024DG

A, A
B. B
C. F
D. I

011988/DG04014   DECKHAND MANUAL

The face wire refers to item _____. See Diagram D024DG

A, I
B. H
C. B
D. A

TOWING TERMINOLOGY

011989/DG03470   **DECKHAND MANUAL**
The section of each end of a barge which is heavily reinforced to take the pressure of pushing is called the _____.
⚓ A. headlog
  B. towhead
  C. collision bulkhead
  D. bullnose

011990/DG04054   **BRADY**
Hanging a barge off means to _____.
⚓ A, moor a barge to the bank and leave
  B. remove and deliver a loaded barge from a multiple tow
  C. remove a barge while locking through
  D. tow an empty barge astern

011991/DG03430   **BRADY**
What is NOT considered "jewelry"?
  A. Steamboat ratchets
  B. Manila lines
⚓ C. Buttons
  D. Shackles

011992/DG03450   **REID**
Kort nozzles are installed around the propellers of some vessels to _____.
⚓ A. increase the thrust of the propeller
  B. protect the propeller from striking sawyers
  C. prevent the propeller from striking barges towed on the hip
  D. prevent the propeller from touching bottom in low water

011993/DG03440   **REID**
The circular steel structure installed around the propeller of a towboat is the _____.
⚓ A. nozzle
  B. shroud
  C. strut
  D. hood

011994/DG03480   **DECKHAND MANUAL**
When barge headlogs do not meet or are not even with one another, the void or opening between them is called a _____.
⚓ A. notch
  B. hole
  C. spacing
  D. gap

011995/DG00640   **BRADY**
Which factor(s) can affect the performance of a river towboat?
  A. The draft of the towboat and the draft of the barges under tow
  B. The placement of the barges within the tow
  C. The presence of flanking rudders and Kort nozzles
⚓ D. All of the above

011996/DG02922   **DECKHAND MANUAL**
A long pole with a hook at one end, used to reach for lines, is known as a _____.
⚓ A. pike pole
  B. jack staff
  C. line rod
  D. hooker

011997/DG03490   **REID; BLANK; BRADY**
A device used to tighten up remaining slack in wire rope when you are making up to a tow in inland waters is a _____.
  A. tripping line
  B. tripping bracket
  C. norman pin
⚓ D. steamboat ratchet

011998/DG03460   **DECKHAND MANUAL**
You would NOT secure a line to a _____.
  A. kevel
⚓ B. stand pipe
  C. button
  D. timber head

EMERGENCY TOWING

EMERGENCY TOWING OPERATIONS

011999/DG01840   **KNIGHTS**
You are approaching a ship that is broken down and are preparing to take her in tow. BEFORE positioning your vessel to pass the towline, you must _____.
⚓ A. compare the rate of drift between the ships
  B. install chafing gear on the towline
  C. secure the bitter end of the towing hawser to prevent loss if the tow is slipped
  D. have traveling lizards rigged to guide the towline while it is paid-out

012000/DG01877   **BRADY**
When casting a heaving line to a disabled vessel, cast the line _____.
⚓ A. well over vessel's center to drop on deck
  B. directly at the most forward positioned crewmember
  C. on the windward side of the cockpit
  D. with a float attached

012001/DG03508   **CHAPMAN**
A situation has occurred in which your vessel must be towed. When the towing vessel passes the towing line to you, you should secure the line _____.
A. to the base of the foremast
⚓ B. to the forward-most bitts
C. to the forward part of the deckhouse
D. at the stern

012002/DG01939   **KNIGHTS**
You are on a ship that has broken down and are preparing to be taken in tow. You will use your anchor cable as part of the towline. Which statement is TRUE?
A. The anchor cable should be veered enough to allow the towline connection to be just forward of your bow.
B. The anchor cable should be veered enough to allow the towline connection to be immediately astern of the towing vessel.
⚓ C. The strain of the tow is taken by the riding pawl, chain stopper, and anchor windlass brake.
D. The anchor cable should be led out through a chock, if possible, to avoid a sharp nip at the hawsepipe lip.

012003/DG01905   **KNIGHTS**
You have a large, broken-down vessel in tow with a wire rope and anchor cable towline. Both vessels have made provision for slipping the tow in an emergency; however, unless there are special circumstances _____.
⚓ A. the towing vessel should slip first
B. the vessel towed should slip first
C. they should slip simultaneously
D. either vessel may slip first

012004/DG00275   **NICHOLLS**
You have taken another vessel in tow at sea. You can tell that the towing speed is too fast when the _____.
A. vessels are not in step
B. tow line feels like it is "jumping" when touched
⚓ C. catenary comes clear of the water
D. towed vessel goes "in irons"

012005/DG01770   **BRADY**
You are attempting to take a dead ship in tow. All lines have been passed and secured. How should you get underway?
A. Order minimum turns until the towing hawser is just clear of the water, then reduce speed to that necessary to keep the line clear of the water.
B. If the towline is properly adjusted and weighted you can order slow or dead slow and the towline will act as a spring to absorb the initial shock.
C. Order minimum turns until the towing hawser is taut and then continue at that speed until towing speed is attained.
⚓ D. Gradually apply power until catenary almost breaks the water, but keep the catenary in the water.

012006/DG03520   **CHAPMAN**
A situation has occurred where it becomes necessary for you to be towed. What action should be taken to prevent your vessel from yawing?
A. Shift weight to the bow
B. Shift weight to the center of the boat
⚓ C. Shift weight to the stern
D. Throw excess weight overboard

DIAGRAM D025DG

012007/DG02150   **KNIGHTS**
The vessel shown has broken down and you are going to take her in tow. The wind is coming from her starboard beam. You are making more leeway than she. Where should you position your vessel when you start running lines? See Diagram D025DG
⚓ A. A
B. B
C. C
D. D

012008/DG02000   **KNIGHTS**
The vessel has broken down and you are going to take her in tow. The wind is on her starboard beam. Both vessels are making the same amount of leeway. Where should you position your vessel when you start running lines? See Diagram D025DG
A. A
B. B
⚓ C. C
D. D

012009/DG02062   **KNIGHTS**

The vessel shown has broken down and you are going to take her in tow. The wind is on her starboard beam. She is making more leeway than you. Where should you position your vessel when you start running lines? See Diagram D025DG

A. A

B. B

C. C

⚓ D. D

PRINCIPLES OF DAMAGED STABILITY
& DAMAGE CONTROL

DAMAGE CONTROL PROCEDURES

012010/DG02207   **PNE**
After an explosion, repair of emergency machinery and services should be accomplished _____.
⚓ A. after control of fire, flooding, and structural repairs
B. immediately, before the emergency is under control
C. after control of fire, but before control of flooding
D. after stability is restored

012011/DG01252   **PNE**
Control of flooding should be addressed _____.
A. first
⚓ B. following control of fire
C. following restoration of vital services
D. only if a threat exists

012012/DG02361   **PNE**
The BEST information on the nature and extent of damage to the vessel is obtained from _____.
A. alarms and monitoring devices
B. the engineroom watch
⚓ C. personnel at the scene of the damage
D. the bridge watch

012013/DG02171   **PNE**
The order of importance in addressing damage control is _____.
A. control flooding, control fire, repair structural damage
B. restore vital services, control fire, control flooding
C. control fire, restore vital services, control flooding
⚓ D. control fire, control flooding, repair structural damage

012014/DG03501   **PNE**
What must be accurately determined to assess the potential for progressive flooding after a vessel has been damaged?
⚓ A. The integrity of the water tight boundaries
B. The capacity of the water sprinkler systems
C. The operation of the machinery space bilge level alarms
D. All of the above

012015/DG02266   **KNIGHTS**
Your vessel has been damaged and is partially flooded. The first step to be taken in attempting to save the vessel is to _____.
⚓ A. establish flooding boundaries and prevent further spread of flood water
B. plug the hole(s) in the outer shell
C. pump out the water inside the vessel
D. calculate the free surface effect and lost buoyancy to determine the vessel's stability

012016/DG02143   **KNIGHTS**
Your vessel was damaged and initially assumed a significant list and trim; however, further increase has been slow. Based on this data, what should you expect?
A. The slowing is only temporary and the vessel will probably suddenly capsize or plunge from loss of stability due to change in the waterplane area.
⚓ B. The vessel can probably be saved if further flooding can be stopped.
C. The vessel will continue to slowly list and/or trim due to the free surface effect and free communication effect.
D. The vessel will suddenly flop to the same or greater angle of list on the other side and may capsize.

012017/DG02065   **PNE**
A continual worsening of the list or trim indicates _____.
A. negative GM
⚓ B. progressive flooding
C. structural failure
D. an immediate need to ballast

012018/DG02047   **PNE**
Progressive flooding is controlled by securing watertight boundaries and _____.
A. transferring water ballast
B. jettisoning cargo
⚓ C. pumping out flooded compartments
D. abandoning ship

012019/DG01864   **PNE**
Progressive flooding may be indicated by _____.
A. ballast control alarms
B. excessive draft
C. excessive list or trim
⚓ D. a continual worsening of list or trim

012020/DG00545   **PNE**
Repairing damage to the hull at or above the waterline reduces the threat of _____.
A. free surface effects
B. capsizing
⚓ C. continued progressive flooding
D. wind heel

012021/DG01482   **HMT**

The two courses of action if the underwater hull is severely damaged are to plug the openings or to _____.

⚓ A. establish and maintain flooding boundaries
   B. dewater the compartment
   C. secure power to the compartment
   D. ballast to maintain even keel

012022/DG04061   **HMT**

The two factors which make underwater hull repair difficult are accessibility and the _____.
   A, availability of tools
   B. shape of the hull
⚓ C. pressure exerted by the water
   D. threat of progressive flooding

012023/DG00652   **HMT**

When plugging holes below the waterline you should _____.

   A. eliminate all water entering the hole
   B. only plug holes in machinery or other vital spaces
⚓ C. reduce the entry of water as much as possible
   D. plug the largest holes first

012024/DG00064   **LADAGE**

Which statement about damage control is TRUE?
⚓ A. A hole in the hull at the waterline is more dangerous than a hole below the inner bottom.
   B. The amount of water entering a ship through a hole varies inversely to the area of the hole.
   C. Water flowing into a lower compartment on a ship is more dangerous than water on deck or flowing into an upper compartment.
   D. Water flowing over the fo'c'sle bulwark is more dangerous than a hole in the hull at the waterline.

012025/DG00263   **PNE**

Which type of hull damage should be repaired FIRST?
   A. Damage below the waterline
   B. Damage to interior watertight boundaries
   C. Damage in way of machinery rooms
⚓ D. Damage at or just above the waterline

012026/DG02639   **DEEP DRILLER**

A wooden plug fitted tightly in the vent of a damaged tank may prevent the tank from _____.
⚓ A. filling completely
   B. developing free surface
   C. developing free surface moment
   D. collapsing

012027/DG02279   **HMT**

In plugging submerged holes; rags, wedges, and other materials should be used in conjunction with plugs to _____.

   A. reduce the water pressure on the hull
   B. reduce the possibility of stress fractures
   C. prevent progressive flooding
⚓ D. reduce the water leaking around the plugs

012028/DG03500   **CHAPMAN**

Small hull leaks can be temporarily repaired by _____.

   A. parceling
   B. parbuckling
⚓ C. caulking
   D. seizing

012029/DG02911   **DEEP DRILLER**

The wooden plug inserted in the vent of a damaged tank should be removed if you are going to _____.

⚓ A. pump from the damaged tank
   B. fight a fire
   C. abandon ship
   D. use the crossover system

012030/DG00123   **HMT**

When patching holes in the hull, pillows, bedding, and other soft materials can be used as _____.
   A. shores
⚓ B. gaskets
   C. strongbacks
   D. wedges

012031/DG00014   **MMOH**

Damaged bulkheads often take a permanent set which is independent of the panting or bulge caused by water pressure. To control this, you should _____.
⚓ A. install shoring so the shoring supports the damaged bulkheads without pushing on them
   B. install shoring so that it pushes on the damaged bulkhead while supporting it
   C. use jacks or chain falls to remove the set before installing shores
   D. place sandbags by the bulkhead without installing shores

012032/DG03519   **AMSM**

Strengthening damaged bulkheads by using wood or steel is called _____.
   A. bracing
   B. battening
   C. blocking
⚓ D. shoring

012033/DG00053   **AMSM**
The objective of shoring a damaged bulkhead is to
_____.

A. force the warped, bulged, or deformed sections
   back into place
⚓ B. support and hold the area in the damaged position
C. withstand subsequent additional damage
D. make a watertight seal at the damaged area

012034/DG01999   **HMT**
When shoring a damaged bulkhead, effort should be
taken to spread the pressure over the _____.
⚓ A. maximum possible area
B. minimum possible area
C. nearest watertight door
D. nearest longitudinal girder

012035/DG02664   **SEATECH**
You must shore up a bulkhead due to solid flooding
forward. The bulkhead approximates a rectangle. The
center of pressure of the shores on the bulkhead should
be located _____.
A. evenly over the surface of the bulkhead
⚓ B. approximately one-third of the way up the
   bulkhead
C. approximately halfway up the bulkhead
D. at the bottom of the bulkhead

012036/DG02622   **SEATECH**
You must shore up the collision bulkhead due to solid
flooding forward. The bulkhead approximates an
inverted triangle. The center of pressure of the shores
on the bulkhead should be located _____.
A. evenly over the surface of the bulkhead
B. approximately two-thirds of the way up the
   bulkhead
⚓ C. approximately halfway up the bulkhead
D. at the bottom of the bulkhead

012037/DG02530   **CHAPMAN; KNIGHTS**
Your vessel has gone aground in waters where the tide
is falling. The BEST action you can take is to
_____.
⚓ A. set out a kedge anchor
B. shift the vessel's load aft and repeatedly surge the
   engine(s) astern
C. shift the vessel's load forward and wait until the
   next high tide
D. slowly bring the engine(s) to full speed astern

012038/DG00054   **LADAGE**
Your vessel has grounded on a bar. What should you
do?
A. If you cannot get clear immediately, lighten the
   ship by pumping all ballast overboard.
B. Run the engine full astern to keep from being set
   further onto the bar.
⚓ C. Switch to the high suction for condenser
   circulating water, if it is submerged.
D. All of the above

012039/DG02321   **KNIGHTS**
Your vessel has run aground and is touching bottom for
the first one-quarter of its length. What is the LEAST
desirable method from the standpoint of stability to
decrease the bottom pressure?
A. Discharge forward deck cargo.
⚓ B. Pump out the forepeak tank.
C. Shift deck cargo aft.
D. Flood an after double-bottom tank.

012040/DG02281   **KNIGHTS**
Your vessel has run hard aground in an area subject to
heavy wave action. Backing full astern failed to free
her. Which action should be taken next?
A. Continue backing to scour out the bottom.
B. Wait for high tide and then try backing.
⚓ C. Flood empty tanks to increase bottom pressure and
   prevent inshore creep.
D. Shift weight aft to reduce the forward draft.

012041/DG02310   **KNIGHTS**
How do you determine the weight of the vessel that is
supported by the ground when a vessel has run
aground?
A. This requires extensive calculation and is usually
   performed only by a naval architect not by a ship's
   officer.
B. Determine the point where aground and the draft at
   that point, then calculate it using the grounding
   formula.
⚓ C. Use the hydrostatic tables and enter with the mean
   draft before grounding and the mean draft after
   grounding.
D. Use the inclining experiment formula and
   substitute the change of trim for the angle of list.

MERCHANT VESSEL HULL DESIGN

HYDRODYNAMIC FEATURES

012042/DG00284   **BAKER**
The beam of a vessel refers to the _____.
A. depth between decks
B. internal cubic capacity
C. molded depth of the vessel
⚓ D. width of the vessel

012043/DG00900   **BAKER**
Camber, in a ship, is usually measured in _____.
A. feet per feet of breadth
B. feet per feet of length
⚓ C. inches per feet of breadth
D. inches per feet of length

012044/DG03342   **EYRES**
Which term refers to a transverse curvature of the deck?
A. Deadrise
⚓ B. Camber
C. Freeboard
D. Flare

012045/DG01690   **PURSEY**
Molded depth is measured from the _____.
⚓ A. inside of the shell
B. outside of the shell
C. top of the center vertical keel
D. top of the garboard stake

012046/DG00950   **BAKER**
The upward slope of a ships bottom from the keel to the bilge is known as _____.
A. camber
B. slope
⚓ C. deadrise
D. keel height

012047/DG03327   **AMSM**
The upward slope of a vessels bottom from the keel to the bilge is called _____.
A. camber
B. sheer
C. rake
⚓ D. rise of bottom

012048/DG03239   **EYRES**
Which term indicates the rise in height of the bottom plating from the plane of the base line?
⚓ A. Deadrise
B. Camber
C. Molded height
D. Sheer

012049/DG00990   ***46 CFR 45.3 (g)**
Freeboard is measured from the upper edge of the _____.
A. bulwark
⚓ B. deck line
C. gunwale bar
D. sheer strake

012050/DG03599   **EYRES**
What term indicates the outward curvature of the hull above the waterline?
A. sheer
B. tumble home
C. deadrise
⚓ D. flare

012051/DG03204   **EYRES**
What term indicates the immersed body of the vessel forward of the parallel mid-body?
A. Run
B. Flare
⚓ C. Entrance
D. Sheer

012052/DG03282   **EYRES**
What term indicates the immersed body of the vessel aft of the parallel mid-body?
⚓ A. Run
B. Stern
C. Counter
D. Flow

012053/DG03324   **EYRES**
What descriptive term indicates that the dimension is measured from the inner face of the shell or deck plating?
⚓ A. Molded
B. Register
C. Tonnage
D. Effective

012054/DG00910   **AMSM**
The purpose of sheer in ship construction is to _____.
⚓ A. allow the ship to ride waves with drier decks
B. eliminate the need for butt straps
C. eliminate the need for margin plates
D. give greater strength at the deck edge

012055/DG03308   **EYRES**
What term indicates a curvature of the decks in a longitudinal direction?
A. Deadrise
B. Camber
⚓ C. Sheer
D. Flare

012056/DG03449   **EYRES**
What term indicates an inward curvature of the ship's hull above the waterline?
A. Camber
⚓ B. Tumble home
C. Deadrise
D. Flare

HULL DIMENSIONS

012057/DG03502   **EYRES**
The point that is halfway between the forward and after perpendicular and is a reference point for vessel construction is the _____.
A. half length
B. mid-body
C. center line
⚓ D. amidships

012058/DG03242   **EYRES**
What term indicates the line drawn at the top of the flat plate keel?
⚓ A. Base line
B. Molded line
C. Designer's waterline
D. Keel line

012059/DG03582   **EYRES**
What term indicates the length measured along the summer load line from the intersection of that load line with the foreside of the stem and the intersection of that load line with the after side of the rudder post?
A. Length overall
B. Register length
⚓ C. Length between perpendiculars
D. Length on the waterline

012060/DG03392   **EYRES**
What term indicates the midships portion of a vessel that has a constant cross section?
A. Half length
B. Amidships
⚓ C. Middle body
D. Molded length

012061/DG00404   **ENCY. NAUT. KNOW.**
A vessel's "quarter" is that section which is _____.
A. abeam
B. dead astern
C. just aft of the bow
⚓ D. on either side of the stern

012062/DG00019   **INT. MARITIME DICTIONARY**
The vessel's "quarter" is located _____.
A. abeam
B. dead astern
C. just forward of the beam on either side
⚓ D. on either side of the stern

MODERN SHIP TYPES

TRANSVERSE CONSTRUCTION

012063/DG00455   **PNE**
A vessel having continuous closely spaced transverse strength members is _____.
A. longitudinally framed
⚓ B. transversely framed
C. cellular framed
D. web framed

012064/DG00143   **PURSEY**
Why are most break bulk vessels built with the transverse framing system rather than the longitudinal system?
A. The transverse system is more resistant to hog and sag stresses.
B. The numerous longitudinal frames cause excessive broken stowage.
C. The transverse system provides better support to the varying cargo densities on a break bulk vessel.
⚓ D. The deep web frames interfere with the stowage of break bulk cargo.

LONGITUDINAL CONSTRUCTION

012065/DG01170   **LADAGE**
Transverse frames are more widely spaced on a ship that is designed with the _____.
A. centerline system of framing
B. isometric system of framing
⚓ C. longitudinal system of framing
D. transverse system of framing

012066/DG01010   **PNE**
When the longitudinal strength members of a vessel are continuous and closely spaced, the vessel is _____.
A. transversely framed
⚓ B. longitudinally framed
C. intermittently framed
D. web framed

TONNAGE MEASUREMENTS

DISPLACEMENT TONNAGE

012067/DG00294   **BAKER; *BOWD 2, PG 655**
Displacement refers to the _____.
A. cubic capacity of a vessel
B. deadweight carrying capacity of a vessel
C. gross tonnage of a vessel
⚓ D. number of long tons of water displaced by a vessel afloat

DEADWEIGHT TONNAGE

012068/DG01780MARINE CARGO OPS.; *BOWD 2, PG 655
The term that indicates how many tons of cargo a vessel can carry is _____.
A. bale cubic
⚓ B. deadweight
C. gross tonnage
D. loaded displacement

012069/DG00264   ***BOWD 2, PG 655**
The total weight of cargo, fuel, water, stores, passengers and crew, and their effects, that a ship can carry, is the _____.
A. bale cubic
⚓ B. deadweight
C. gross tonnage
D. loaded displacement

GROSS TONNAGE

012070/DG00960   ***BOWD 2, PG 655; *46 CFR 69.9; *46 CFR 69.57; *46 CFR 69.117**
Gross tonnage indicates the vessel's _____.
A. displacement in metric tons
B. total weight including cargo
⚓ C. volume in cubic feet
D. draft in feet

012071/DG01800   ***BOWD 2, PG 655; *46 CFR 69.9; *46 CFR 69.57; *46 CFR 69.117**
The figure obtained by dividing the total volume of the ship in cubic feet (after omission of exempted spaces) by 100 is the _____.
A. bale cubic
⚓ B. gross tonnage
C. light displacement
D. net tonnage

012072/DG01790   ***BOWD 2, PG 655; *46 CFR 69.9; *46 CFR 69.57; *46 CFR 69.117**
Which space(s) is(are) exempt when measuring gross tonnage?
A. Auxiliary machinery spaces above the uppermost continuous deck
B. Steering gear room
C. Part of the wheelhouse used to control vessel
⚓ D. All of the above

012073/DG01040   ***BOWD 2, PG 655; *46 CFR 69.9; *46 CFR 69.57; *46 CFR 69.117**
A well in the uppermost deck of a shelter deck vessel which has only a temporary means of closing for the purpose of gaining an exemption from tonnage measurement is called a(n) _____.
A. exemption space
B. tonnage deck
C. cofferdam
⚓ D. tonnage opening

012074/DG01300   ***46 CFR 92.07-10 (e)**
Tonnage openings must be closed by means of _____.
A. press board
B. steel hatch boards
⚓ C. steel plates
D. wooden hatch boards

012075/DG00293   ***BOWD 2, PG 655; *46 CFR 69.9; *46 CFR 69.57; *46 CFR 69.117**
Which space(s) is(are) NOT exempt when measuring gross tonnage?
A. Auxiliary machinery spaces above the deck
B. Steering gear room
⚓ C. Cargo holds
D. Galley in a deckhouse

NET TONNAGE

012076/DG00391   ***BOWD 2, PG 655; *46 CFR 69.9; *46 CFR 69.63; *46 CFR 69.119**
A tonnage tax is levied according to the _____.
A. deadweight cargo tonnage aboard
B. displacement tonnage of vessel
C. gross tonnage of vessel
⚓ D. net tonnage of vessel

012077/DG00274   ***BOWD 2, PG 655; *46 CFR 69.9; *46 CFR 69.63; *46 CFR 69.119**
What is the difference between net tonnage and gross tonnage?
⚓ A. Net tonnage is the gross tonnage less certain deductible spaces.
B. Net tonnage is tonnage of cargo compared to tonnage of whole ship.
C. Net tonnage is gross tonnage minus engine and bunker spaces.
D. Net tonnage is the net weight of the ship.

012078/DG00970   *BOWD 2, PG 655; *46 CFR 69.9;
                         *46 CFR 69.63; *46 CFR 69.119

What is the difference between net tonnage and gross tonnage?
- ⚓ A. Net tonnage is the gross tonnage less certain deductions for machinery and other areas.
- B. Net tonnage is tonnage of cargo compared to tonnage of whole ship.
- C. Net tonnage is the net weight of the ship.
- D. There is no difference.

012079/DG00495   *BOWD 2, PG 655; *46 CFR 69.9;
                         *46 CFR 69.63; *46 CFR 69.119

Which space(s) is (are) deducted from gross tonnage to derive net tonnage?
- ⚓ A. Boatswain's stores
- B. Companions and booby hatches
- C. Passenger spaces
- D. All of the above

012080/DG00363   *BOWD 2, PG 655; *46 CFR 69.9;
                         *46 CFR 69.63; *46 CFR 69.119

Which space(s) is(are) deducted from gross tonnage to derive net tonnage?
- A. Companions and booby hatches
- ⚓ B. Chart room
- C. Open structures
- D. All of the above

012081/DG00657   *BOWD 2, PG 655; *46 CFR 69.9;
                         *46 CFR 69.63; *46 CFR 69.119

Which space(s) is(are) deducted from gross tonnage to derive net tonnage?
- A. Companions and booby hatches
- B. Open structures
- ⚓ C. Spaces for the exclusive use of the officers or crew
- D. Water ballast spaces

012082/DG00063   *BOWD 2, PG 655; *46 CFR 69.9;
                         *46 CFR 69.63; *46 CFR 69.119

Which space(s) is(are) deducted from gross tonnage to derive net tonnage?
- A. Boatswain's stores
- B. Chart room
- C. Spaces for the exclusive use of the officers or crew
- ⚓ D. All of the above

012083/DG00727   *BOWD 2, PG 655; *46 CFR 69.9;
                         *46 CFR 69.63; *46 CFR 69.119

Which space(s) is(are) deducted from gross tonnage to derive net tonnage?
- A. Galley fitted with range or oven
- B. Open structures
- C. Passenger spaces
- ⚓ D. Boatswain's stores

012084/DG00561   *BOWD 2, PG 655; *46 CFR 69.9;
                         *46 CFR 69.63; *46 CFR 69.119

Which space cannot be deducted from gross tonnage when calculating net tonnage?
- A. Crew messroom
- ⚓ B. Forepeak ballast tank
- C. Master's cabin
- D. Chain locker

STRENGTH OF MATERIALS

HULL CRACKS

012085/DG00024   **NVIC 7-68**

A crack in the deck plating of a vessel may be temporarily prevented from increasing in length by _____.
- A. cutting a square notch at each end of the crack
- ⚓ B. drilling a hole at each end of the crack
- C. slot-welding the crack
- D. welding a doubler over the crack

HULL STRESSES

SAGGING

012086/DG01430   **MODSHIPS**

A vessel's bottom will be subjected to tension when weight is concentrated _____.
- ⚓ A. amidships
- B. aft
- C. at both ends of the vessel
- D. forward

012087/DG01460   **MODSHIPS**

Weight concentration in which area will cause a vessel's bottom to be subjected to tension stresses?
- A. Aft
- ⚓ B. Amidships
- C. At both ends
- D. Forward

RACKING

012088/DG01470   **BAKER**

Signs of racking stresses generally appear at the _____.
- A. bow and stern shell frames and plating
- ⚓ B. junction of the frames with the beams and floors
- C. garboard strake, at each side of the keel
- D. thrust bearing of the main shaft

SHEAR

012089/DG01420   **MODSHIPS**
Tensile stress is a result of two forces acting in
_____.

⚓ A. opposite directions on the same line, tending to pull the material apart
   B. opposite directions on the same line, tending to compress the object
   C. opposite directions along parallel lines
   D. the same direction along parallel lines

012090/DG02659   **MODSHIPS**
The shearing stresses on a ship's structure are usually greatest at _____.
   A. the bow
   B. the stern
   C. midships
⚓ D. the ship's quarter-length points

TENSILE STRESS

012091/DG01410   **MODSHIPS**
The result of two forces acting in opposite directions and along parallel lines, is an example of what type of stress?
   A. Tensile
   B. Compression
⚓ C. Shear
   D. Strain

BENDING MOMENTS

012092/DG02688   **MODSHIPS**
What would have the greatest affect on a vessel's longitudinal strength?
   A. Collision damage to the bow, forward of the collision bulkhead
⚓ B. Grounding damage to the bilge strake, just aft of midships
   C. Extensive corrosion to the centerline deck plating
   D. Damage to the side shell, midway between the bilge and the stringer plate

012093/DG03096   **MARINE CARGO OPS.**
When loading a cargo of taconite, proper sequencing of loading by hatch number is necessary to _____.
   A. provide the proper trim
   B. prevent negative stability from developing
⚓ C. prevent excessive longitudinal stresses
   D. control list

012094/DG00309   **BAPTIST; MARTON**
When planning the loading or discharging of a VLCC (100,000 DWT+) what is the most important consideration?
   A. Draft and trim
⚓ B. Limits of the bending moments
   C. Rate of discharging
   D. Rate of loading

DYNAMIC VESSEL MOTIONS

012095/DG03576   **LADAGE; *BOWD 2, PG 911**
Heave is motion along the _____.
   A. longitudinal axis
   B. transverse axis
⚓ C. vertical axis
   D. centerline axis

012096/DG00395   **LADAGE; *BOWD 2, PG 911**
The vertical motion of a floating vessel in which the entire hull is lifted by the force of the sea is known as _____.
   A. surge
   B. sway
⚓ C. heave
   D. pitch

012097/DG03328   **LADAGE; *BOWD 2, PG 911**
The vertical motion of a floating vessel is known as _____.
   A. surge
   B. sway
⚓ C. heave
   D. yaw

012098/DG03456   **PETEX; *BOWD 2, PG 911**
The vertical movement of a vessel in the water is called _____.
   A. pitch
   B. sway
⚓ C. heave
   D. roll

012099/DG03339   **LADAGE; *BOWD 2, PG 911**
Pitching is angular motion of the vessel about what axis?
   A. Longitudinal
⚓ B. Transverse
   C. Vertical
   D. Centerline

012100/DG03374   **LADAGE; *BOWD 2, PG 911**
Angular motion about the longitudinal axis of a vessel is known as _____.
   A. pitch
   B. surge
   C. sway
⚓ D. roll

012101/DG03234   LADAGE; *BOWD 2, PG 911

Rolling is angular motion of the vessel about what axis?

⚓ A. Longitudinal
B. Transverse
C. Vertical
D. Centerline

012102/DG03288   PETEX; *BOWD 2, PG 911

The angular movement of a vessel about a horizontal line drawn from its bow to its stern is _____.

A. pitching
⚓ B. rolling
C. heaving
D. swaying

012103/DG03439   LADAGE; *BOWD 2, PG 911

Horizontal fore or aft motion of a vessel is known as _____.

A. pitch
⚓ B. surge
C. sway
D. roll

012104/DG04069   PETEX; *BOWD 2, PG 911

The horizontal fore-and-aft movement of a vessel is called _____.

A, yaw
B. sway
C. heave
⚓ D. surge

012105/DG03654   LADAGE; *BOWD 2, PG 911

Horizontal transverse motion of a vessel is known as _____.

A. pitch
B. surge
⚓ C. sway
D. heave

012106/DG03608   PETEX; *BOWD 2, PG 911

The horizontal port or starboard movement of a vessel is called _____.

A. yaw
⚓ B. sway
C. surge
D. heave

012107/DG03488   LADAGE; *BOWD 2, PG 911

Angular motion about the vertical axis of a vessel is called _____.

⚓ A. yaw
B. surge
C. sway
D. roll

012108/DG04096   LADAGE; *BOWD 2, PG 911

Yawing is angular motion of the vessel about what axis?

A, Longitudinal
B. Transverse
⚓ C. Vertical
D. Centerline

VESSEL LINES PLANS & DRAWINGS

BODY PLAN

012109/DG01390   INT. MARITIME DICTIONARY

The body plan of a vessel is a(n) _____.

⚓ A. endwise view of the ship's molded form
B. longitudinal side elevation view
C. plan made looking down on the ship, showing it's hull cut horizontally by the first set of planes
D. vertical view made looking up in the ship, with the keel at the center

SHEER/PROFILE PLAN

012110/DG02872   EYRES

The Sheer Plan _____.

⚓ A. shows a longitudinal side elevation
B. is an endwise view of the ship's molded form
C. is usually drawn for the port side only
D. has the forebody to the right of centerline and afterbody to the left of centerline

HALF-BREADTH PLAN

012111/DG01400   BAKER

The half-breadth plan is _____.

A. an endwise view of the ship's molded form
B. a plan with the forebody to right of centerline and afterbody to the left of centerline
C. a longitudinal side elevation
⚓ D. usually drawn for the port side only

DOCKING PLAN

012112/DG00074   MODSHIPS

The best information on the location of the blocks when dry docking a vessel is contained in the _____.

A. shell expansion plan
B. docking diagram
⚓ C. ship's docking plan
D. general arrangement plan

CAPACITY PLAN

012113/DG00018 **MARINE CARGO OPS.**

To determine the weight capacity of a deck in a cargo hold, you would refer to the _____.

   A. deadweight scale
⚓ B. deck capacity plan
   C. cubic capacity tables
   D. general arrangement plan

WELDING PROCEDURES

WELDING TECHNIQUES

012114/DG01510 **BAKER**

The type of welding employed in shipyards is primarily _____.

   A. brazing
⚓ B. electric arc
   C. pressure welding
   D. thermite welding

012115/DG01520 **BAKER**

A welded joint's effectiveness is considered _____.

   A. 48%
   B. 90%
⚓ C. 100%
   D. 121%

012116/DG02566 **PURSEY**

The welds used to join shell plates in flush construction are known as _____.

⚓ A. butt welds
   B. seam welds
   C. fillet welds
   D. continuous welds

012117/DG02554 **PURSEY**

The welds used to attach stiffeners to a plate are known as _____.

   A. butt welds
   B. seam welds
⚓ C. fillet welds
   D. plate welds

012118/DG02551 **PURSEY**

What welding pattern is NOT used to permanently attach a stiffener to a plate?

   A. Chain intermittent
⚓ B. Tack
   C. Continuous
   D. Staggered intermittent

012119/DG02486 **EYRES**

Which weld fault can only be detected by a method that examines the internal structure of a weld?

   A. Undercut
   B. Lack of reinforcement
   C. Overlap
⚓ D. Lack of penetration

012120/DG02648 **EYRES**

The smallest size of flaw that can be detected on a radiograph examination of a weld will be indicated by the _____.

   A. film speed
⚓ B. penetrometer
   C. exposure reading
   D. time of exposure

012121/DG02649 **EYRES**

Which type of weld testing can be used to detect internal flaws?

⚓ A. Radiographic
   B. Magnetic particle
   C. Dye penetrant
   D. Chemical reaction

012122/DG02512 **EYRES**

Ultrasonic testing is used to determine the thickness of a vessel's shell plating and to _____.

   A. provide tail shaft clearances
⚓ B. test welds for subsurface defects
   C. check the wear of the rudder carrier bearing
   D. test the links of the anchor cables while being ranged

012123/DG02479 **EYRES**

Which type of weld testing can be used to detect internal flaws?

   A. Magnetic particle
   B. Dye penetrant
⚓ C. Ultrasonic
   D. Chemical reaction

WELDING & RIVETING

012124/DG01500 **BAKER**

Sometimes it is desirable to connect a member both by riveting and welding. Which statement is TRUE concerning this procedure?

   A. Tearing through the member is more likely in this type connection.
   B. The weld may be broken by the stresses caused by riveting.
   C. The weld increases the tensile stress on the rivet heads.
⚓ D. The welding must be completed before the riveting commences.

012125/DG02646   **MODSHIPS**
Which statement is true concerning repairs on the hull of a vessel which is to be riveted and welded?
A. Riveting must be completed before welding begins.
B. Riveting and welding should be done alternately.
⚓ C. Welding must be completed before the riveting begins.
D. It does not matter in what order the operations are done.

RIVETING PROCEDURES

RIVET NOMENCLATURE & MATERIALS

012126/DG02588   **MODSHIPS**
Rivets are usually made of _____.
A. wrought-iron
B. aluminum
C. high-tensile steel
⚓ D. mild steel

LINERS

012127/DG02472   **MODSHIPS**
A "liner" in riveted construction of a vessel is a(n) _____.
⚓ A. small plate which fills the aperture between riveted strakes and the vessel framing
B. backing plate which is used to level the strakes while riveting, and then removed
C. internal frame to which the side shell is riveted
D. seam that is welded after riveting is completed

RIVETED JOINTS

012128/DG02636   **BAKER**
When riveted joints occur at the ends of plating they are called _____.
A. trailers
B. terminals
C. seams
⚓ D. butts

012129/DG02689   **MODSHIPS**
After riveting is completed, the joints on the shell of a vessel are generally made watertight by _____.
A. faying
⚓ B. caulking
C. felt or canvas packing
D. red lead

012130/DG02626   **MODSHIPS**
The "grip" of a joint represents the _____.
⚓ A. thickness of the connected members
B. diameter of the head
C. entire length of the rivet
D. diameter of the shank

012131/DG02539   **MODSHIPS**
The distance between rivets in a row is known as the _____.
A. arm
⚓ B. pitch
C. gage
D. rivet distance

012132/DG02860   **EYRES**
How are riveted lap joints made watertight?
A. The faying surfaces are coated with white lead (or similar product) before the rivets are set.
B. A sealing weld bead of 1/8" or less pitch is run along the plate edge.
⚓ C. The plate edge is split close to an adjacent plate and mechanically forced into contact with the adjacent plate.
D. A properly riveted joint will be watertight; any leakage is stopped by setting up on the rivets.

012133/DG02484   **MODSHIPS;**
INT. MARITIME DICTIONARY; ENCY. NAUT. KNOW.
The type of joint formed when an edge of one plate is laid over the edge of the plate to which it is riveted is a _____.
A. grip joint
B. strap joint
C. thread joint
⚓ D. lap joint

012134/DG02556   **MODSHIPS**
The type of joint formed when a third small plate is riveted over two plates butted together is called a _____.
A. butted joint
B. lap joint
⚓ C. strap joint
D. stringer joint

RIVETED SYSTEMS

012135/DG02475   **MODSHIPS**
The use of liners in riveted construction is eliminated by using _____.
A. lapped construction
B. strapped construction
⚓ C. joggled construction
D. belted construction

LAUNCHING & DRYDOCKING

DRYDOCKING

012136/DG01565   **MODSHIPS**
While in dry dock your vessel will be belt-gauged. This
process involves _____.
A. measuring the thickness of the tail shaft liner
B. taking the vessel's offsets to check for hull
   deformation
C. testing and examining the anchor cables for
   defective links
⚓ D. drilling or sonic-testing the hull to determine the
   plate thickness

012137/DG02094   **MODSHIPS**
A large basin cut into the shore, closed off by a caisson,
and used for dry docking of ships is known as a

_____.
A. slipway
⚓ B. graving dock
C. ground warp
D. caisson dock

012138/DG02120   **MODSHIPS**
Wale shores would be used when dry docking a vessel
with _____.
A. tumble home
⚓ B. excessive deadrise
C. excessive trim
D. a list

012139/DG01637   **MODSHIPS**
Which statement about a vessel's stability while dry-
docking is TRUE?
⚓ A. Every ton of weight bearing on the blocks acts as if
   a ton of weight was removed at keel level.
B. When the ship touches the blocks, the beam for
   stability purposes increases to the beam of the dry-
   dock.
C. The stability of the vessel increases as a dock is
   pumped out due to the support of the keel blocks.
D. As the dock begins to support the weight of the
   vessel, stability calculations are based on the ship
   and dock as a single unit.

012140/DG02109   **MODSHIPS**
What is NOT an item that requires the vessel to be dry-
docked?
A. Inspection of tail shaft liner
B. Repacking and grinding of skin valves
⚓ C. Verification of load line measurements
D. Belt gauging

VESSEL CONSTRUCTION NOMENCLATURE

MISCELLANEOUS HULL FITTINGS

012141/DG00012   **LADAGE**
The maximum length allowed between main, transverse
bulkheads on a vessel is referred to as the _____.
A. floodable length
B. factor of subdivision
C. compartment standard
⚓ D. permissible length

012142/DG02458   **BAKER**
A carling is used aboard ship _____.
A. as a connecting strap between the butted ends of
   plating
⚓ B. to stiffen areas under points of great stress between
   beams
C. to prevent the anchor from fouling when the brake
   is released
D. to provide an extra heavy fitting in a heavy lift
   cargo rig

012143/DG02466   **BAKER**
The pillar shape that gives the greatest strength for the
least weight is the _____.
A. octagonal pillar
B. H Beam pillar
C. I Beam pillar
⚓ D. circular type pillar

012144/DG02672   **BAKER**
The term "scantlings" refers to the _____.
A. draft of a vessel
⚓ B. measurements of structural members
C. requirements for ship's gear
D. placement of a vessel's load line

BRACKETS

012145/DG01380   **BAKER**
The deck beam brackets of a transversely framed vessel
resist _____.
A. hogging stresses
B. sagging stresses
⚓ C. racking stresses
D. shearing stresses

012146/DG01370   **D'ARCANGELO**
The strength of a deck will be increased by adding

_____.
A. camber
⚓ B. deck beam brackets
C. hatch beams
D. sheer

012147/DG01340   **BAKER**
The usual depth of a beam bracket is _____.
A. 2-1/2 times the depth of the beam
B. 5 times the depth of the beam
C. 10 times the depth of the beam
D. same depth as the beam

BEAMS

012148/DG01330   **BAKER**
Beams are cambered to _____.
A. increase their strength
B. provide drainage from the decks
C. relieve deck stress
D. All of the above

012149/DG01350   **INT. MARITIME DICTIONARY**
A deck beam does NOT _____.
A. act as a beam to support vertical deck loads
B. lessen the longitudinal stiffness of the vessel
C. act as a tie to keep the sides of the ship in place
D. act as a web to prevent plate wrinkling due to twisting action on the vessel

BULWARKS & FITTINGS

012150/DG01110   **BAKER**
One function of a bulwark is to _____.
A. help keep the deck dry
B. prevent stress concentrations on the stringer plate
C. protect against twisting forces exerted on the frame of the vessel
D. reinforce the side stringers

012151/DG00324   **ENCY. NAUT. KNOW.**
A "chock" is a _____.
A. deck fitting used to secure mooring lines
B. casting fitted at the side of a weather deck, used as a fairlead
C. sharp block of wood used to support hygroscopic cargo
D. smoke pipe for the galley stove

012152/DG01090BAKER; INT. MARITIME DICTIONARY;
ENCY. NAUT. KNOW.; AMSM
A chock _____.
A. is a deck fitting used to shackle gear to the deck
B. permits easy jettisoning of deck cargo in an emergency
C. prevents stress concentration in the bulwark
D. provides openings through the bulwark for mooring lines

012153/DG01122   **BAKER**
Freeing ports on a vessel with solid bulwarks _____.
A. prevent stress concentration in the bulwark
B. permit easy jettison of deck cargo in an emergency
C. provide openings through the bulwarks for mooring lines
D. allow water shipped on deck to flow off rapidly

012154/DG00374   **BAKER**
Holes in the bulwark, which allow deck water to drain into the sea, are _____.
A. doggers
B. fidleys
C. freeing ports
D. swash ports

012155/DG01100   **INT. MARITIME DICTIONARY**
What is the purpose of the freeing ports on a vessel with solid bulwarks?
A. Allow water which may be shipped on deck to flow off rapidly
B. Permit easy jettisoning of deck cargo in an emergency
C. Prevent the formation of any unusual stress concentration points
D. Lighten the above deck weight caused by a solid bulwark

DECK HOUSE & FITTINGS

012156/DG00087   **AMSM**
A set of interior steps on a ship leading up to a deck from below is know as _____.
A. a companion way
B. 'tween-decks
C. stairs
D. All of the above are acceptable

012157/DG00810   **INT. MARITIME DICTIONARY**
In nautical terminology a "dog" is a _____.
A. crow bar
B. device to force a water tight door against the frame
C. heavy steel beam
D. wedge

012158/DG01130   **AMSM**
The fittings used to secure a watertight door are known as _____.
A. clamps
B. clasps
C. dogs
D. latches

012159/DG00334   ENCY. NAUT. KNOW.
The space above the engine room is called the
_____.
⚓ A. fidley
   B. gold locker
   C. middle hatch
   D. noble

012160/DG00384   BAKER; ISGOTT
A "strongback" refers to a _____.
⚓ A. bar securing a cargo port
   B. centerline vertical bulkhead
   C. deep beam
   D. spanner stay

DECK STRUCTURE

012161/DG00325   AMSM
A deck fitting, used to secure line or wire rope,
consisting of a single body with two protruding horns is
called a _____.
   A. bitt
   B. bollard
   C. capstan
⚓ D. cleat

012162/DG00820   INT. MARITIME DICTIONARY
A partial deck in a hold is called a(n) _____.
   A. weather deck
⚓ B. orlop deck
   C. shelter deck
   D. main deck

012163/DG02842   INT. MARITIME DICTIONARY
By definition, a "spar deck" is the _____.
   A. lower most continuous deck not broken by water
      tight bulkheads
   B. after most weather deck above the main strength
      deck
⚓ C. upper or weather deck above the main strength
      deck
   D. deck of light construction below the main or
      strength deck

012164/DG01630   MMOH
The fore and aft run of deck plating which strengthens
the connection between the beams and the frames and
keeps the beams square to the shell is called the
_____.
   A. garboard strake
   B. limber strake
   C. sheer strake
⚓ D. stringer strake

DOUBLE BOTTOM STRUCTURE (FLOORS)

012165/DG00073   AMSM
Aboard ship, vertical flat plates running transversely
and connecting the vertical keel to the margin plates are
called _____.
⚓ A. floors
   B. intercostals
   C. girders
   D. stringers

012166/DG00015   AMSM
Floors aboard ship are _____.
⚓ A. frames to which the tank top and bottom shell are
      fastened on a double bottomed ship
   B. transverse members of the ships frame which
      support the decks
   C. longitudinal beams in the extreme bottom of a ship
      from which the ship's ribs start
   D. longitudinal angle bars fastened to a surface for
      strength

012167/DG00082   AMSM
Floors aboard ship are _____.
   A. also called decks
⚓ B. vertical transverse plates connecting the vertical
      keel with the margin plates
   C. large beams fitted in various parts of the vessel for
      additional strength
   D. found in passenger and berthing spaces only

012168/DG00075   AMSM
Frames to which the tank top and bottom shell are
fastened are called _____.
⚓ A. floors
   B. intercostals
   C. stringers
   D. tank top supports

012169/DG01230   BAKER; EYRES
Which statement concerning solid floors is TRUE?
   A. They must be watertight.
⚓ B. They may have lightening, limber, or air holes cut
      into them.
   C. They are built of structural frames connected by
      angle struts and stiffeners, with flanged plate
      brackets at each end.
   D. They are lighter than open floors.

012170/DG01290   BAKER
What is NOT an advantage of double bottom ships?
   A. The tank top forms a second skin for the vessel.
   B. The center of gravity of a loaded bulk cargo ship
      may be raised to produce a more comfortable roll.
   C. The floors and longitudinals distribute the upward
      push of the water on the ship's bottom.
⚓ D. They are less expensive to construct because of
      increased access space.

DOUBLE BOTTOM STRUCTURE
(INNER & OUTER BOTTOMS)

012171/DG01080   AMSM; ENCY. NAUT. KNOW.
The "inner bottom" is the _____.
⚓ A. tank top
 B. compartment between the tank top and shell of the vessel
 C. inner side of the vessel's shell
 D. space between two transverse bottom frames

012172/DG00084   BAKER;
INT. MARITIME DICTIONARY; McEWEN
The ceiling is _____.
 A. the overhead in berthing compartments
⚓ B. a wooden protection placed over the tank top
 C. material driven into seams or cracks to prevent leaking
 D. None of the above are correct

012173/DG00870   PURSEY
The terms "ceiling" and "margin plate" are associated with the _____.
 A. crew's quarters
 B. engine room
 C. main deck
⚓ D. tank top

012174/DG00085   BAKER;
INT. MARITIME DICTIONARY; McEWEN
The wooden planking that protects the tank top from cargo loading is called _____.
⚓ A. ceiling
 B. shores
 C. frames
 D. toms

012175/DG00890   MMOH
A term applied to the bottom shell plating in a double-bottom ship is _____.
 A. bottom floor
⚓ B. outer bottom
 C. shear plating
 D. tank top

DOUBLE BOTTOM STRUCTURE (INTERNALS)

012176/DG01250   BAKER
The floors in a vessel's hull structure are kept from tripping, or folding over, by _____.
 A. face plates
⚓ B. bottom longitudinals
 C. longitudinal deck beams
 D. transverse deck beams

012177/DG02452   LADAGE
Which is an advantage of using watertight longitudinal divisions in double bottom tanks?
⚓ A. Cuts down free surface effect
 B. Increases the rolling period
 C. Decreases weight because extra stiffeners are unneeded
 D. Lowers the center of buoyancy without decreasing GM

012178/DG01280   BAKER
Vertical structural members attached to the floors that add strength to the floors are called _____.
 A. boss plates
 B. buckler plates
⚓ C. stiffeners
 D. breast hooks

MARGIN

012179/DG01050   BAKER
The "margin plate" is the _____.
⚓ A. outboard strake of plating on each side of an inner bottom
 B. outer strake of plating on each side of the main deck of a vessel
 C. plate which sits atop the center vertical keel
 D. uppermost continuous strake of plating on the shell of a vessel

LIMBER & BILGE SYSTEMS

012180/DG02722   BAKER
Limber is a term associated with _____.
 A. emergency gear
⚓ B. drainage
 C. deck cargo storage
 D. securing gear

012181/DG01007   MARINE CARGO OPS.
When using the term "limber system" one is referring to a _____.
 A. cleaning system
⚓ B. drainage system
 C. strengthening system
 D. weight reduction system

012182/DG00344   ENCY. NAUT. KNOW.
The purpose of a bilge well is to _____.
 A. afford access to the shell through the double bottoms
⚓ B. collect water to be pumped out
 C. provide access for the pneumercator
 D. provide a base line for sounding measurements

FRAMES

012183/DG01150   **EYRES**
In ship construction, frame spacing is _____.
A. greater at the bow and stern
⚓ B. reduced at the bow and stern
C. uniform over the length of the vessel
D. uniform over the length of the vessel, with the exception of the machinery spaces, where it is reduced due to increased stresses

012184/DG00198   **MARINE CARGO OPS.**
Battens are fitted in cargo holds across the frames of the vessel from the turn of the bilge upward. The purpose of these cargo battens is _____.
A. for securing a snatch block when snaking cargo into the wings of the hold
⚓ B. to prevent cargo from coming in contact with the vessel's frames or shell plating
C. to provide fittings to which cargo lashings may be secured
D. to support the dunnage floors which are laid down between tiers of cargo

012185/DG02509   **PURSEY**
What is the purpose of cant frames in steel vessels?
A. To support the overhang of the stern
⚓ B. To provide strength to shell plating at the stern
C. To add strength to the deck beams which support the weather decks
D. To support the plating of a cylindrical tank

012186/DG00850   **BAKER; MMOH; EYRES**
Panting frames are located in the _____.
A. after double bottoms
B. centerline tanks on tankships
⚓ C. fore and after peaks
D. forward double bottoms

012187/DG00750   **BAKER**
On a single-screw vessel the stern frame _____.
⚓ A. furnishes support to the rudder, propeller shaft, and transom frame
B. provides foundations for after mooring winches
C. provides foundations for the main propulsion engines
D. transfers the driving force of the propeller to the hull

012188/DG00742   **PNE**
Lighter longitudinal stiffening frames on the vessel's side plating are called _____.
⚓ A. stringers
B. side frames
C. side stiffeners
D. intercostals

012189/DG01302   **PNE**
Reinforcing frames attached to a bulkhead on a vessel are called _____.
A. side longitudinals
B. intercostals
⚓ C. stiffeners
D. brackets

012190/DG01160   **BAKER**
In a longitudinally-framed ship, the longitudinal frames are held in place and supported by athwartship members called _____.
A. floors
B. margin plates
C. stringers
⚓ D. web frames

012191/DG01140   **BAKER**
In a transversely framed ship, the transverse frames are supported by all of the following EXCEPT _____.
A. girders
B. longitudinals
C. side stringers
⚓ D. web plates

BOW CONSTRUCTION

012192/DG01210   **MMOH**
To rigidly fasten together the peak frames, the stem, and the outside framing, a horizontal plate is fitted across the forepeak of a vessel. This plate is known as a(n) _____.
A. apron plate
⚓ B. breasthook
C. intercostal plate
D. joiner

STERN CONSTRUCTION

012193/DG00840   **BAKER**
The terms "cant frame" and "counter" are associated with the vessel's _____.
A. cargo hatch
B. forecastle
C. steering engine
⚓ D. stern

KEEL

012194/DG01540   **BAKER**
In ship construction, keel scantlings should be the greatest _____.
A. at each frame
⚓ B. amidships
C. one-third the distance from the bow
D. one-third the distance from the stern

012195/DG01550   **MODSHIPS**
Keel scantlings of any vessel are greatest amidships because _____.
A. connections between forebody and afterbody are most crucial
⚓ B. of maximum longitudinal bending moments
C. of severest racking stresses
D. resistance to grounding is at a maximum amidships

012196/DG00740   **BAKER**
The extension of the after part of the keel in a single-screw vessel upon which the stern post rests is called the _____.
A. boss
B. knuckle
⚓ C. skeg
D. strut

BILGE KEELS

012197/DG01240   **BAKER**
Bilge keels are fitted on ships to _____.
A. assist in dry dock alignment
B. improve the vessel's stability
C. protect the vessel from slamming against piers
⚓ D. reduce the rolling of the vessel

012198/DG00780   **MODSHIPS**
Bilge keels are more effective at dampening rolls as the _____.
A. pitching increases
B. list increases
⚓ C. rolling increases
D. draft decreases

012199/DG01260   **BAKER**
The function of the bilge keel is to _____.
⚓ A. reduce the rolling of the vessel
B. serve as the vessel's main strength member
C. add strength to the bilge
D. protect the vessel's hull when alongside a dock

012200/DG02684   **EYRES**
Which statement about bilge keels is CORRECT?
A. They are critical strength members and require careful design consideration.
⚓ B. They increase resistance to rolling.
C. They attach to a low stress area.
D. They provide support when the vessel is dry docked.

PLATING SYSTEMS

012201/DG01530   **BAKER**
Shell plating is _____.
A. the galvanizing on steel
B. a hatch cover
⚓ C. the outer plating of a vessel
D. synonymous with decking

012202/DG01560   **BAKER**
Which arrangement of shell plating is used most in modern shipbuilding?
A. Clinker
⚓ B. Flush
C. In-and-Out
D. Joggled

012203/DG02594   **PURSEY**
Which is NOT an advantage of the flush method of welded shell plating?
A. Reduces weight
B. Reduces frictional resistance
C. Keeps practically 100% of tensile strength at the joints
⚓ D. Reduces plate stress

012204/DG01570   **BAKER**
What is NOT an advantage of ship construction methods using welded butt joints in the shell plating?
A. Keeps practically 100% of tensile strength at the joints
B. Reduces frictional resistance
⚓ C. Reduces plate stress
D. Reduces weight

PLATE MATERIALS

012205/DG02488   **EYRES**
A vessel is constructed with a steel hull and an aluminum superstructure. Which statement is TRUE?
A. The aluminum will provide greater resistance to the spread of fire by conduction.
⚓ B. The aluminum structure is usually attached to a steel coaming by a method that insulates the two metals.
C. If the superstructure is stressed, an aluminum structure requires additional expansion joints to prevent fracture.
D. The steel at the area of the aluminum-to-steel connection must be closely checked for galvanic corrosion.

012206/DG02302   ***46 CFR 94.05-5;**
                        *46 CFR 147.40 (a) (2); *46 CFR 94.60-1
What is NOT required to be approved or certified by the U.S. Coast Guard before being used on inspected vessels?
A. Lifesaving equipment that is in excess of the regulatory minimum
B. Ship's stores that are Class A poisons or Class A explosives
⚓ C. Steel plate used in hull construction
D. EPIRBs

STRAKE NAMES

012207/DG01670   **AMSM**
The term "strake" is used in reference to _____.
A. rudder mountings
B. anchor gear
⚓ C. hull plating
D. vessel framing

012208/DG02236   **BAKER**
Another name for the garboard strake is the _____.
⚓ A. A strake
B. Z strake
C. side keel plate
D. stringer plate

012209/DG01680   **AMSM**
In vessel construction, the garboard strake is _____.
⚓ A. located next to and parallel to the keel
B. located next to and parallel to the gunwale
C. another term for the bilge keel
D. another term for the rub rail

012210/DG01640   **ENCY. NAUT. KNOW.**
The garboard strake is the _____.
A. raised flange at the main deck edge
B. riveted crack arrester strap on all-welded ships
C. riveting pattern most commonly used in ship construction
⚓ D. row of plating nearest the keel

012211/DG01660   **AMSM**
The strake on each side of the keel is called a _____.
A. sheer strake
B. gatewood strake
C. insulation strake
⚓ D. garboard strake

012212/DG01650   **BAKER**
To reduce the number of strakes at the bow, two strakes are tapered and joined at their ends by a single plate. This plate is known as a _____.
A. cover plate
B. joiner
C. lap strake
⚓ D. stealer plate

012213/DG01620   **BAKER**
Owing to the greater girth of a ship amidships than at the ends, certain strakes are dropped as they approach the bow and stern to reduce the amount of plating at the ends. These strakes are called _____.
⚓ A. drop strakes
B. stealers
C. throughs
D. voids

PLATE LAY-UP

012214/DG01580   **BAKER**
Shell plating that has curvature in two directions and must be heated and hammered to shape over specially prepared forms is called _____.
A. compound plate
⚓ B. furnaced plate
C. flat plate
D. rolled plate

012215/DG02604   **PURSEY**
The joint formed when two steel plates are placed end-to-end is called a _____.
A. bevel
B. seam
⚓ C. butt
D. bond

012216/DG01610   **BAKER**
The joint formed when two steel shell plates are placed longitudinally side to side is called a _____.
A. bevel
B. bond
C. strake
⚓ D. seam

PROPULSION SYSTEMS

012217/DG00236   **MODSHIPS**
As the propeller turns, voids are formed on the trailing and leading edges of the propeller blades causing a loss of propulsive efficiency, pitting of the blades, and vibration. These voids are known as _____.
A. advance
⚓ B. cavitation
C. edging
D. slip

012218/DG00266   **BOWD**
The distance that a ship moves forward with each revolution of its propeller, if there is no slip, is called _____.
A. advance
B. head reach
⚓ C. pitch
D. transfer

012219/DG00253   **BOWD**
The forward movement of a vessel in one revolution of its propeller is measured by _____.
A. advance
B. head reach
C. the pitch
D. transfer

012220/DG00827   **H.O. 220**
The pitch of a propeller is a measure of the _____.
A. angle that the propeller makes with a free stream of water
B. angle that the propeller makes with the surface of the water
C. number of feet per revolution the propeller is designed to advance in still water without slip
D. positive pressure resulting from the difference of the forces on both sides of the moving propeller in still water without slip

NOZZLES

012221/DG00800   **BRADY**
A Kort nozzle is a(n) _____.
A. hollow tube surrounding the propeller used to improve thrust
B. nozzle attached to a firefighting hose
C. intake valve on a diesel engine
D. piston cylinder on a diesel engine

TUNNEL BOW THRUSTERS

012222/DG02958   **SHIPHAND**
The bow thruster generally is ineffective at _____.
A. over 3 knots headway
B. at any speed astern
C. at any speed ahead
D. over 1 knot sternway

012223/DG00006   **SHIPHAND**
Which statement about a tunnel bow thruster is TRUE?
A. It provides lateral control without affecting headway.
B. It is fully effective at speeds up to about six knots.
C. It can be used to slow the ship in addition to backing down.
D. It will allow you to hold a position when the current is from astern.

012224/DG04046   **WILLERTON**
Which statement about tunnel bow thrusters fitted to large vessels is TRUE?
A. They are effective on most vessels at speeds up to 10 knots.
B. Because of their location, most modern installations have as much power as a tug.
C. They are fully effective at all drafts.
D. When going astern at slow speed, they provide effective steering control.

RUDDERS

012225/DG00770   **MODSHIPS**
The ratio of the height of a vessel's rudder to its width is referred to as the _____.
A. aspect ratio
B. constriction ratio
C. rudder ratio
D. steering ratio

012226/DG02478   **BAKER**
A "contra-guide" is a type of _____.
A. bow thruster
B. cargo gear
C. steering engine
D. rudder

RUDDER FITTINGS

012227/DG00880   **BAKER**
The projecting lugs of the rudderpost which furnish support to the rudder are called _____.
A. bases
B. gudgeons
C. pintles
D. rudder lugs

012228/DG00862   **BAKER**
The term "pintle" and "gudgeon" are associated with the _____.
A. anchor windlass
B. jumbo boom
C. rudder
D. steering engine

012229/DG02632   **EYRES**
The horizontal flat surfaces where the upper stock joins the rudder are the _____.
A. rudder keys
B. rudder palms
C. lifting flanges
D. shoes of the rudder

TANKAGE

012230/DG01320   **AMSM**

A cofferdam is _____.
- A. any deck below the main deck and above the lowest deck
- B. a member that gives fore-and-aft strength
- ⚓ C. made by placing two bulkheads a few feet apart
- D. a heavy fore-and-aft beam under the deck

012231/DG00199   **AMSM; INTRO. NAVAL ARCH.; BAKER; ENCY. NAUT. KNOW.; INT. MARITIME DICTIONARY; *46 CFR 30.10-13**

What is a cofferdam?
- A. Tube fitted to an ullage hole
- B. Area the product is loaded into
- ⚓ C. Void or empty space separating two tanks
- D. Opening in the deck used for cleaning a tank

012232/DG00980   **AMSM**

The perforated, elevated bottom of the chain locker, which prevents the chains from touching the main locker bottom and allows seepage water to flow to the drains, is called a _____.
- A. cradle
- B. draft
- C. harping
- ⚓ D. manger

012233/DG00239   **MARTON; MFPFFS**

Flame screens are used to _____.
- A. contain flammable fumes
- B. protect firefighters from flames
- ⚓ C. prevent flames from entering tanks
- D. keep flames and sparks from getting out of an engine's exhaust system

012234/DG01310   **BAKER; ABS**

Which statement is TRUE concerning protection of double bottom tanks against excessive pressure?
- A. Each vent for the tank must be equal to the area of the tank filling line.
- B. The tanks must be protected by overflows.
- ⚓ C. The total area of the vents or the overflow shall be at least 125% of the area of the fill line.
- D. There must be twice as much vent area as the area of the fill line.

012235/DG02862 MERCHANT SHIP CONSTRUCTION

What is used to prevent accidental flooding of a double bottom or peak tanks in the event of a pipe rupture due to collision?
- A. Separate lines are provided for filling and pumping these tanks.
- B. Pipe lines must run vertically from the tank to a point above the margin line before turning fore or aft towards the pump.
- C. All tanks must be served by the fewest possible number of pipes to reduce the possibility of rupture.
- ⚓ D. Suction lines are fitted with a non-return valve

DIAGRAM D001DG

012236/DG01700   **BAKER**

Which letter designates the bilge strake of the vessel? See Diagram D001DG
- A. A
- B. B
- C. C
- ⚓ D. D

DIAGRAM D033DG

012237/DG01832   **BAKER**

The run of plating labeled A is known as the _____. See Diagram D033DG
- A. sheer strake
- ⚓ B. stringer plate
- C. deck strake
- D. deck longitudinal

012238/DG01819   **BAKER**

The stringer plate is represented by which letter? See Diagram D033DG
- ⚓ A. A
- B. C
- C. I
- D. N

012239/DG02222   **MODSHIPS**

The lower seam of the strake indicated by the letter B is sometimes riveted. This is done to _____. See Diagram D033DG
- A. increase the strength in a highly stressed area
- B. provide the flexibility inherent in a riveted seam
- ⚓ C. serve as a crack arrestor and prevent hull girder failure
- D. reduce construction costs

012240/DG01902   **BAKER**
The joint indicated by letter D is a _____. See Diagram D033DG
A. seam
⚓ B. butt
C. span
D. sheet line

012241/DG01915   **BAKER**
A butt is indicated by which letter? See Diagram D033DG
A. J
B. F
C. E
⚓ D. D

012242/DG01875   **BAKER**
A seam is indicated by which letter in illustration D033DG? See Diagram D033DG
⚓ A. E
B. H
C. L
D. M

012243/DG01854   **BAKER**
The structural member indicated by the letter F is known as a(n) _____. See Diagram D033DG
A. erection
⚓ B. pillar
C. girder
D. deck support

012244/DG01357   **BAKER**
The area indicated by the letter G is known as the _____. See Diagram D033DG
A. entrance
B. stringer plate
⚓ C. turn of the bilge
D. garboard

012245/DG01957   **BAKER**
The strake of shell plating indicated by letter H is known as the _____. See Diagram D033DG
A. sheer strake
B. outboard keel plate
⚓ C. garboard strake
D. bilge strake

012246/DG01944   **BAKER**
The garboard strake is indicated by which letter? See Diagram D033DG
A. A
B. B
C. G
⚓ D. H

012247/DG02046   **BAKER**
The structural member indicated by the letter I is the _____. See Diagram D033DG
A. garboard strake
B. center pillar
⚓ C. keel
D. girder

012248/DG02251   **BAKER**
The letter I indicates the keel. Which of the following plates is NOT part of the keel? See Diagram D033DG
A. Center vertical keel
B. Rider plate
⚓ C. Longitudinal girder
D. Flat plate keel

012249/DG01994   **BAKER**
The space indicated by the letter J is known as the _____. See Diagram D033DG
⚓ A. double bottom
B. flooding barrier
C. floor space
D. bilge tank

012250/DG02011BAKER; AMSM; ENCY. NAUT. KNOW.
The structural member indicated by the letter K is a _____. See Diagram D033DG
A. longitudinal frame
B. stringer
C. girder
⚓ D. floor

012251/DG02002   **BAKER**
The structural member indicated by the letter K was fitted in segments between continuous longitudinals. It is known as which type of floor? See Diagram D033DG
⚓ A. Intercostal
B. Open
C. Lightened
D. Non-watertight

012252/DG01970   **BAKER**
The structural member indicated by the letter L is a _____. See Diagram D033DG
A. web frame
B. bilge keel
C. side keel
⚓ D. longitudinal

012253/DG01976   **BAKER**
Which letter indicates a longitudinal? See Diagram D033DG
A. C
B. E
⚓ C. L
D. M

012254/DG02241   **BAKER**

The letter M indicates a(n) _____. See Diagram D033DG

⚓ A. web frame
B. intercostal
C. stringer
D. cant frame

012255/DG02191   **BAKER**

A wooden deck installed on top of the plating lettered N is known as _____. See Diagram D033DG

A. spar decking
B. furring
⚓ C. ceiling
D. flooring

012256/DG02040   **BAKER**

The plating indicated by the letter N is known as the _____. See Diagram D033DG

⚓ A. inner bottom
B. floor riders
C. tank-top rider plating
D. ceiling

VESSEL DESIGN COMPUTATIONS

PLATE THICKNESS

012257/DG01590   **BAKER**

A thirty pound plate would be _____.

A. 3/8" thick
B. 1/2" thick
⚓ C. 3/4" thick
D. 1" thick

012258/DG02699   **BAKER**

The thickness of a 30.6 pound plate is _____.

A. 3/8"
B. 1/2"
⚓ C. 3/4"
D. 1"

WEIGHT OF STEEL PLATE

012259/DG02392   ***BOWD 2; CHAP. 1**

Determine the weight of a rectangular piece of 12.75 lbs. steel measuring 5 feet by 8 feet.

⚓ A. 510.00 lbs.
B. 255.00 lbs.
C. 198.89 lbs.
D. 165.75 lbs.

012260/DG02390   ***BOWD 2; CHAP. 1**

Determine the weight of a rectangular piece of 20.4 lb. steel measuring 4 feet by 6 feet.

A. 204.0 lbs.
⚓ B. 489.6 lbs.
C. 734.4 lbs.
D. 979.2 lbs.

012261/DG02393   ***BOWD 2; CHAP. 1**

Determine the weight of a rectangular piece of 25.5 lbs. steel measuring 4.5 feet by 6.7 feet.

A. 285.6 lbs.
B. 329.7 lbs.
C. 591.2 lbs.
⚓ D. 768.8 lbs.

012262/DG02391   ***BOWD 2; CHAP. 1**

Determine the weight of a rectangular piece of 40.8 lbs. steel measuring 3 feet by 5 feet.

A. 326.4 lbs
B. 453.6 lbs
⚓ C. 612.0 lbs
D. 1224.0 lbs

DEADWEIGHT TONNAGE

012263/DG00920   **MMOH**

A vessel's light displacement is 12,000 tons. Its heavy displacement is 28,000 tons. When fully loaded it carries 200 tons of fuel and 100 tons of water and stores. What is the cargo carrying capacity in tons?

A. 11,700 tons
⚓ B. 15,700 tons
C. 16,000 tons
D. 27,700 tons

VESSEL DOCUMENTATION

LOAD LINE REGULATIONS

012264/DG00361   **MODSHIPS**
The strictest load line regulations apply to _____.
A. gas carriers
B. freighters (break-bulk)
⚓ C. passenger ships
D. tankers

012265/DG00351   **MMOH**
Which certificate is issued by the American Bureau of Shipping?
A. Certificate of Inspection
⚓ B. Load Line Certificate
C. Safety Equipment Certificate
D. Permit to Proceed for repairs

012266/DG00372   **KNIGHTS**
Keeping the draft at or below the load line mark will insure that the vessel has adequate _____.
A. ballast
⚓ B. reserve buoyancy
C. displacement
D. rolling periods

012267/DG02100   **MODSHIPS; *46 CFR 42.07-5**
The primary purpose of a load line is to establish required _____.
⚓ A. minimum freeboard
B. GM
C. transverse stability
D. fresh water allowances

012268/DG00341   **ENCY. NAUT. KNOW.**
The Certificate of Freeboard is the _____.
⚓ A. Load Line Certificate
B. Certificate of Inspection
C. Admeasurer's Certificate
D. Forecastle Card

012269/DG02132   **HOPKINS**
Which statement concerning dual-tonnage vessels is TRUE?
A. The dual-tonnage mark is always marked above the load line marks.
B. The tonnages referred to are the displacement tonnage and gross tonnage.
⚓ C. A single-deck vessel may not be assigned dual tonnages.
D. The dual-tonnage mark must never be submerged beyond the freshwater allowance.

012270/DG01730   **AMSM**
A disk with a horizontal line through its center, equivalent to the summer load line, is called the _____.
A. deadrise mark
B. maximum allowable draft mark
⚓ C. Plimsoll mark
D. tonnage mark

012271/DG01020   **BAKER**
The Plimsoll mark on a vessel is used to _____.
A. align the vessel's tail shaft
B. determine the vessel's trim
⚓ C. determine the vessel's freeboard
D. locate the vessel's centerline

012272/DG01731   ***46 CFR 35.07-10**
You are in charge of a 225-gross ton tug preparing to depart from Houston, Texas, with a loaded 2500-gross ton tank barge bound for New York. Prior to departure, regulations require that you _____.
A. record the status of all firefighting equipment
⚓ B. record the barge's load line and draft readings
C. record the condition of the towing gear
D. have on board an Official Logbook in lieu of other forms of records

012273/DG01962   ***46 CFR 42.01-10**
The maximum draft to which a vessel can legally be submerged is indicated by the _____.
⚓ A. load line mark
B. Certificate of Inspection
C. Muster List ("Station Bill")
D. tonnage mark

012274/DG02135   ***46 CFR 42.07-45**
A load line certificate is valid for how many years?
A. 1
B. 2
C. 3
⚓ D. 5

012275/DG01041   ***46 CFR 42.07-45; MARTIN**
The document on a vessel, annually endorsed by an American Bureau of Shipping surveyor, is called the _____.
A. Certificate of Inspection
B. Classification Certificate
⚓ C. Load Line Certificate
D. Seaworthy Certificate

012276/DG01984 ***46 CFR 42.07-45 (d) (1)**
Your load line certificate expires on 27 May 1988. The
vessel is surveyed on that date and is found
satisfactory. You are sailing foreign the same day.
Which statement is TRUE?
A. A new certificate must be issued before you sail.
B. The existing certificate is endorsed as valid for a
     five year period commencing 27 May 1988.
⚓ C. The existing certificate is extended for a period of
     up to 150 days.
D. The existing certificate is extended until the first
     foreign port of call where a new certificate will be
     issued by the local surveyor.

012277/DG01765 ***46 CFR 42.09-15 (d)**
The annual survey for endorsement of a Load Line
Certificate must be held within _____.
A. the three month period immediately following the
     certificate's anniversary date
B. the three month period immediately preceding the
     certificate's anniversary date
⚓ C. three months either way of the certificate's
     anniversary date
D. the three month period centered on the certificate's
     anniversary date

012278/DG02735 ***46 CFR 42.09-15**
Periodic surveys to renew the load line assignment
must be made at intervals NOT exceeding _____.
A. 18 months
B. two years
C. three years
⚓ D. five years

012279/DG02027 ***46 CFR 42.09-15**
Your vessel is issued a load line certificate dated 27
May 1992. What is NOT an acceptable date for one of
the surveys for endorsements?
A. 28 February 1993
⚓ B. 27 November 1993
C. 26 August 1994
D. 27 May 1995

012280/DG02042 ***46 CFR 42.13-20**
Which statement about the deck line is TRUE?
A. The top of the deck line is marked at the highest
     point of the freeboard deck, including camber, at
     the midships point.
⚓ B. A vessel with wooden planks on a steel deck will
     have the deck line marked at the intersection of the
     upper line of the wood sheathing with the side
     shell.
C. The deck edge is marked at the intersection of the
     freeboard deck with the side shell, at the lowest
     point of sheer, with the vessel at even trim.
D. On a vessel with a rounded stringer-sheer plate, the
     deck line is marked where the stringer plate turns
     down from the plane of the deck line.

012281/DG01791 ***46 CFR 44**
Which factor does NOT affect the required freeboard of
a cargo vessel?
A. Season of the year
B. Geographic zone of operation
C. Density of the water
⚓ D. Condition of trim in normal operation

012282/DG00437 ***46 CFR 109.433 (j)**
Prior to getting underway in fresh or brackish water,
the Master must _____.
⚓ A. log the density of the water
B. secure all overboard discharges
C. take on fresh water ballast
D. clean the sides with fresh water

012283/DG02690 ***46 CFR 109.433 (j)**
When must the Master of a vessel log the position of
load line marks in relation to the surface of the water in
the Official Logbook?
A. Once a day
B. At the change of every watch
C. Only when in fresh or brackish water
⚓ D. Prior to getting underway

012284/DG02112 ***46 USC 4209-30**
What is NOT surveyed at an annual load line survey?
A. The overall structure and layout of the vessel for
     alterations to the superstructure
⚓ B. The bilge pumping system
C. Main deck hatch covers
D. Portholes and deadlights in the side plating

012285/DG02152 ***46 CFR 69.177; *46 CFR 69.183 (a)**
Your vessel has the symbol shown inscribed on the
side. Which statement concerning this symbol is
TRUE? See Diagram D022DG
A. This represents the load line marks when engaged
     on a voyage upon the Great Lakes.
B. The line directly under the triangle is at the same
     level as the summer load line.
C. The symbol is the equivalent of a load line marking
     and is used by government vessels (USN, MSC,
     USCG) only.
⚓ D. The applicable gross and net tonnage of the ship
     will change if this mark is submerged and the load
     line mark is visible.

012286/DG01042   *46 CFR 69.177; *46 CFR 69.183
Your vessel has the symbol shown inscribed on the sides amidships. Which statement is TRUE? See Diagram D022DG
A. This line represents the load line mark for a Great Lakes voyage.
⚓ B. The gross and net tonnage of the ship will change if this mark is submerged and the load line is visible.
C. The line directly under the triangle is at the same level as the summer load line.
D. This is the equivalent of a load line marking for government (COE, NOAA, MSC) vessels.

012287/DG02089   MODSHIPS
In addition to the load lines indicated in illustration D003DG, some vessels have a Winter North Atlantic line. Which statement about this load line mark is TRUE? See Diagram D003DG
A. It is carried on VLCC/ULCC type vessels and allows reduced freeboard considering their size.
B. It is marked above line B in the diagram.
C. It is applied to vessels on restricted trade routes between the United Kingdom, Iceland, and Northern European countries.
⚓ D. It applies only to vessels not exceeding 328 ft. navigating in the Winter North Atlantic zones.

012288/DG01740   AMSM
The group of markings shown is called a _____.
See Diagram D003DG
A. loft mark
⚓ B. load line mark
C. test mark
D. water mark

012289/DG02107   KNIGHTS; *46 CFR 42.20-75 (d)
What is the name of the mark indicated by the letter A? See Diagram D003DG
A. Winter North Atlantic load line
B. Fresh Water load line
⚓ C. Deck line
D. Plimsoll line

012290/DG02054   MODSHIPS; KNIGHTS
What is the name of the mark indicated by the letter B in the diagram? See Diagram D003DG
A. Timber summer load line
⚓ B. Tropical fresh water load line
C. Tropical load line
D. Summer load line

012291/DG01980   MODSHIPS
What is the name of the mark indicated by the letter C? See Diagram D003DG
⚓ A. Fresh water line
B. Tropical water line
C. Summer water line
D. Winter North Atlantic water line

012292/DG01675   MODSHIPS
What is the name of the mark indicated by the letter D? See Diagram D003DG
⚓ A. Tropical load line
B. Summer load line
C. Fresh load line
D. Winter load line

012293/DG01767   MODSHIPS
What is the name of the mark indicated by the letter E? See Diagram D003DG
A. Fresh water line
B. Winter water line
C. Tropical water line
⚓ D. Summer water line

012294/DG01792   MODSHIPS; KNIGHTS
What is the name of the mark indicated by the letter F? See Diagram D003DG
A. Fresh water load line
B. Summer load line
⚓ C. Winter load line
D. Tropical load line

TONNAGE CERTIFICATE

012295/DG00421   *46 CFR 69.5
An International Tonnage Certificate will be issued to a vessel when it meets several requirements, one of which is that the vessel must _____.
A. admeasure over 100 GT
⚓ B. be 79 or more feet in length
C. engage in intercoastal or international trade
D. be issued a Certificate of Inspection

012296/DG00411   INT. MARITIME DICTIONARY
Tonnage tax is officially based upon the figures obtained from the _____.
⚓ A. Admeasurement Certificate
B. deadweight scale
C. displacement scale
D. Load Line Certificate

012297/DG01207   MMOH; MARTIN; *46 CFR 69.71
The Tonnage Certificate indicates _____.
A. deadweight tons
B. displacement tons
⚓ C. net tons
D. light displacement tons

CERTIFICATE OF DOCUMENTATION & ENROLLMENT

012298/DG00511   *46 CFR 67.17-3; MARTIN
All U.S. Flag vessels engaged in foreign trade are required to have a(n) _____.
A. enrollment
B. license
⚓ C. registry
D. sea letter

012299/DG01422   MARTIN
A U.S. vessel engaged in foreign trade must be _____.
A. classed
B. enrolled
C. licensed
⚓ D. registered

012300/DG02889   *46 CFR 67.5
What is the minimum size required before a vessel can be documented?
⚓ A. 5 net tons
B. 100 gross tons
C. 26 feet length
D. 65 feet length

012301/DG04013   *46 CFR 67.01
What is the minimum size required before a vessel can be documented?
A, 26 feet; end-to-end over the deck excluding sheer
B. 100 gross tons
⚓ C. 5 net tons
D. 26 feet between perpendiculars

012302/DG00645   *46 CFR 67.45
A vessel's Certificate of Documentation _____.
A. may be retained by the owner at the home port OR kept on the vessel
B. must be posted under transparent material in the pilothouse
⚓ C. must be carried on board
D. must be kept on file at the corporate offices of the owner or operator

012303/DG00471   CHAPMAN; MARTIN
The official identification of a vessel is found in the _____.
A. Certificate of Inspection
B. Classification Certificate
C. Load Line Certificate
⚓ D. Certificate of Documentation

012304/DG00431   MARTIN; *46 CFR 67.01-3
Official proof of an American vessel's nationality is contained in the _____.
A. Certificate of Inspection
B. Official Log
⚓ C. Certificate of Documentation
D. Shipping Articles

012305/DG00441   *46 CFR 67.01-3
The document which shows a vessel's nationality, ownership, and tonnage is the _____.
A. Manifest Certificate
B. Bill of Lading Certificate
⚓ C. Certificate of Documentation
D. Official Logbook

012306/DG00451   MMOH; *46 CFR 67.05-1
What is official proof of a vessel's ownership?
⚓ A. Certificate of Documentation
B. Bill of Lading
C. Transfer Certificate
D. Logbook

012307/DG00541   *46 CFR 67.15
The official number of a documented vessel is _____.
A. not required to be marked anywhere on the vessel
⚓ B. required to be permanently marked on the vessel's structure
C. required to be painted on the vessel's stern
D. required to be painted on the vessel's bow

012308/DG00551   *46 CFR 67.15
The name and hailing port of a documented commercial vessel is _____.
A. not required to be marked anywhere on the vessel
B. required to be marked on both bows and on the keel
⚓ C. required to be marked on the stern with the name of the vessel marked on both bows
D. required to be marked on the keel, stern, and both bows

012309/DG03110   *46 USC 46; *46 CFR 67.15-3
The number or name of a tank barge shall be _____.
A. displayed in at least 4 different positions on the barge
B. carved on a wooden board and attached to the barge's hull
C. displayed as close to the navigation lights as possible
⚓ D. displayed at the highest point of the barge's hull such that it can be seen from either side

U.S. COAST GUARD CERTIFICATE OF INSPECTION

012310/DG03130   ***46 CFR 10.16; *46 CFR 24.05;**
***46 CFR 67.45**

What is NOT required on an uninspected towing vessel?

A. Certificate of Documentation
⚓ B. Certificate of Inspection
C. Operators Merchant Marine license
D. FCC Station License

012311/DG00902   ***46 CFR 15.501**

The number of able seamen required on board is stated in the _____.

A. American Bureau of Shipping code
B. SOLAS Certificate
C. Classification Certificate
⚓ D. Certificate of Inspection

012312/DG03631   ***46 CFR 15.501**

The number of certificated able seamen and lifeboatmen required on board is listed in the _____.

⚓ A. Certificate of Inspection
B. American Bureau of Shipping code
C. Muster List ("Station Bill")
D. Safety of Life at Sea Convention

012313/DG00661   ***46 CFR 15.501**

The number of certificated lifeboatmen required for a vessel is found on the _____.

⚓ A. Certificate of Inspection
B. Muster List ("Station Bill")
C. lifeboats
D. Register or Enrollment

012314/DG02471   ***46 CFR 15.501**

To determine the number of able seamen required on an inspected vessel, you should check the _____.

A. Load Line Certificate
B. operations manual
C. Safety of Life at Sea Certificate
⚓ D. Certificate of Inspection

012315/DG02245   ***46 CFR 15.501**

To determine the number of certificated lifeboatmen required on a vessel, you should check the _____.

A. Load Line Certificate
⚓ B. Certificate of Inspection
C. Safety of Life at Sea Certificate
D. operations manual

012316/DG00641   ***46 CFR 15.501; MARTIN**

Which document shows the minimum required crew a vessel must have to navigate from one port in the United States to another?

A. Articles
⚓ B. Certificate of Inspection
C. Crew List
D. Register

012317/DG02271   ***46 CFR 15.501 (a)**

You are signing on a crew. You can determine the minimum number and qualifications of the crew that you are required to carry by consulting which document?

A. Crew list
⚓ B. Certificate of Inspection
C. Articles of Agreement
D. Fo'c'sle card

012318/DG01325   ***46 CFR 15.501 (a)**

You are signing on crew members. The minimum number of people required aboard, and the qualifications of each, is listed on the _____.

A. Crew list
⚓ B. Certificate of Inspection
C. Articles of Agreement
D. Fo'c'sle card

012319/DG02197   ***46 CFR 15.501 (a)**

You are signing on crew members. The minimum number of people required aboard, and the qualifications of each, is listed on the _____.

A. Crew list
B. Fo'c'sle card
⚓ C. Certificate of Inspection
D. Articles of Agreement

012320/DG03083   ***46 CFR 15.501 (a)**

You are signing on crew members. The minimum number of people required aboard, and the qualifications of each, is listed on the _____.

A. Fo'c'sle card
B. Crew list
C. Articles of Agreement
⚓ D. Certificate of Inspection

012321/DG01671   ***46 CFR 15.501 (b)**

The number of certificated able seamen and lifeboatmen required on a vessel is determined by the _____.

A. International Maritime Organization
B. Corps of Engineers
⚓ C. Coast Guard
D. American Bureau of Shipping

012322/DG00004
*46 CFR 15.840
Considering manning requirements for US flag vessels, your 2 watch cargo vessel has a deck crew of 20 people, exclusive of officers. How many of these people do the manning regulations require to be able seamen?
A. 13
⚓ B. 10
C. 7
D. 5

012323/DG03120
*46 CFR 24.05-1 (a) (1)
You are operating a 150-GT towing vessel. What is NOT required on the vessel?
A. Certificate of Documentation
B. FCC station license
C. Your Coast Guard license
⚓ D. Certificate of Inspection

012324/DG00313
*46 CFR 25.25-5
With the exception of a Coast Guard approved commercial hybrid Personal Flotation Device (PFD), which type of life preserver must be carried for each person on board an uninspected passenger vessel?
⚓ A. Type I
B. Type II
C. Type III
D. None of the above

012325/DG00621
*46 CFR 31.05-1 (b)
Which document shows details of a tank vessel, cargoes it may carry, manning and safety equipment required?
A. Safety Construction Certificate
B. Cargo Gear Certificate
⚓ C. Certificate of Inspection
D. Declaration of Inspection

012326/DG00591
*46 CFR 31.05
What will NOT be found on the Certificate of Inspection of an ocean going tankship?
A. Manning requirements
⚓ B. Minimum freeboard permitted
C. Grade(s) of cargoes that the vessel may carry
D. Waters upon which the vessel may be operated

012327/DG03140
*46 CFR 31.10-35
If the Certificate of Inspection of a damaged tank barge has expired, which certificate may be issued to allow its movement to a repair facility?
A. Change of employment
⚓ B. Permit to proceed
C. Application for inspection
D. Temporary Certificate of Inspection

012328/DG01057
*46 CFR 31.10-35
The Certificate of Inspection of a damaged tank barge has expired. What certificate authorizes the barge to move to a repair facility for repair and inspection?
A. Application for Inspection
B. Change of Employment
⚓ C. Permit to Proceed
D. Temporary Certificate of Inspection

012329/DG00611
*46 CFR 91.01
The Certificate of Inspection for a containership _____.
⚓ A. must be posted under transparent material in a conspicuous place
B. is issued by the Coast Guard and is usually valid for 2 years.
C. lists all of the stability limitations and conditions imposed on the vessel
D. shows the due date of the quadrennial test of the cargo gear

012330/DG00957
*46 CFR 91.01-15
Your vessel has completed an inspection for certification and is issued a Temporary Certificate of Inspection. The Temporary Certificate _____.
⚓ A. has the full force of the regular Certificate of Inspection
B. expires six months after it is issued
C. must be exchanged for a regular Certificate of Inspection within 3 months
D. is retained in the custody of the Master

012331/DG00601
*46 CFR 91.01-15
Your vessel has completed an inspection for certification and is issued a temporary certificate. This _____.
A. expires six months after it is issued
B. must be exchanged for a regular Certificate of Inspection before going foreign or out of state
⚓ C. has the full force of a regular Certificate of Inspection
D. must be posted in the vicinity of the officers' licenses

012332/DG00671
*46 CFR 91.05
A Permit to Proceed is issued by the _____.
A. American Bureau of Shipping
B. National Cargo Bureau
⚓ C. U.S. Coast Guard
D. U.S. Department of Labor

012333/DG00571   ***46 CFR 91.05***
You are in port A in the United States, and your Certificate of Inspection has expired. You wish to go to port B in the United States for repairs and to complete the inspection. If the Officer-in-Charge Marine Inspection deems it safe, he may issue a _____.
A. Certificate of Seaworthiness
B. Limited Certificate of Inspection
C. Temporary Certificate of Inspection
D. Permit to Proceed

012334/DG00651   ***46 CFR 91.20-15***
Fire fighting equipment requirements for a particular vessel may be found on the _____.
A. Certificate of Inspection
B. Certificate of Seaworthiness
C. Classification Certificate
D. Certificate of Registry

012335/DG01532   ***46 CFR 91.20-15***
To determine the number of portable fire extinguishers required on an inspected vessel, you should check the _____.
A. hot work permit
B. Certificate of Inspection
C. Safety of Life at Sea Certificate
D. Muster List ("Station Bill")

012336/DG02810ENCY. NAUT. KNOW.; *46 CFR 91.20-15*
Which document lists all the lifesaving equipment required for a vessel?
A. Certificate of Inspection
B. American Bureau of Shipping Classification Certificate
C. International Convention for the Safety of Life at Sea Certificate
D. Certificate of Registry

012337/DG02601   ***46 CFR 91.25; PETEX***
To determine the number of inflatable liferafts required on a vessel, you should check the _____.
A. Load Line Certificate
B. SOLAS Certificate
C. Stability Letter
D. Certificate of Inspection

012338/DG00631   ***46 CFR 91.27***
At least one reinspection shall be made on each vessel holding a Certificate of Inspection valid for two years. This inspection shall be held between the tenth and fourteenth months of the duration period of the certificate and shall be _____.
A. at the discretion of the inspector, but in no greater detail than required for original certification
B. at the discretion of the inspector, but in no lesser detail than required for original certification
C. generally similar in scope to the inspection required for certification, but in less detail
D. equivalent to the inspection required for certification

012339/DG00799   ***46 CFR 107.223***
Temporary Certificates of Inspection are effective until the _____.
A. SOLAS Certificate is issued
B. Load Line Certificate is renewed
C. classification society approval is issued
D. permanent Certificate of Inspection is issued

012340/DG02852   ***46 CFR 177.085 (j) (1) (2)***
On a small passenger vessel the collision bulkhead is _____.
A. amidships forward of the engine room
B. just forward of the steering compartment
C. in the engine room
D. A distance of 5% to 15% of the waterline length abaft the stem measured at the load waterline

012341/DG00315*46 CFR 180.70 (a) (1); *46 CFR 25.25-5 (d)*
A vessel must have one approved ring life buoy on board if its length is over how many feet?
A. 6 feet
B. 16 feet
C. 26 feet
D. 36 feet

012342/DG02629   ***46 CFR 199.155 (d)***
Each open lifeboat carried on a vessel on an international voyage must have _____.
A. hand-propelling gear
B. a davit span with at least 2 lifelines
C. a mast and a sail
D. a motor

012343/DG03542   ***46 CFR 71.01-5***
The Certificate of Inspection on a passenger vessel of over 100 gross tons must be posted _____.
A. in the Master's office
B. on the bridge
C. in a conspicuous place where observation by the passengers is likely
D. in the passengers' dining room or, where there is no dining room, in the lounge area

INTERNATIONAL CERTIFICATES

012344/DG02898   ***46 CFR 91.60-40***
What is the period of validity of the SOLAS required Cargo Ship Safety Construction Certificate?
A. 12 months
B. 24 months
C. 48 months
⚓ D. 60 months

012345/DG00691   ***46 CFR 91.60-10; MARTIN***
On U.S. flag vessels, which certificate is always issued by the Coast Guard?
A. Load Line Certificate
⚓ B. Safety Equipment Certificate
C. Safety Construction Certificate
D. Register of cargo gear

012346/DG00701*46 CFR 91.60-10; SOLAS; ARMSTRONG
The Safety Equipment Certificate shows that the vessel conforms to the standards of the _____.
A. U.S. Coast Guard
B. American Bureau of Shipping
C. American Salvage Association
⚓ D. S.O.L.A.S. Convention

012347/DG02791   ***46 CFR 91.60-10***
What is the period of validity of a Cargo Ship Safety Equipment Certificate?
A. 72 months
⚓ B. 60 months
C. 48 months
D. 42 months

012348/DG00915   ***46 CFR 91.60-15***
What is the period of validity of a Cargo Ship Safety Radio Certificate?
A. 6 months
B. 12 months
C. 24 months
⚓ D. 60 months

012349/DG02890   ***46 CFR 91.60-25***
A vessel cannot comply with all of the SOLAS requirements due to its construction. Where will this be indicated?
A. Nowhere; the vessel must comply to engage in international trade.
B. On the reverse of the SOLAS certificate
⚓ C. On the Exemption Certificate
D. On the Certificate of Inspection

012350/DG02618   ***46 CFR 91.60-25***
Due to the nature of a vessel's construction for a particular trade, it does not fully comply with the provisions of SOLAS. Where will this be indicated?
⚓ A. On the Exemption Certificate
B. On the reverse of the particular SOLAS certificate affected
C. On the face of the Certificate of Inspection
D. Nowhere; the vessel must comply to engage in international trade.

012351/DG00917   ***46 CFR 91.60-30***
What is the period of validity of a Safety Management Certificate?
⚓ A. 60 months
B. 48 months
C. 42 months
D. 36 months

IOPP CERTIFICATE & OIL RECORD BOOK

012352/DG01363   ***33 CFR 151.25***
According to 33 CFR, on board which type of vessel described below is required to maintain Part II (Cargo/Ballast Operations) of the Oil Record Book?
A. A ship of 150 gross tons and above, other than an oil tanker.
⚓ B. A non-tanker that carries more than 200 cubic meters of oil in bulk.
C. Any oil tanker of 100 gross tons and above.
D. An oil tanker of 150 gross tons and above on domestic voyages only.

012353/DG01378   ***33 CFR 151.25 (a)***
Container vessels are required to maintain an Oil Record Book when the vessel is _____?
A. 150 gross tons and above
B. 200 gross tons and above
C. 300 gross tons above
⚓ D. 400 gross tons and above

012354/DG01377   ***33 CFR 151.25 (a)***
On a passenger vessel over 400 gross tons, routine entries for the Oil Record Book are recorded in _____.
A. Oil Record Book is not required
⚓ B. Part I (Machinery Space Operations)
C. Part II (Cargo Oil/Ballast Operations)
D. Part III (Emergency Discharge/Spillage)

012355/DG01382   ***33 CFR 151.25 (c)***
The Oil Record Book for all fixed or floating drilling rigs is the property of the _____.
⚓ A. U.S. government
B. state in whose water the drilling rig is located
C. drilling rig's owner
D. company leasing the drilling rig

012356/DG01372   ***33 CFR 151.25 (c)**
The Oil Record Book for all U.S. ships is the property of the _____.
⚓ A. U.S. government
B. master of the vessel
C. vessel's owner
D. charterer of the vessel

012357/DG01383   ***33 CFR 151.25 (h)**
According to Pollution Prevention Regulations (33CFR), after every designated operation, the Oil Record Book is to be signed by _____.
A. the master
B. a licensed officer present at the operation designated by the master
⚓ C. person(s) in charge of the operation
D. person(s) in charge of the operation and a licensed officer present at the operation

012358/DG01385   ***33 CFR 151.25 (h)**
According to Pollution Prevention Regulations (33CFR), each completed page in the Oil Record Book is to be signed by _____.
A. Coast Guard representative designated by COTP
⚓ B. the master
C. person(s) in charge of the operation
D. oil terminal representative

012359/DG01373   ***33 CFR 151.25 (h)**
After each operation involving the transfer of oil or oily mixture, an entry shall be recorded in the Oil Record Book _____.
⚓ A. without delay
B. within 1 hour of completion of the inspection
C. within 6 hours of completion of the operation
D. as the operation permits

012360/DG01362   ***33 CFR 151.25**
Under normal operating conditions aboard a ship, who has the overall responsibility in maintaining the Oil Record Book?
A. Chief Engineer
B. First Assistant Engineer
⚓ C. Master
D. Chief Mate

012361/DG01037*33 CFR 151.17 (a) (3); *33 CFR 151.19 (e)
After an IOPP Certificate is issued to an inspected vessel, how many other surveys of the vessel's pollution prevention equipment are conducted during the period of validity of the certificate?
A. None
B. One
C. Two
⚓ D. Three

012362/DG01527   ***33 CFR 151.19 (a)**
A 30,000 DWT tankship is required to have an IOPP certificate when _____.
A. engaged in the coastwise trade
B. going foreign
⚓ C. calling at ports in another country signatory to MARPOL 73/78
D. carrying cargoes listed in the MARPOL regulations

012363/DG00758   ***33 CFR 151.19 (e)**
An IOPP Certificate on an inspected vessel is valid for what period of time?
A. 6 months
B. 1 year
C. 2 years
⚓ D. 5 years

012364/DG01062   ***33 CFR 151.19 (e)**
An IOPP Certificate on an inspected vessel is valid for what period of time?
A. 6 months
B. 12 months
C. 18 months
⚓ D. 5 years

012365/DG01577   ***33 CFR 151.19 (e)**
You are the Chief Mate of a 30,000-DWT tankship. The vessel is engaged in trade with another country signatory to MARPOL 73/78. Which statement is TRUE?
A. The Certificate of Inspection serves as prima facie evidence of complying with MARPOL 73/78.
⚓ B. The IOPP Certificate for an inspected vessel is valid for 5 years.
C. An IOPP Certificate is invalidated if the ship carries cargoes outside the classes authorized thereon.
D. An IOPP Certificate is renewed at each inspection for certification.

012366/DG00955   *33 CFR 151.17 (a); *33 CFR 151.19 (e)
In which case is the IOPP Certificate of an inspected vessel NOT invalidated?
⚓ A. The required oily-water separator malfunctions.
B. The ship is transferred to Liberian registry.
C. An annual survey is conducted fifteen months after the date of certificate issuance.
D. A 15 ppm oily-water separator is replaced by a 100 ppm oily-water separator.

012367/DG00791   ***33 CFR 151; OIL RECORD BOOK**
The oil record book is required to be carried aboard _____.
A. tankers
B. passenger vessels
C. cargo vessels
⚓ D. All of the above

012368/DG00801   *33 CFR 151
When oil is discharged overboard, an entry is required in the _____.
  A. engine rough log
⚓ B. Oil Record Book
  C. Official Logbook
  D. deck rough log

012369/DG00811   *33 CFR 151
When oily ballast has been pumped overboard, an entry must be made in the _____.
⚓ A. Oil Record Book
  B. Official Logbook
  C. deck rough log
  D. engine rough log

012370/DG00821   *33 CFR 151.35
The Master must maintain the Oil Record Book on board for at least _____.
  A. 1 month
  B. 12 months
  C. 24 months
⚓ D. 36 months

012371/DG01386   OIL RECORD BOOK
Which of the following is not an acceptable unit of measure to be used consistently through out an Oil Record Book?
  A. cubic meters
  B. gallons
⚓ C. tons
  D. barrels

012372/DG00831   *33 CFR 151.35
The Oil Record Book on a vessel NOT engaged on a foreign voyage shall be maintained on board for not less than _____.
  A. 12 months
  B. 24 months
⚓ C. 36 months
  D. 48 months

012373/DG01505   MARPOL
The supplement to the IOPP Certificate contains what type of data?
  A. The grades of cargo that an oil tanker is permitted to carry.
⚓ B. A checklist of the equipment installed for controlling the discharge of oil.
  C. The trade routes upon which the vessel may operate.
  D. A list of the underwriters who will assume financial responsibility in the event of an oil spill.

MISCELLANEOUS CERTIFICATES

012374/DG00711   MARTIN
If an alien stowaway is discovered aboard your vessel, his name must be placed on the _____.
  A. Alien Crew List
  B. Crew List
  C. Passenger List
⚓ D. separate Passenger List marked stowaways

012375/DG00771   MARTIN
What does a Visaed Alien Crew List which is made and submitted to the U.S. Consul for visa show?
  A. All aliens aboard
  B. All crew members
⚓ C. Nonresident aliens aboard
  D. Registered aliens aboard

012376/DG00751   MARTIN
A document which has a list of names, birthplaces, and residences of persons employed on a merchant vessel bound from a U.S. port on a foreign voyage and is required at every port is called the _____.
⚓ A. Certified Crew List
  B. Crew Manifest
  C. Shipping Articles
  D. Muster List ("Station Bill")

012377/DG00761   MARTIN
The Immigration and Naturalization Service is concerned with which document on a vessel making preliminary entry into a U.S. port from a foreign port?
  A. Cargo Manifest
⚓ B. Certified Crew List
  C. Curio List
  D. Shipping Articles

012378/DG00731   ARMSTRONG
A Deratization Exemption Certificate is valid for a period of _____.
  A. no time limit so long as Certificate of Sanitation is valid
  B. no time limit so long as no evidence of rodents aboard
  C. 1 year
⚓ D. 6 months

012379/DG02918   SEATECH
What is the period of validity of a De-Rat certificate?
  A. Specific voyage
⚓ B. 6 months
  C. 1 year
  D. 2 years

012380/DG00717   *46 CFR 97.13-15; *46 CFR 109.505

It is the responsibility of the Master to ensure that _____.

A. the muster list is posted in each compartment

⚓ B. temporary personnel and visitors are advised of emergency stations

C. names of crew members are listed on the muster list

D. no changes are made to the muster list

012381/DG00982   *46 CFR 97.13-15; *46 CFR 109.505 (b)

The muster list must be posted in conspicuous locations and signed by the _____.

A. safety officer

B. Coast Guard Officer approving the bill

C. owner

⚓ D. Master

012382/DG01033   *46 CFR 97.13-15; *46 CFR 109.505

Each crewmember has an assigned firefighting station. This assignment is shown on the _____.

A. fire fighting plan

B. shipping articles

C. Certificate of Inspection

⚓ D. muster list

012383/DG01368   *46 CFR 199.80

Fire and abandon ship stations and duties may be found on the _____.

A. crewman's duty list

B. Certificate of Inspection

C. shipping articles

⚓ D. muster list

012384/DG01348   *46 CFR 97.13-15; *46 CFR 109.505

Preparation of muster lists and signing of same is the responsibility of the _____.

A. Chief Officer of the vessel

B. owner of the vessel

⚓ C. Master of the vessel

D. United States Coast Guard

012385/DG01358   *46 CFR 199.80

Seeing that all hands are familiar with their duties, as specified in the muster list, is the responsibility of the _____.

⚓ A. Master

B. Chief Mate

C. safety officer

D. department heads

012386/DG01165   *46 CFR 109.501; *46 CFR 97.13-1

The Muster List ("Station Bill") shows each person's lifeboat station, duties during abandonment, basic instructions, and _____.

⚓ A. all emergency signals

B. instructions for lowering the lifeboats

C. the time each weekly drill will be held

D. work schedule

012387/DG01285   *46 CFR 109.501

Which information MUST be entered on the muster list?

A. Names of all crew members

B. Use and application of special equipment

C. Listing of approved emergency equipment

⚓ D. Duties and station of each person during emergencies

CLASSIFICATION CERTIFICATE

012388/DG01261   INT. MARITIME DICTIONARY

A vessel operating "in class" has met all the requirements of the _____.

⚓ A. ABS or similar society

B. insurance company

C. U.S. Coast Guard

D. U.S. Customs

012389/DG01021   MMOH

A vessel's Classification Certificate is issued by the _____.

⚓ A. American Bureau of Shipping

B. National Cargo Bureau

C. United States Coast Guard

D. United States Customs

012390/DG01031   MARTIN

Which certificate is NOT issued by the Coast Guard?

A. Award of official number

B. Certificate of Inspection

⚓ C. Classification of Hull and Machinery

D. Safety Equipment Certificate

RECORD KEEPING PROCEDURES

012391/DG01011   *46 CFR 04.05-15

After your vessel has been involved in a casualty, you are required to make your logbooks, bell books, etc., available to _____.

A. attorneys for opposition parties

B. marine surveyors

⚓ C. U.S. Coast Guard officials

D. All of the above

012392/DG00871   **MMOH; WATCH GUIDE**
In writing up the logbook at the end of your watch, you make an error in writing an entry. What is the proper means of correcting this error?
  A. Cross out the error with a single line, and write the correct entry, then initial it.
  B. Carefully and neatly erase the entry and rewrite it correctly.
  C. Remove this page of the log book, and rewrite all entries on a clean page.
  D. Blot out the error completely and rewrite the entry correctly.

012393/DG02461   **MMOH; WATCH GUIDE**
In writing up the logbook at the end of your watch, you make an error in writing an entry. What is the proper way of correcting this error?
  A. Carefully and neatly erase the entry and rewrite it correctly.
  B. Cross out the error with a single line, write the correct entry, and initial it.
  C. Blot out the error completely and rewrite the entry correctly.
  D. Remove this page of the log book and rewrite all entries on a clean page.

012394/DG01217   **MMOH; WATCH GUIDE**
The proper way to correct a mistake in the logbook is to _____.
  A. erase the entry and rewrite
  B. draw a line through the entry, rewrite, and initial the correction
  C. draw several lines through the entry, rewrite, and initial the correction
  D. completely black out the entry, rewrite, and initial the correction

OFFICIAL LOG BOOK

012395/DG01127   **MARTIN**
All entries in the Official Logbook must be signed by the Master and _____.
  A. the Chief Engineer
  B. the person about whom the entry concerns
  C. one other crew member
  D. No other signature is required.

012396/DG00841   **MARTIN**
All entries in the Official Logbook must be signed by the Master and _____.
  A. the Union Representative
  B. the person about whom the entry concerns
  C. no one else
  D. one other crew member

012397/DG00094   **MMOH**
All of the following records are usually maintained by the watch-standing officers aboard a vessel EXCEPT the _____.
  A. deck logbook
  B. official logbook
  C. compass record book
  D. chronometer error book

012398/DG01001   **MARTIN**
Which is supplied to the vessel by the U.S. Coast Guard?
  A. Bell book
  B. Cargo gear register
  C. Official Logbook
  D. Rough Logbook

012399/DG00873   ***46 CFR 109.213 (a)**
At the required fire drill, all persons must report to their stations and demonstrate their ability to perform the duties assigned to them _____.
  A. by the Coast Guard regulations
  B. in the Muster List ("Station Bill")
  C. by the person conducting the drill
  D. at the previous safety meeting

012400/DG00961   ***46 USC 201**
Which log includes a statement of the conduct, ability, and character of each crew member on the completion of a voyage?
  A. Official Logbook
  B. Department Logbook
  C. Crew Logbook
  D. Smooth Logbook

012401/DG00861   ***46 USC 202; ARMSTRONG**
Every entry required to be made in the Official Logbook shall be signed by the _____.
  A. Mate on watch
  B. Master and Chief Mate or other member of the crew
  C. Master only
  D. Purser, one of the Mates, and some other member of the crew

012402/DG01077   ***46 USC 10702; MARTIN**
A seaman dies during a voyage. What is NOT required to be entered into the Official Log?
  A. Statement that the Master has taken custody of the deceased's MMD and passport
  B. An inventory of the money and property
  C. Statement of the wages due
  D. Statement as to the total deductions to be made from the wages

012403/DG00891 ***33 CFR 20.1305**
A seaman assaults the Second Mate and injures him with a beer bottle while the ship is at sea. The incident is logged in the Official Logbook. In subsequent suspension and revocation proceedings against the seaman, according to the regulations, _____.
A. the Second Mate and the Master must testify as to the facts of the assault
B. the case will be dismissed if the logbook entries are improperly made
⚓ C. the logbook entry is prima facie evidence of the facts if it complies with the law
D. the logbook is inadmissible if the logbook entries do not conform to the law

012404/DG01748 ***46 CFR 35.07-5; MARTIN**
An Official Logbook is required on which vessel?
A. A 150-G.T. tug going from Boston to New Orleans.
⚓ B. A 100-G.T. tug going from New York to San Pedro, California.
C. A 50-G.T. tug going from Miami to Seattle.
D. A 199-G.T. tug on a coastwise trip of 650 miles.

012405/DG03492 ***46 CFR 78.37-10 (b)**
The Master of a passenger vessel which is not required to maintain an Official Logbook must keep a record of the number of passengers received and delivered from day to day. This record must be available for a period of _____.
A. 6 months
⚓ B. 12 months
C. 24 months
D. 36 months

012406/DG00951 ***46 CFR 95.10**
The responsibility for maintaining the Official Logbook on voyages between the Atlantic and Pacific coasts of the United States rests with the _____.
A. Chief Mate of the vessel
⚓ B. Master of the vessel
C. Deck Officer of the watch at the time of the occurrence
D. Purser of the vessel

012407/DG01758 ***46 CFR 97.35**
As operator of a 199-GT towing vessel sailing foreign, it shall be your duty to enter in the Official Logbook or other permanent record _____.
A. all information contained on the barge's Certificate of Inspection
B. the condition of all towing gear to be used
C. all navigational aids to be used
⚓ D. the barges load line and draft readings

012408/DG01738 ***46 CFR 97.35; MARTIN**
Which vessel is required by regulations to have an Official Logbook?
⚓ A. A 100-gross ton tug on a trip between Baltimore, Maryland, and San Pedro, California.
B. A 199-gross ton tug on a coastwise trip of 610 miles.
C. A 66-gross ton tug operating between states.
D. All of the above

012409/DG00851 ARMSTRONG; *46 USC 201; MARTIN
Your vessel (185-GT) is on a voyage between New York and San Francisco. Which statement is TRUE?
A. The maintenance of an Official Logbook is optional.
B. The vessel must be on foreign articles.
C. This is considered a coastwise voyage.
⚓ D. An Official Logbook must be maintained.

012410/DG01413 ***46 CFR 97.35-3 (a)**
The official logbook is filed with the Officer in Charge, Marine Inspection (OCMI) _____.
⚓ A. upon completion of the voyage
B. at the next Certificate of Inspection
C. within 30 days of the date of arrival of the first U.S. port
D. at the end of the year with all other official logbooks

012411/DG01412 ***46 CFR 97.35-3 (a)**
Upon completion of a voyage, the official logbook shall be filed with the _____.
A. nearest Regional Exam Center (REC)
⚓ B. the Officer in Charge, Marine Inspection (OCMI)
C. Captain of the Port (COTP)
D. None of the above

012412/DG01415 ***46 CFR 97.35-3 (b)**
When an Official logbook is not required, an unofficial logbook is required to be kept aboard for review by a marine inspector for _____.
A. one month
B. six months
⚓ C. 12 months
D. None of the above

012413/DG00941 ***46 CFR 97.35-3**
Which logbook is required to be submitted to the Coast Guard?
⚓ A. Official Log
B. Smooth log
C. Rough log
D. Bell log

012414/DG00901   *46 CFR 97.35-5; MARTIN
What is required to be entered into the Official Logbook?
⚓ A. Opening a sideport at sea to renew a gasket
   B. The annual required stripping and cleaning of the lifeboats
   C. The biennial weight test of the lifeboats and falls
   D. The drafts on entering port

012415/DG00921   *46 CFR 97.35-5; MARTIN
Which item must be entered in the official log?
   A. All engine orders
⚓ B. Drafts upon leaving port
   C. Names of night mates and engineers
   D. Number of cargo gangs on board

012416/DG00911   *46 CFR 97.35-5; MARTIN
Which entry is NOT required in the Official Logbook?
   A. Steering gear tests
   B. Position of the load line and freeboard upon sailing
⚓ C. Commencement and termination of cargo operations
   D. Closure of hatches and sideports upon sailing

012417/DG00931   *46 CFR 97.35-5; MARTIN
Which is NOT a required entry in the ship's Official Logbook?
   A. Sale of effects of a deceased crew member
   B. Medical treatment of an injury
   C. Inspections of cargo gear
⚓ D. Dry docking of the vessel

012418/DG01921   *46 CFR 97.35-5; MARTIN
Which is NOT a required entry in the ship's Official Logbook?
   A. Reason for weekly emergency drill not being held
   B. Medical treatment of an injury
   C. Inspections of cargo gear
⚓ D. Dry docking of the vessel

012419/DG01820   *46 CFR 109.433 (h)
If a drill required by regulations is not completed, the Master or person in charge must _____.
   A. report this immediately to the Commandant of the Coast Guard
⚓ B. log the reason for not completing the drill
   C. conduct two of the required drills at the next opportunity
   D. All of the above

CARGO GEAR REGISTER

012420/DG02579   *46 CFR 91.37-75
Where are the test certificates, for wire rope used as cargo runners, and loose gear certificates usually maintained?
⚓ A. With the Cargo Gear Register on the ship
   B. In the Official Log
   C. At the Coast Guard Marine Safety Office with the vessel's inspection records
   D. At the central records center of the agency testing the cargo gear

MISCELLANEOUS LOGS & RECORDS

012421/DG00981   INT. MARITIME DICTIONARY
When a vessel is entering or leaving a port, a record of engine speeds is kept in the _____.
⚓ A. bell book
   B. deck rough log
   C. Official Logbook
   D. engine rough log

012422/DG00991   MMOH
When an azimuth of the Sun has been taken and the deviation of the standard magnetic compass computed, the watch officer should record the results _____.
   A. in the vessel's Official Logbook
   B. on the compass deviation card
⚓ C. in the compass deviation log
   D. on a Napier diagram

012423/DG00971   ENCY. NAUT. KNOW.
A journal kept by the officer of the watch in which day to day happenings are recorded regarding the deck department is the _____.
   A. cargo record book
⚓ B. deck rough log
   C. bell book
   D. Official Logbook

CARGO DOCUMENTS

012424/DG01407   MASTER'S HANDBOOK OF SHIP'S BUSINESS
If there is a discrepancy in the cargo totals, between the cargo onboard the vessel and the cargo listed in the cargo manifest, the more accurate account of cargo totals can be found in the _____.
   A. Notice of Readiness
   B. Charter Party
⚓ C. Bill of Lading
   D. Portage Bill

012425/DG02129   **HOPKINS**
The exact and complete identification of all cargo on board must be found on the _____.
   A.   Cargo Manifest
      B.   Mate's Receipt
      C.   Hatch Report
      D.   Loading List

012426/DG01138   **MMOH**
A vessel arrives in the port of Los Angeles from a foreign port and discharges some of its inward foreign cargo. What additional manifest is required?
      A.   Discharge Manifest
      B.   Inward Foreign Manifest
      C.   Pro Forma Manifest
   D.   Traveling Manifest

012427/DG01248   **MARTIN**
A declaration made by the Master before a U.S. Consul, giving particulars regarding heavy weather or other incidents which may have caused damage to the vessel or cargo, through no fault of the vessel, her officers, or crew is a(n) _____.
      A.   cargo addendum
      B.   exception report
      C.   Master's declaration
   D.   note of protest

012428/DG01288   **MARTIN**
A document used to indicate suspected cargo damage caused by rough weather would be the _____.
      A.   cargo report
      B.   hull damage report
   C.   Master's Note of Protest
      D.   Unseaworthy Certificate

012429/DG01298   **MARTIN**
A Master should file a marine note of protest if _____.
      A.   cargo was received at ship side which was damaged in land transit
      B.   longshore labor went on strike in the port causing undue vessel delay
      C.   portions of his vessel's cargo were illegally impounded in a foreign port
   D.   the vessel encountered heavy weather which might have caused cargo damage

012430/DG01328   **MARTIN**
The declaration made by the Master when he anticipates hull and/or cargo damage due to unusual weather conditions is a _____.
   A.   Note of Protest
      B.   Notice of Casualty
      C.   Portage Bill
      D.   Bottomry Bond

012431/DG01278   **MARTIN**
The document that establishes the facts of a casualty and is the prima facie relief from liability for the damage is the _____.
      A.   adjuster's report
      B.   insurance policy
      C.   invoice
   D.   Master's protest

012432/DG01268   **MARTIN**
The S.S. Ossel Hitch arrives in Capetown, South Africa, and the Master affects a note of protest with the U.S. Consul. Why would the Master affect this document?
      A.   Crew misconduct
      B.   Inability of vessel to comply with voyage charter
      C.   Suspicion of cargo pilferage by crew
   D.   Suspicion of heavy weather damage to vessel or cargo

012433/DG01308   **MARTIN**
The S.S. Sheet Bend arrives in New York after encountering heavy weather on a voyage from Cape Town. Who will note the maritime protest for the Master?
      A.   Collector of Customs
   B.   Notary Public
      C.   Officer in Charge Marine Inspection
      D.   U.S. Shipping Commissioner

BILL OF LADING

012434/DG01238   **MARTIN**
A contract of affreightment is a _____.
   A.   Bill of Lading
      B.   Bottomry Bond
      C.   manifest
      D.   Portage Bill

012435/DG01168   **MARTIN**
A vessel has completed loading cargo in the port of San Francisco. What document is signed by the Master stating the terms that goods were delivered and received by the ship?
      A.   Bill of Goods
   B.   Bill of Lading
      C.   Cargo Manifest
      D.   Cargo Receipt

012436/DG01188   **INT. MARITIME DICTIONARY**
An implied warranty of seaworthiness on the part of the vessel's owner lies in the _____.
      A.   Cargo Manifest
      B.   Certificate of Inspection
      C.   Classification Certificate
   D.   contract of carriage, i.e. Bill of Lading

012437/DG01218   ENCY. NAUT. KNOW.
Which is a negotiable document?
⚓ A. Bill of Lading
  B. Cargo Manifest
  C. Export Declaration
  D. Receiving Report

012438/DG01178   MARTIN
A shipper of cargo aboard your vessel offers a letter of
indemnity for the cargo. This is done in order to obtain
a(n) _____.
⚓ A. Clean Bill of Lading
  B. Order Bill of Lading
  C. Straight Bill of Lading
  D. Through Bill of Lading

012439/DG02161   THOMAS
A vessel loads 5000 tons of manganese ore. The
railroad cars that brought the ore to the vessel were
previously loaded with iron ore so the ore is
contaminated. The agent requests the Master to sign a
Clean Bill of Lading and in return the shipper will give
him a Letter of Indemnity. What is the best procedure
to follow?
  A. Sign a Clean Bill of Lading and accept the Letter
      of Indemnity.
⚓ B. Refuse to sign a Clean Bill of Lading.
  C. Sign the Clean Bill of Lading and have the agent
      countersign it.
  D. Sign a Clean Bill of lading under protest.

012440/DG01158   MARTIN
A vessel loads 100 tons of glass jars. The mate on
watch discovers that some of the cartons have been
damaged and has an exception made on the Bill of
Lading. What is this document called?
  A. Damage Bill of Lading
  B. Letter of Indemnity
  C. Non-negotiable Bill of Lading
⚓ D. Unclean Bill of Lading

012441/DG02165   KENDELL
The original Bill of Lading, once signed by the Master,
is NOT _____.
  A. a receipt and proof that goods have been received
      on board
⚓ B. surrendered to the customs agency of the country
      where the cargo is discharged
  C. used to transfer ownership of the cargo while the
      ship is enroute
  D. proof of title or ownership of the cargo

DRY CARGO SHIPPING DOCUMENTS

012442/DG01148   INT. MARITIME DICTIONARY
The document which acknowledges that the cargo has
been received and is in the carrier's custody is called
the _____.
⚓ A. Dock Receipt
  B. Hatch Report and Recapitulation
  C. Cargo Manifest
  D. Stowage Plan

012443/DG01228   McFARLANDS & WALLS
A cargo exception would appear on _____.
⚓ A. a Bill of Lading
  B. the cargo manifest
  C. the Export Declaration
  D. a Letter of Indemnity

LIQUID CARGO SHIPPING DOCUMENTS

012444/DG03290   *46 CFR 35.01-10
What will be accepted as the shipping papers for an
unmanned tank barge but will not be accepted if the
tank barge is manned?
  A. Bill of Lading
⚓ B. Logbook entry
  C. Manifest
  D. Shipping document

012445/DG02153   *46 CFR 35.01-10
The shipping papers for the products being carried in
your tankship are NOT required to contain the
_____.
⚓ A. exact quantity of the cargoes
  B. grades of the cargoes
  C. location of the delivery point(s)
  D. name of the consignee(s)

012446/DG03280   *46 CFR 35.01-10
What is NOT accepted as the required shipping papers
on a manned and loaded tank barge?
  A. Bill of Lading
  B. Manifest
  C. Shipping document
⚓ D. Logbook entry

GOVERNMENT AGENCIES
& REGULATORY BODIES

AMERICAN BUREAU OF SHIPPING (ABS)
012447/DG01894   *46 CFR 42.05-10
A load line is assigned by _____.
  A. the U.S. Customs
  B. the U.S. Department of Energy
  C. the U.S. Army Corps of Engineers
⚓ D. a recognized classification society approved by the
      U.S. Coast Guard

012448/DG00371   **MARTIN**

In the United States, the load line markings are set by the _____.

⚓ A.   American Bureau of Shipping
     B.   Coast Guard
     C.   Federal Maritime Board
     D.   IMO

012449/DG01761   ***46 CFR 42.05-10**

Load lines for U.S. vessels are assigned by _____.

     A.   the U.S. Coast Guard
⚓ B.   the American Bureau of Shipping
     C.   Lloyd's Register of Shipping
     D.   the National Cargo Bureau

012450/DG01771   ***46 CFR 42.05-10**

The agency which assigns load lines and issues Load Line Certificates is the _____.

⚓ A.   American Bureau of Shipping
     B.   Secretary of Commerce
     C.   U.S. Customs
     D.   U.S. Coast Guard

012451/DG01751   ***46 CFR 42.05-10**

The load line certificate is issued by _____.

⚓ A.   the American Bureau of Shipping
     B.   the National Cargo Bureau
     C.   the United States Coast Guard
     D.   United States Customs

012452/DG01781   ***46 CFR 42.05-10**

Which organization usually assigns load lines to U.S. vessels?

     A.   National Load-Line Agency
     B.   National Shipping Bureau
⚓ C.   American Bureau of Shipping
     D.   American Regulations Council

012453/DG01223   **MARINE CARGO OPS.**

The organization that certifies the safe working load of cargo cranes on a vessel is the _____.

⚓ A.   classification society
     B.   National Cargo Bureau
     C.   U.S. Coast Guard
     D.   none of the above

012454/DG00795   **MARINE CARGO OPS.**

Who certifies the safe working load of cargo booms on a vessel?

     A.   U.S. Coast Guard
⚓ B.   American Bureau of Shipping
     C.   Society of Naval Architects and Marine Engineers
     D.   The Ship's Master

012455/DG01222   **MARINE CARGO OPS.**

Who certifies the safe working load of cargo cranes on a vessel?

⚓ A.   American Bureau of Shipping
     B.   National Cargo Bureau
     C.   U.S. Coast Guard
     D.   None of the above

012456/DG01220   **MARINE CARGO OPS.**

Who certifies the safe working load of cargo cranes on a vessel?

     A.   U.S. Coast Guard
⚓ B.   American Bureau of Shipping
     C.   Society of Naval Architects and Marine Engineers
     D.   National Cargo Bureau

012457/DG01808   **MARINE CARGO OPS.**

Which organization would conduct a survey of the insulation in a reefer compartment prior to loading cargo?

     A.   U.S. Customs Service
     B.   OSHA
⚓ C.   American Bureau of Shipping
     D.   National Cargo Bureau

U. S. IMMIGRATION SERVICE (INS)

012458/DG01281   **MARTIN**

The agency most concerned with a stowaway is _____.

     A.   Customs
⚓ B.   Immigration
     C.   Public Health
     D.   U.S.D.A.

012459/DG01271   **MARTIN ; MMOH**

The citizenship of a crew member of a vessel in a U.S. port is determined solely by the _____.

     A.   Customs Officer
⚓ B.   Immigration Officer
     C.   Coast Guard
     D.   Union Official

NATIONAL CARGO BUREAU (NCB)

012460/DG00708   **MARINE CARGO OPS.**

The National Cargo Bureau represents the _____.

     A.   agent
     B.   operator
     C.   shipper
⚓ D.   All of the above

012461/DG00490   ***49 CFR 176.18***
Which agency is authorized to assist the Coast Guard in the inspection of vessels for the suitability of loading hazardous materials?
A. American Bureau of Shipping
B. Environmental Protection Agency
⚓ C. National Cargo Bureau, Inc.
D. U.S. Navy explosive loading details

012462/DG00678   ***46 CFR 93.20-15 (a) (b)***
Prior to being able to sail, each vessel that carries grain in bulk must have a certificate of loading issued by the _____.
A. American Bureau of Shipping
B. Lloyds of London
⚓ C. National Cargo Bureau
D. U.S. Salvage

012463/DG02624   ***46 CFR 93.20-15; *46 CFR 93.20-01***
The certificate of loading required by each vessel carrying grain in bulk is issued by the _____.
A. owner or charterer of the vessel
B. American Bureau of Shipping
C. shipper of the cargo
⚓ D. National Cargo Bureau

012464/DG00698   ***46 CFR 93.20-10***
Which agency issues a certificate of loading that is evidence that the rules and regulations concerning bulk grain cargoes have been observed?
A. American Bureau of Shipping
B. Department of Agriculture
⚓ C. National Cargo Bureau
D. Public Health Service

012465/DG00688   ***46 CFR 93.20-10***
Who would normally certify that all preparations have been made and all regulations observed prior to loading a cargo of bulk grain?
A. American Bureau of Shipping
B. U.S. Coast Guard
⚓ C. National Cargo Bureau
D. Master of the vessel

012466/DG01812   **MARINE CARGO OPS.**
A survey of refrigerated cargo, to certify that proper methods of stowage were utilized, can be conducted by the _____.
A. American Bureau of Shipping
B. Occupational Safety and Health Administration
C. U.S. Coast Guard
⚓ D. National Cargo Bureau

U. S. COAST GUARD (USCG)

012467/DG01741   ***46 CFR 42.07-50; *46 CFR 42.07-60***
The load line regulations are administered by the _____.
⚓ A. U.S. Coast Guard
B. Maritime Administration
C. Lloyd's Register of Shipping
D. National Cargo Bureau

012468/DG01018   ***46 CFR 42.07-50***
Which U.S. Government agency can suspend or revoke a Merchant Mariner's license for violating the load line act?
A. American Bureau of Shipping
⚓ B. U.S. Coast Guard
C. U.S. Customs Service
D. U.S. Maritime Administration

012469/DG00481   **MMOH**
Which U.S. agency assigns an official number to a vessel?
A. American Bureau of Shipping
B. Collector of Customs
C. Treasury Department
⚓ D. Coast Guard

012470/DG00491   ***46 CFR 67.13-5; *46 CFR 67.117***
A change of a documented vessel's name can only be made by the _____.
A. American Bureau of Shipping
B. Commissioner of Customs
C. Treasury Department
⚓ D. Coast Guard

012471/DG00781   ***46 CFR 70; *46 CFR 93.10***
The trim and stability booklet must be approved by the _____.
A. International Maritime Organization
B. National Cargo Bureau
C. Society of Naval Architects and Marine Engineers
⚓ D. United States Coast Guard

012472/DG02030   ***46 CFR 160; *46 CFR 199***
Safety equipment on board vessels must be approved by the _____.
⚓ A. U.S. Coast Guard
B. Safety Standards Bureau
C. Occupational Safety and Health Administration (OSHA)
D. National Safety Council

SHIPMENT OF SEAMEN

MANNING REQUIREMENTS

012473/DG01322   ***46 USC 11104; NORRIS; THE LAW OF SEAMEN**

The American Consul has asked the Master of a vessel bound for a port in the U.S. to transport a destitute seaman back to the U.S. Which action may the Master take?

A. He may refuse to take the seaman if the ship will not stop at a U.S. port within 30 days.

B. He is required to accept the seaman only if the seaman is medically unfit.

⚓ C. He may refuse to take the seaman if the seaman has a contagious disease.

D. He is required to take the seaman under any circumstance.

012474/DG03166   ***46 USC 11104; NORRIS; THE LAW OF SEAMEN**

The American Consul has asked the Master of a vessel bound for a port in the U.S. to transport a destitute seaman back to the U.S. Which action may the Master take?

A. He must always take the seaman.

B. He is required to accept the seaman only if the seaman is medically unfit.

⚓ C. He may refuse the seaman if the seaman has a contagious disease.

D. He may refuse to take the seaman if he is being held by shore authorities.

012475/DG00021   **NORRIS; THE LAW OF SEAMEN**

The American Consul has asked the Master of a vessel bound for a port in the U.S. to transport a destitute seaman back to the U.S. Which action may the Master take?

A. He is normally required to take the seaman.

B. He may refuse to take the seaman if the seaman has a contagious disease.

C. He may refuse to take the seaman if it will violate the Certificate of Inspection.

⚓ D. All of the above

012476/DG00473   **NORRIS; THE LAW OF SEAMEN; *46 USC 11104**

The American Consul has asked the Master of a vessel bound for a port in the U.S. to transport a destitute seaman back to the U.S. Which action may the Master take?

A. He may refuse to accept the seaman if the seaman is medically unfit.

B. He must take the seaman even if the seaman has a contagious disease.

C. He is always required to take the seaman.

⚓ D. He may refuse to take the seaman if it will violate the Certificate of Inspection.

012477/DG02148   ***46 CFR 15.401**

You are the Master of an uninspected diesel towing vessel of 190-GT operating on a regular run from New York to the Gulf of Mexico. Which statement is TRUE?

⚓ A. All crew members must have Merchant Mariner's Documents.

B. A licensed Chief Engineer is required.

C. Deck watches may be 6 and 6.

D. Able Seamen are not required in the deck crew.

012478/DG00457   ***46 CFR 15.401**

You are the operator of an uninspected diesel towing vessel of 190-GT operating on a regular run from New York to the Gulf of Mexico. Which statement is TRUE?

A. Deck watches may be 6 and 6.

B. Able seamen are not required in the deck crew.

⚓ C. All crew members must have Merchant Mariner's Documents.

D. A licensed Chief Engineer is required.

012479/DG00855   ***46 CFR 15.610; *46 CFR 15.710**

Which party must ensure that legal work hour limitations (for both officers and crew members), rest periods and regulations governing work on Sundays and holidays are followed when the vessel is in a safe harbor?

A. The owner of the vessel

B. The company operating the vessel

⚓ C. The Master of the vessel

D. The company chartering the vessel

012480/DG00813   ***46 CFR 15.701 (a)**

The Officers Competency Certificates Convention of 1936 applies to all of these vessels operating seaward of the boundary line EXCEPT a/an _____.

A. offshore supply vessel over 200 gross tons

B. passenger vessel of 295 gross tons

⚓ C. uninspected towing vessel of less than 200 gross tons

D. inspected towing vessel of 305 gross tons

012481/DG00815   ***46 CFR 15.701 (c)**

A U.S. or foreign flag vessel that does not comply with the Officers Competency Certificates Convention of 1936 may be detained by certain designated officials. These officials include all of the following EXCEPT a/an _____.

⚓ A. State Police officer

B. Coast Guard officer

C. Coast Guard petty officer

D. officer of the U.S. Customs Service

012482/DG00797   *46 CFR 15.701 (c)
A U.S. or foreign flag vessel that does not comply with the Officers Competency Certificates Convention of 1936 may be detained by certain designated officials. These officials include all of the following EXCEPT a/an _____.
- A. Coast Guard officer
- B. employee of the U.S. Customs Service
- C. Coast Guard petty officer
- ⚓ D. State Police officer

012483/DG00061   *46 CFR 15.705
Deckhands onboard towing vessels shall be divided into 3 watches when on a trip exceeding _____.
- ⚓ A. 600 miles
- B. 700 miles
- C. 800 miles
- D. 1000 miles

012484/DG03463   *46 CFR 15.705
Deckhands onboard towing vessels shall be divided into 3 watches when the trip exceeds _____.
- A. 1000 miles
- B. 800 miles
- C. 700 miles
- ⚓ D. 600 miles

012485/DG00830   *46 CFR 15.705 (c); *46 USC 8104 (g)
On which vessels are the officers and deck crew allowed to operate under a two-watch system on voyages of less than 600 miles?
- A. Towing vessels
- B. Offshore supply vessels
- C. Barges, when manned
- ⚓ D. All of the above

012486/DG00877   *46 CFR 15.705 (d); *46 USC 8104 (h)
On which vessels may licensed individuals be required to stand watch under the two-watch system, on voyages of more than 600 miles in length?
- ⚓ A. Uninspected towing vessels
- B. Offshore supply vessels
- C. Cargo ships
- D. Tank vessels

012487/DG00829   *46 CFR 15.705 (a)
In terms of vessel manning, a watch is the _____.
- ⚓ A. direct performance of deck or engine operations in a scheduled and fixed rotation
- B. performance of maintenance work necessary for the vessel's safe operation, on a daily basis
- C. performance of lookout duties
- D. direct performance of cargo loading and discharge operations only

012488/DG00963   *46 CFR 15.705
You are the person in charge of a 199-GT uninspected towing vessel engaged in towing from Galveston to Savannah and then returning, a distance in excess of 600 miles. Which statement is FALSE?
- A. The sailors shall be divided into three watches.
- B. All deck crew members are to have a Merchant Mariner's Document.
- C. Able seamen are required in the deck crew.
- ⚓ D. The crew members are NOT required to sign articles.

012489/DG00962   *46 CFR 15.705
You are the person in charge of a 199-GT uninspected towing vessel engaged in towing from New York to Mexico and then returning, a distance in excess of 600 miles. Which statement is FALSE?
- ⚓ A. The crew members are required to sign articles.
- B. All deck crew members are to have a Merchant Mariner's Document.
- C. Able seamen are required in the deck crew.
- D. The sailors shall be divided into three watches.

012490/DG00071   *46 CFR 15.705 (b)
You are the licensed Master of a 199-GT uninspected towing vessel making a 500 mile coastwise trip. You carry a deck crew of six (6). Which statement is TRUE?
- A. There must be 3 separate watches stood.
- B. There must be at least 5 able seamen among the deck crew.
- C. Only the able seamen require Merchant Mariner's Documents.
- ⚓ D. None of the above

012491/DG03100   *46 CFR 15.705 (d)
A holder of a license as Master of towing vessels may work each 24 hours for a period not to exceed _____.
- A. 6 hours
- ⚓ B. 12 hours
- C. 18 hours
- D. 24 hours

012492/DG03561   *46 CFR 15.705 (d)
A holder of a license as Operator of Uninspected Towing Vessels may work each 24 hours for a period not to exceed _____.
- A. 24 hours
- B. 18 hours
- ⚓ C. 12 hours
- D. 6 hours

012493/DG00091   ***46 CFR 15; *46 CFR 14.307**
You are the person in charge of a 199-GRT uninspected towing vessel engaged in coastwise towing from the Gulf of Mexico to New York, a distance in excess of 600 miles. Which statement is FALSE?
A. The deckhands shall be divided into 3 watches.
B. Able seamen are required in the deck crew.
C. All crew members shall have Merchant Mariner's Documents.
⚓ D. Certificates of Discharge are not required to be issued.

012494/DG00347   ***46 CFR 15; *46 CFR 14.307**
You are the person in charge of a 199-GRT uninspected towing vessel engaged in coastwise towing from the Gulf of Mexico to the New York area, a distance in excess of 600 miles. Which statement is FALSE?
⚓ A. Certificates of Discharge are not required to be issued.
B. All crew members shall have Merchant Mariner's Documents.
C. Able seamen are required in the deck crew.
D. The sailors shall be divided into 3 watches.

012495/DG03143   ***46 CFR 15.705**
You are the person in charge of a 199-GRT uninspected towing vessel engaged in coastwise towing from the Gulf of Mexico to the New York area, a distance in excess of 600 miles. Which statement is FALSE?
A. The deckhands shall be divided into 3 watches.
⚓ B. Certificates of Discharge are not required to be issued.
C. Able seamen are required in the deck crew.
D. All crew members shall have Merchant Mariner's Documents.

012496/DG03493   ***46 CFR 15.705**
You are the Master of an uninspected diesel towing vessel of 190-GT operating on a regular run from New York to the Gulf of Mexico. Which statement is TRUE?
A. Able Seamen are not required in the deck crew.
⚓ B. All crew members must have Merchant Mariner's Documents.
C. A licensed Chief Engineer is required.
D. Deck watches may be 6 and 6.

012497/DG00833   ***46 CFR 15.710**
The Master may require part of the crew to work when needed for _____.
A. maneuvering, shifting berth, mooring and unmooring
B. performing work necessary for the safety of the vessel, its passengers, crew or cargo
C. performing fire, lifeboat or other drills in port or at sea
⚓ D. All of the above

012498/DG00843   ***46 CFR 15.720;***
                            46 CFR 15.805; *46 CFR 15.910
If the Master of a US-flag towing vessel replaces any crew member with a non-US citizen, he/she must ensure that the _____.
A. replacement holds a license or document equivalent in experience and training to a mariner holding US credentials
B. replacement can communicate with other crew members to the extent required by regulations
C. vessel is on a foreign voyage, outside US jurisdiction, and not operating above the US outer continental shelf
⚓ D. all of the above

012499/DG00842   ***46 CFR 15.720;***
                            46 CFR 15.805; *46 CFR 15.910
When can the US citizenship requirement for the Master of a US-flag uninspected towing vessel be waived?
A. When US-licensed Masters are not readily available
B. When it costs too much to hire a US-licensed Master
C. When the towing vessel operates shoreward of the boundary line
⚓ D. Never, under any circumstances

012500/DG00823   ***46 CFR 14.307; NVIC 4-01***
Which statement concerning a 298-GRT inspected tug engaged in towing from Seattle, WA, to Alaska is TRUE?
A. A licensed Master of Towing Vessels may serve as Master.
B. Crew must be signed on before a Shipping Commissioner.
⚓ C. Each crew member must be issued a certificate of discharge at the time of discharge.
D. No able seamen are required.

012501/DG00852   *46 CFR 15.730 (d)
How can the Coast Guard determine that a crew member is "able to understand any order spoken by the officers"?

⚓ A. Require a demonstration by the officer and the crew member
B. Require a written test
C. Require that an interpreter be provided
D. All of the above

012502/DG00337   *46 CFR 15.840
On a coastwise tugboat of 199-GT, on a voyage over 600 miles, what percentage of the deck crew (excluding licensed officers) must hold a document of able seaman?

⚓ A. 65%
B. 50%
C. 25%
D. 0%

012503/DG00845   *46 CFR 15.730 (c); *46 USC 8702 (b)
The terminology "able to understand any order spoken by the officers" refers to all of the following situations EXCEPT _____.
A. in response to a fire
B. directing the use of lifesaving equipment
⚓ C. for deck department crew members to understand the terminology used in the engine room
D. in response to a man overboard

012504/DG00051   *46 CFR 15.730; *46 USC 8702
You are the licensed Master of a 100-GT towing vessel sailing coastwise. What percentage of the deck crew must be able to understand any order spoken by the officers?
A. 50%
B. 65%
⚓ C. 75%
D. 100%

012505/DG01034   *46 CFR 15.730
You are the licensed operator of a 100-GT towing vessel sailing coastwise. What percentage of the deck crew must be able to understand the language commonly used onboard the vessel?
A. 100%
⚓ B. 75%
C. 65%
D. 50%

012506/DG00041   *46 CFR 15.840
Considering the manning requirements for U.S. vessels (100 gross tons and above), your cargo vessel has a deck crew of 20 men, exclusive of the officers. How many of these men do the manning regulations require to be Able Seamen?
A. 5
B. 7
C. 10
⚓ D. 13

012507/DG00893   *46 CFR 15.840
Considering the manning requirements for U.S. vessels, your three watch cargo vessel has a deck crew of 20 people, exclusive of the officers. How many of these people do the manning regulations require to be Able Seamen?
⚓ A. 13
B. 10
C. 7
D. 5

012508/DG00835   *46 CFR 15.840 (a); *46 CFR 15.730
For towing vessels over 100 gross tons that are permitted to maintain a two-watch system, what percentage of the deck crew must be able seamen?
⚓ A. 50%
B. 65%
C. 75%
D. 100%

012509/DG00141   *46 CFR 15.840; *46 CFR 15.705
On a sea going towing vessel of 150 gross tons, there are six (6) seamen in the deck crew. How many certificated able seamen are required if the voyage is over 600 miles?
A. 1
B. 2
C. 3
⚓ D. 4

012510/DG03105   *46 CFR 15.840; *46 CFR 15.705
On a sea going towing vessel of 150-GT, there are six (6) seamen in the deck crew. How many certificated able seamen are required if the voyage is over 600 miles?
⚓ A. 4
B. 3
C. 2
D. 1

012511/DG00860 *46 CFR 15.840 (b); *46 USC 7312 (d)
Which category of able seaman is not authorized to be counted as an able seaman on a seagoing tug of over 100 gross tons?
A. Unlimited
B. Limited
C. Special
⚓ D. Special (OSV)

012512/DG00522 *46 CFR 15.840
You are onboard a 120-GT uninspected sea going tug which carries one Master and one Mate of Towing Vessels and four (4) seamen when underway. How many of the four seamen must have a rating as able seamen if the voyage is under 600 miles?
A. 4
B. 3
⚓ C. 2
D. 1

012513/DG00131 *46 CFR 15.840; *46 CFR 15.705
You are onboard a 120-GT uninspected sea going tug which carries one Master and one mate of towing vessels, and four seamen when underway. How many of the four seamen must have a rating as able seamen if the voyage is under 600 miles?
A. 1
⚓ B. 2
C. 3
D. 4

012514/DG03491 *46 CFR 15.840; *46 CFR 15.705
You are the licensed Master of a towing vessel operating between New York and Tampa, Florida. If you carry four (4) deckhands onboard, how many must be able seamen?
A. 4
⚓ B. 3
C. 2
D. 1

012515/DG00111 *46 CFR 15.840; *46 CFR 15.705
You are the licensed Master of a towing vessels operating between New York and Tampa, Florida. If you carry four (4) deckhands onboard, how many must be able seamen?
A. 1
B. 2
⚓ C. 3
D. 4

012516/DG00121 *46 CFR 15.840
You are the Master of an uninspected diesel towing vessel of 190-GT operating on a regular run from New York to the Gulf of Mexico. Which statement is TRUE?
A. Able Seamen are not required in the deck crew.
B. Sailors may stand watch for 6 hours on and 6 hours off.
C. A licensed Chief Engineer is required.
⚓ D. All crew members must have Merchant Mariner's Documents.

012517/DG00081 *46 CFR 15.840; *46 CFR 15.730
Your 199-GT tugboat is on a 675 mile coastwise voyage. What percentage of the deck crew must be Able Bodied Seamen?
A. 0%
B. 25%
C. 50%
⚓ D. 65%

012518/DG00857 *46 CFR 15.840 (c)
On vessels over 100 gross tons, whose responsibility is it to ensure that all able seamen in the vessel's crew have the documents and qualifications required by law and regulation?
⚓ A. Master of the vessel
B. USCG Officer in Charge of Marine Inspection
C. Owner or operator of the vessel
D. Company's personnel director

012519/DG00837 *46 CFR 15.910; *46 CFR 15.720 (a)
When may foreign licensed or documented personnel be employed on a US-flag towing vessel?
⚓ A. While on a foreign voyage and outside US jurisdiction, in order to meet manning requirements
B. While operating above the US outer continental shelf
C. On vessels operating on domestic voyages only
D. Never, under any circumstances

012520/DG00875 *46 CFR 15.810 (b) (4); *46 CFR 15.1109
Which statement, concerning offshore supply vessel operations, correctly defines the length of a voyage?
A. The distance from the point of departure to the vessel's first stop
B. The distance from the point of departure to the most distant point offshore
⚓ C. The total distance from the port of departure to the port of arrival, not including stops at offshore points
D. The shortest measurable distance from the port of departure to the port of arrival

012521/DG00825   *46 CFR 15.1109; *46 CFR 15.705 (a)
Who is responsible for establishing watches aboard a U.S. vessel?
- A. The owner of the vessel
- B. The company that operates the vessel
- C. The company that charters the vessel
- ⚓ D. The Master of the vessel

012522/DG00853   *46 CFR 15.801; *46 CFR 15.1109
Who is responsible for properly manning a vessel in accordance with all applicable laws, regulations and international conventions?
- A. The (USCG) Officer in Charge of Marine Inspection
- B. The (USCG) Captain of the Port
- C. The owner or operator of the vessel
- ⚓ D. The Master of the vessel

012523/DG00769   *33 CFR 164.78; *46 CFR 15.405
The owner or Master of a towing vessel must ensure that each person that directs and controls the movement of the vessel knows all of the following EXCEPT _____.
- A. the effects of maneuvering on the vessel and its tow
- B. the speed and direction of any current for the area being transited
- C. how to apply variation and deviation to readings from a magnetic compass
- ⚓ D. the ownership of the vessel(s) being towed

012524/DG00783   *33 CFR 164.78 (a); *46 CFR 15.405
The owner or Master of a towing vessel shall ensure that each person that directs and controls the movement of the vessel can accomplish all of the following EXCEPT _____.
- A. evaluate the danger of each closing visual or radar contact
- B. adjust speed with due regard for the weather and visibility
- ⚓ C. reduce speed only where local speed limits are posted
- D. enter all required test and inspection results in the vessel's log or other record carried on board

012525/DG00782   *33 CFR 164.78 (a); *46 CFR 15.405
The owner or Master of a towing vessel shall ensure that each person that directs and controls the movement of the vessel can accurately fix the vessel's position using all of the following EXCEPT _____.
- A. installed navigational equipment
- ⚓ B. buoys alone
- C. all available aids to navigation
- D. depths soundings and hydrographic contour lines

FORECASTLE CARD

012526/DG02084   *46 CFR 14.05; MARTIN
A copy of the Articles of Agreement, less the signatures, is required to be posted. This document is called the _____.
- ⚓ A. Fo'c'sle Card
- B. Articles Copy
- C. Voyage Agreement
- D. Shipping Articles

012527/DG02145   MARTIN
The fo'c'sle card _____.
- A. is posted in the crews quarters and lists the emergency stations
- ⚓ B. advises the crew of the conditions of employment
- C. is also known as a Merchant Mariner's Document
- D. designates the quarters a seaman will occupy during a voyage

012528/DG00151   MARTIN
The forecastle card is a copy of the _____.
- A. quarters allocation
- ⚓ B. shipping agreement
- C. Muster List ("Station Bill")
- D. unlicensed shipping card from the union

012529/DG01324   MARTIN
The forecastle card is a(n) _____.
- ⚓ A. copy of the shipping agreement
- B. quarters allocation
- C. Muster List ("Station Bill")
- D. unlicensed shipping card from the union

012530/DG03292   MARTIN
The forecastle card is a(n) _____.
- A. unlicensed shipping card from the union
- B. quarters allocation
- ⚓ C. copy of the shipping agreement
- D. Muster List ("Station Bill")

012531/DG02188   MARTIN
The forecastle card is a(n) _____.
- A. quarters allocation
- B. Muster List ("Station Bill")
- C. unlicensed shipping card from the union
- ⚓ D. copy of the shipping agreement

012532/DG01283   MARTIN
Which statement about the fo'c'sle card is TRUE?
- A. The fo'c'sle card is a blank sample of the articles.
- B. It contains copies of the crew's signatures from the articles.
- ⚓ C. Is an exact copy of shipping articles.
- D. Each crewmember is given a copy of the fo'c'sle card.

CREW VACANCIES & SHORTAGES

012533/DG00161   **NORRIS; *46 USC 11501**
A seaman leaves a vessel before it sails from a foreign port. He informs the Chief Officer that he won't return. After the vessel sails, the Chief Officer finds the seaman's work clothes in his locker. How should the Master handle this matter?
⚓ A. Log the seaman as a deserter.
B. Log the seaman as a fail to join.
C. Log the seaman for misconduct.
D. Take no action.

012534/DG00191   **MARTIN**
An alien crewmember with a D-1 permit leaves the vessel in a U.S. port and fails to return. The first report you make should be to the _____.
A. Customs Service
⚓ B. Immigration Service
C. local police
D. OCMI

012535/DG00172   **NORRIS**
While a vessel is in a foreign port where there is no American Consul, a seaman becomes violent prior to sailing. The Master should _____.
A. call local police, put the seaman in prison ashore, and sail the vessel
B. pay off the seaman and make arrangements with the agent to return him to the original port of signing on in the U.S.
⚓ C. put the seaman in irons and sail to the next port where there is an American Consul
D. send the seaman ashore and arrange with the agent to repatriate him by armed guard

012536/DG00201   **MARTIN**
Your vessel is in a foreign port and you find that one of the crew members has been incarcerated for drunkenness. The Official Logbook shows that the seaman doesn't have funds to cover the costs of the fine. Which action should the Master take?
A. Inventory his gear and send it and a pay voucher ashore with the agent.
B. Leave the seaman in jail and log him as a fail to join after the vessel sails.
C. Leave the seaman in jail and log him as a deserter after the vessel sails.
⚓ D. Pay the seaman's fine.

012537/DG00181   ***46 CFR 15.720**
Your vessel is on an extended foreign voyage. Several vacancies have occurred in your unlicensed crew through sickness and repatriation. Which statement is correct?
A. Aliens may be employed except that all U.S. flag vessels must maintain no less than 90% U.S. citizens in the crew.
⚓ B. Qualified aliens may be employed to fill the vacancies.
C. Seamen to fill vacancies must be flown from U.S. to join the vessel in the foreign port.
D. Vacancies can only be filled by U.S. citizens with valid Merchant Mariner's Documents.

SIGN-ON & SIGN-OFF PROCEDURES

012538/DG00107   ***46 USC 10314; NORRIS**
When may a seaman on a vessel engaged in foreign trade be paid before earning the wages?
⚓ A. The seaman may only draw an advance on earned wages.
B. Wages up to fifty percent of the seaman's base wage maybe advanced upon proof of serious family illness.
C. Wages equivalent to three days base wage may be advanced upon arrival in a foreign port.
D. The advance of wages is at the discretion of the master; however, a seaman cannot be in an overpaid status at signoff.

012539/DG00311   ***46 CFR 14.01.5 (a); MARTIN**
The Shipping Articles shall be signed by each seaman and the _____.
⚓ A. Master of the vessel
B. Shipping Commissioner
C. U.S. Coast Guard
D. U.S. Customs Service

012540/DG00577   ***46 CFR 14**
You are signing on a crew. A man presents a Merchant Mariner's Document that you suspect has been tampered with. Which action should you take?
A. Confiscate the document and deliver it to the Coast Guard.
B. Sign the man on and notify the Coast Guard at the first U.S. port of call.
⚓ C. Refuse to sign the man on articles until authorized by the Coast Guard.
D. Refuse to sign the man on and notify the FBI of unauthorized use of a federal document.

012541/DG02092   *46 CFR 12.10-1; *46 CFR 12.25-10
You are signing on a crew. When they present their Merchant Mariner's Documents, you should suspect a fraudulent document if it has a single endorsement that says _____.
A. see Certificate of Registry
B. any unlicensed rating in the deck department including AB
C. Steward's Department (F.H.)
⚓ D. Bosun

012542/DG00301   *46 CFR 12.25-10; *46 CFR 12.10-1
You are signing on a crew. Which person is presenting a Merchant Mariner's Document (MMD) that you should suspect as being invalid?
A. An AB with an endorsement of "Any unlicensed rating in the deck department including Able Seaman"
⚓ B. A seaman with an MMD only endorsed as "Bosun"
C. A Purser with an MMD only endorsed "See certificate of registry"
D. A Chief Steward with an MMD only endorsed as "Steward's Dept. (FH)"

012543/DG02103   *46 CFR 10.801
You are signing on the Purser. He should present a Merchant Mariner's document with which endorsement?
⚓ A. See Certificate of Registry
B. Steward's Department
C. Purser
D. Staff Officer

012544/DG00507   *46 CFR 12.02-1 (d) (1)
You are signing on your crew. Which is NOT authorized?
⚓ A. A man presenting his Chief Mate's license to sign on as able seaman
B. An engineer presenting an MMD endorsed "QMED - any rating" to sign on as an Electrician
C. A man presenting an MMD endorsed as "Able Seaman" to sign on as Bosun
D. A man presenting an MMD endorsed "Steward's Department (F.H.)" to sign on as Chief Cook

012545/DG00211   *46 USC 10906; NORRIS
A seaman is entitled by law to a release from Foreign Articles when _____.
A. intoxicated
⚓ B. the vessel is overloaded
C. there is a change of home port
D. there is a change of Master

012546/DG03081   *46 USC 10906; NORRIS
A seaman is entitled by law to a release from Foreign Articles when _____.
A. intoxicated
B. deductions are made from wages
C. injured
⚓ D. the vessel is overloaded

012547/DG00221   *46 USC 11105
A vessel arrives in a foreign port and the Master is informed that the vessel is being sold to foreign interests. The new owners request that the crew remain on board to complete the voyage. Under these circumstances, the crew _____.
⚓ A. has the right to an immediate discharge and transportation to original port of engagement
B. must remain on board
C. must comply with the decision made by the Master
D. must remain aboard until the vessel is delivered to the new owners at a mutually agreed upon port

012548/DG00271   *46 CFR 14-16
Total responsibility for shipping and discharging the seamen is that of the _____.
⚓ A. Master of the vessel
B. steamship company
C. U.S. Custom Service
D. U.S. Coast Guard

012549/DG00702   *46 CFR 14.05-7
When paying off seamen in a foreign port, where a United States consul is not available, the release must be executed by the seamen and the _____.
A. representative of the foreign country
B. local port authority representative
⚓ C. Master of the vessel
D. ship's union delegate

012550/DG00261*46 CFR 14.10-1 (b); *46 CFR 14.10-1 (e)
A seaman about to be discharged has a Continuous Discharge Book. Which statement is TRUE?
A. A Certificate of Discharge Form should be attached to the book.
B. An entry should be made in the book and a Certificate of Discharge Form issued to the seaman.
C. If a vessel was on coastwise articles, the record of discharge will be made in the Official Logbook.
⚓ D. The record of entry in the book must be submitted to the Coast Guard.

012551/DG00251   ***46 CFR 14.10-15**
A seaman lost his continuous discharge book during the voyage. Upon discharge from Articles, he should be issued a _____.
A. letter of service on company letterhead signed and sealed by the master
B. Record of Entry in a Continuous Discharge Book for use in applying for a duplicate book
C. Certificate of Discharge with the white copy forwarded to the Commandant
D. Mutual Release (CG-2119), and the articles should be annotated as to the loss

012552/DG02289   ***46 CFR 14.10-1 (b);**
     *46 CFR 14.10-1 (e); *46 CFR 14.704 (c)
A seaman you have just discharged has a Continuous Discharge Book. Which statement is TRUE?
A. The record of entry in the continuous discharge book shall agree with the entry made in the Ship's Articles.
B. If the vessel was on coastwise articles, the record of discharge will be made in the Official Logbook.
C. An entry should be made in the book and a Certificate of Discharge issued to the seaman.
D. A Certificate of Discharge form should be attached to the book.

012553/DG01418   ***46 CFR 97.35-3 (a)**
The master or individual in charge of a vessel prepares a certificate of discharge for each mariner being discharged from the vessel where the original discharge goes to the _____.
A. National Maritime Center
B. Officer In Charge, Marine Inspection (OCMI)
C. Shipping Company
D. Mariner

012554/DG00792   **MARTIN**
When the vessel is on coastwise articles, the original certificate of the seaman's certificate of discharge is _____.
A. given to the seaman
B. retained on board
C. sent to Commandant, U.S. Coast Guard
D. sent to the shipping company

012555/DG01423   **MARTIN**
Which statement is FALSE regarding certificates of discharge?
A. The mariner receives the original copy of the discharge
B. The mariner only signs the original copy of the discharge
C. Computer generated signatures are not authorized
D. Copies of the certificate of discharge are furnished by the shipping company

012556/DG00291   ***46 CFR 14.05-10 (c)**
You are the licensed operator of a 100-GT towing vessel making coastwise runs. Whenever a crew member is discharged from your vessel you must _____.
A. issue a Certificate of Discharge and make an entry in his Continuous Discharge Book
B. issue a Certificate of Discharge or make an entry in his Continuous Discharge Book
C. retain the crew member's Continuous Discharge Book onboard
D. retain the crew member's Certificate of Discharge onboard

012557/DG00241   **MARTIN**
If there are any changes in the crew in a foreign port, the changes will be made by _____.
A. the Master on the Certified Crew List
B. the Master on the Shipping Articles
C. U.S. Consul on the Certified Crew List
D. U.S. Consul on the Shipping Articles

012558/DG00281   **MARTIN**
Which action will take place if a crew member is replaced in a U.S. port after foreign articles have been signed, and the ship proceeds foreign?
A. The Master will remove the replaced man's name from the Certified Crew List but not from the articles.
B. The name of the new man is added to the articles but not to the Certified Crew List.
C. The U.S. Consul will remove the replaced man's name from the Certified Crew List.
D. The U.S. Consul will add the new man's name to the Certified Crew List.

012559/DG00872   ***46 CFR 14.10-20 (c) (i)**
In a foreign port with a consulate, the U.S. Consul may excuse the Master from personally appearing before him to consent to the mutual release of an injured seaman, when the _____.
A. injury requires immediate inpatient hospitalization of the seaman
B. Master authorizes the agent to act in his place
C. ship is still in port and the seaman can appear before the Consul after medical treatment
D. seaman also consents to the absence, and there is no dispute as to the wages due

012560/DG04443   IMO

You are signing on a deck officer, who will be designated as one of the GMDSS operators, before sailing foreign. Which statement is TRUE?

⚓ A, He/she must have an STCW certificate endorsed as "Valid for Service on Vessels Operating in the GMDSS System".

B. He/she must present either an FCC-issued license or a Coast Guard-issued license.

C. You must consult the "List of Qualifications" on the reverse of his/her FCC-issued license.

D. His/her Merchant Mariners Document must have an added endorsement as "Radio Electronics Officer".

ARTICLES OF AGREEMENT

012561/DG00331   MARTIN; *46 USC Chapter 105

Shipping articles are a contract of agreement between the members of the crew and the _____.

A. charterers

B. Coast Guard

⚓ C. Master

D. vessel's owner

012562/DG01292   MARTIN

The Articles of Agreement _____.

A. is also known as a Merchant Mariner's Document

B. designates the quarters a seaman will occupy during a voyage

⚓ C. advises the crew of the conditions of employment

D. are signed by each crewmember at the end of the voyage

012563/DG02057   *46 USC 103; *46 USC 105;
           MARTINS; NORRIS; *46 CFR 14.201 (b) (2)

While assigned to a 106-GRT vessel, you are required to sign "foreign" articles on a voyage from San Francisco to which port?

A. Mazatlan, Mexico (west coast)

B. Vera Cruz, Mexico (east coast)

⚓ C. New York, NY

D. Vancouver, Canada (west coast)

012564/DG00787   *46 USC 103; *46 USC 105;
           MARTINS; NORRIS; *46 CFR 14.201 (b) (2)

While assigned to a 120-GRT vessel, you are required to sign "foreign" articles on a voyage from New York City to which port?

A. Halifax, Canada

⚓ B. Long Beach, California

C. Veracruz, Mexico

D. Saint Maarten, Netherlands Antilles

012565/DG02077   *46 USC 103; *46 USC 105;
           MARTINS; NORRIS; *46 CFR 14.201 (b) (1)

While assigned to a 150-GRT vessel, you are required to sign "foreign" articles on a voyage from New Orleans to which port?

A. Houston, Texas

B. Veracruz, Mexico

C. Kingston, Jamaica

⚓ D. Cristobal Colon, Panama

012566/DG00907   *46 USC 103; *46 CFR 105;
           MARTINS; NORRIS; *46 CFR 14.201 (b) (2)

While assigned to a 90-GRT vessel, you are required to sign "foreign" articles on a voyage from Philadelphia to which port?

⚓ A. San Francisco, CA

B. Baltimore, MD

C. Tampico, Mexico

D. Montreal, Canada

012567/DG00205   MARTIN; *46 USC CHAP 103, 105

A vessel is to make a voyage between New York and San Juan, Puerto Rico, and return. The crew should be signed on _____.

⚓ A. Coastwise Articles

B. Foreign Articles

C. Intercoastal Articles

D. no articles

012568/DG02035   *46 CFR 14

A seaman signed on articles on 16 January 1987 and signed off on 2 March 1987. How should you enter this under the Time of Service column in the articles?

A. 1 Month 18 Days

B. 1 Month 16 Days

C. 2 Months

⚓ D. 46 Days

ENTRY PROCEDURES

012569/DG01151   ENCY. NAUT. KNOW.

The term used in levying customs duties when such are fixed at rates proportioned to estimated value of goods concerned is _____.

⚓ A. ad valorem

B. infinite

C. secure

D. specific

012570/DG02174   **MARTIN**

A vessel puts into the port of Kobe, Japan to discharge cargo. While awaiting completion of the cargo operation, the vessel contracts with a local shipyard to have the hull chipped, scaled, and painted. How is the cost of this maintenance handled with the Collector of Customs?

⚓ A. A declaration is required and duty is involved on the total cost.

B. No declaration is required since this is considered routine maintenance.

C. A declaration is made and duty is charged on the materials only.

D. A declaration is made, but duty is charged on the labor only.

012571/DG01101   **MARTIN**

A vessel puts into the port of Kobe, Japan, to discharge cargo. The vessel contracts a local shipyard to have the hull chipped and scaled. If the vessel provides the primer and paint, which statement is TRUE?

A. You need NOT declare the cost of labor, since no duty is involved.

B. You need NOT declare the cost of labor, since this is considered ship's personnel work.

⚓ C. You MUST declare the cost of labor and pay duty.

D. You MUST declare the cost of labor, but no duty is charged since labor is involved.

012572/DG01081   **MMOH**

You are Master of a U.S. flag vessel which was dry docked for bottom cleaning in Rotterdam, Netherlands. Upon return to a U.S. port, you must _____.

⚓ A. file a customs' form for duty on this repair

B. file no extra reports

C. file a report of the dry docking with the U.S.C.G. Officer in Charge, Marine Inspection

D. obtain a U.S. Coast Guard diver to certify the work

012573/DG01071   **MARTIN**

In some cases, the 50% duty on all foreign repairs made to American flag merchant vessels may be remitted. Which work does NOT come under the remitting policy of U.S. Customs?

⚓ A. Chipping, painting, and scaling by foreign labor

B. Repairs to hull structural damage

C. Repairs due to damage done by heavy weather

D. Repairs to the main propulsion machinery

012574/DG01051   **MARTIN**

A vessel arrives in San Francisco from a foreign voyage. When MUST the Master make formal entry at the custom house?

A. Within 24 hours after arrival, Sundays and holidays excepted

⚓ B. Within 48 hours after arrival, Sundays and holidays excepted

C. Within 48 hours and before all foreign cargo is discharged for that port

D. Within 24 hours after arrival

012575/DG01141   **MMOH; ARAGON**

A vessel has arrived in a U.S. port from a foreign voyage. Preliminary entry has been made. Formal entry at the U.S. Custom House must be made within how many hours after arrival (Sundays and holidays excepted)?

A. 12

B. 24

⚓ C. 48

D. 72 without exception

012576/DG01171   ***USCP 6**

If you intend to land tulip bulbs from Holland in a U.S. port, they must be inspected by the _____.

⚓ A. Animal and Plant Health Service Inspector

B. Captain of the Port personnel

C. Quarantine Officer

D. All of the above

012577/DG01131   **MARTIN**

U.S. Customs, upon boarding a vessel desiring entry into a U.S. port, would inspect which document?

A. Cargo Manifest

B. Certified Crew List

C. Stores List

⚓ D. All of the above

012578/DG01311   **MARTIN**

Before arriving at the first U.S. port from foreign, you must fill out a Crewman's Landing Permit for each _____.

A. alien crewmember

B. crew member

⚓ C. nonresident alien crewmember

D. unlicensed crew member

012579/DG01181   **MARTIN**

Uncleared crew curios remaining on board during a domestic coastwise voyage after returning from foreign should be _____.

A. listed in the Official Logbook

B. cleared prior to the next foreign voyage

⚓ C. noted in the Traveling Curio Manifest

D. retained under locked security by the owner

012580/DG01061   **MARTIN**
A vessel arrives at the port of San Francisco from Yokohama, Japan. The passengers fill out the Baggage Declaration and Entry form. A passenger has baggage arriving on another vessel. How must this baggage be handled for U.S. Customs purposes?

A. It need not be declared at this time.

⚓ B. It must be declared on the same form and marked "Unaccompanied Baggage".

C. It must be declared on another form entitled "Continuation Sheet".

D. It must be declared only if the other vessel's name is known.

012581/DG01111   **MARTIN**
A vessel sailing from Liverpool to New York puts into Boston, Mass. for emergency repairs. If no inward foreign cargo is to be discharged at that port, which of the following documents is required?

A. Customs Manifest

B. Inward Foreign Manifest

⚓ C. Pro Forma Manifest

D. Traveling Manifest

012582/DG01161   **INT. MARITIME DICTIONARY**
The document that the Master uses to attest to the truth of the manifest of cargo is called _____.

A. Master's Protest

⚓ B. Oath of Entry

C. Owner's Oath

D. Shipper's Certification

012583/DG01291   **MARTIN**
Free pratique means that _____.

A. clearance requirements for all regulatory bodies have been met

⚓ B. health requirements have been met and no further quarantine formalities are required

C. shipment will be made at no cost

D. tonnage taxes are not required to be paid

012584/DG01301   **SHIPS MEDICINE CHEST; MMOH**
If, after examination by the Quarantine Officer, your vessel is found to have a specific deficiency, you may be issued _____.

A. Bill of health

B. Free Pratique

C. Notice to Comply

⚓ D. Controlled Free Pratique

CLEARANCE PROCEDURES

012585/DG01221   **MARTIN**
Your vessel is in Charleston, S.C. You need not clear Customs if _____.

⚓ A. all the cargo on board is of U.S. origin and destined for New York

B. you took on no new cargo in Charleston, S.C. and are bound for Puerto Rico and thence foreign

C. you did not discharge any cargo in Charleston and are bound for Panama

D. you did not load any cargo in Charleston and are bound for Halifax

012586/DG01201   **MARTIN**
When clearing customs for a foreign voyage, which of the following is processed at the custom's house and returned to the vessel?

⚓ A. Shipping Articles

B. Traveling Curio Manifest

C. Official Logbook

D. Cargo Gear Register

012587/DG01211   **MARTIN**
When clearing a vessel for a foreign voyage, the original crew list is duly certified by proper authority. In a U.S. port, this authority is the U.S. _____.

A. Coast Guard

⚓ B. Customs

C. Immigration Service

D. Public Health Service

SALVAGE

CONDITIONS FOR MARINE SALVAGE

012588/DG02599   **HOPKINS**
When several salvors are on-scene at the same time to assist a vessel that has not been abandoned, which principal governs the decision as to which one's services will be accepted?

⚓ A. The Master of the ship needing assistance has the absolute right to decide.

B. The first salvor on-scene has the prior claim providing he has adequate facilities to assist the vessel needing assistance.

C. The salvors must agree to a division of any salvage among themselves with the major share allotted to those doing the most work.

D. The first salvor on-scene has the absolute right to provide assistance; however, he is liable if the ship is lost due to his lack of experience, equipment, etc.

012589/DG01231   **HOPKINS**

What is NOT a requirement for a salvage claim?

A. The property saved must be "maritime property."

⚓ B. The salvors must save or attempt to save any life in peril.

C. The salvage service must be voluntary.

D. The property must be in peril.

012590/DG01825   **HOPKINS**

What is NOT true regarding a Lloyd's Open Form (LOF) Salvage Agreement?

A. The agreement between vessels can be made via VHF

B. If salvage is not successful, vessel owes salvor nothing

C. There is a bonus to the salvage award if environmental casualty is averted

⚓ D. The LOF is subject to the law of the country the two parties agree upon

012591/DG01834   **HOPKINS**

What statement is true regarding a Contract Salvage Agreement?

A. Lloyd's Open Form (LOF) Salvage Agreement is a Contract Salvage Agreement

⚓ B. There cost of the salvage is set at a fixed price

C. The crew is allotted the largest percentage of the salvage award

D. There is a "no cure-no pay" agreement

012592/DG02170   **HOPKINS**

Your vessel is disabled and in imminent danger of grounding on a lee shore. The Master agrees to salvage services using Lloyd's Open Form of Salvage Agreement. Which is TRUE?

A. The salvage award will be decided by suit in Admiralty Court.

⚓ B. The salvage service is on a "no cure-no pay" basis.

C. Underwriters will repudiate the agreement if it is unsuccessful, due to their increased liability.

D. The salvor becomes the owner of the vessel until the salvage award, if any, is paid.

012593/DG01757   **HOPKINS**

What is NOT considered maritime property in a salvage claim?

⚓ A. buoys

B. semi-submerged shipwreck

C. sea plane

D. cargo

012594/DG01744   **HOPKINS**

What is NOT considered maritime property in a salvage claim?

A. tug boat

B. rafts

⚓ C. light-vessels

D. cargo

BAREBOAT CHARTER

012595/DG01331   **MARTIN**

The S.S. Microwave has been chartered to the Longline Steamship Company. The Longline Steamship Company agrees to pay all expenses and employ and pay the crew. Which type of contract is involved?

⚓ A. Bareboat Charter Party

B. Lease Charter Party

C. Time Charter Party

D. Voyage Charter Party

012596/DG01398   **MARTIN**

The owners of the S.S. Short Haul agree to a charter with the Longsplice Steamship Company. The owners stipulate in the charter party that they must approve the Master of the vessel for the entire life of the contract. Which charter has been affected?

⚓ A. Bareboat

B. Lease

C. Time

D. Voyage

TIME CHARTER

012597/DG01351   **MARTIN**

Your vessel is chartered under a time charter party. Under this type of charter party, your responsibility is _____.

A. solely to the charterer for all matters pertaining to cargo and ship administration

B. solely to the cargo shippers and consignees

C. solely to the owner, as under normal conditions

⚓ D. to the owner for vessel administration and to the charterer for cargo operations and schedule

VOYAGE CHARTER

012598/DG02080   **MARTIN**

A Contract of Affreightment covering the movement of a particular cargo from one designated port to another at a specified rate for each ton of goods loaded is called a _____.

A. bareboat charter party

B. demise charter party

C. time charter party

⚓ D. voyage charter party

012599/DG02154   MARTIN
A vessel has a charter party for one voyage to carry a full load of manganese from Durban, South Africa, to Baltimore, Maryland, at a stipulated rate per ton. Which type of contract is involved?
A. Bareboat charter party
⚓ B. Voyage charter party
C. Demise charter party
D. Time charter party

012600/DG01361   MARTIN
On a voyage charter, when a vessel is ready to load cargo, the Master should render to the charterer a _____.
⚓ A. Notice of Readiness
B. Master Certificate of Service
C. Shipmasters Declaration
D. Vessel Utilization and Performance Report

012601/DG02133   MARTIN
The S.S. Hollowpoint has a charter party in which the charterer assumes no responsibility for the operation of the vessel but pays stevedoring expenses. What is the name of the charter party?
A. Bareboat
B. Dispatch
⚓ C. Voyage
D. Demise

CHARTERING TERMINOLOGY

012602/DG01391   MARTIN
The basic shipping paper that forms an agreement between a shipowner and a charterer is a _____.
A. Cargo Declaration
B. Charter Commission
⚓ C. Charter Party
D. Letter of Intent

012603/DG01972   INT. MARITIME DICTIONARY
Payment of penalty for a ship's delay after the expiration of lay days due to some fault of the charterer or his agent is known as _____.
⚓ A. demurrage
B. late fee
C. miscibility
• D. volatility

012604/DG01431   MARTIN
A charterer is unable to complete the loading of a vessel during the lay days specified in the charter party. Under these circumstances, the _____.
⚓ A. vessel operator can collect demurrage
B. ship is authorized extra time to discharge the cargo
C. charterer must pay dispatch money
D. effective period of the charter is extended

012605/DG01411   MARTIN
The time allowed for loading and discharging cargo in a charter party is referred to as _____.
A. charter hire
B. demurrage
C. dispatch
⚓ D. lay days

012606/DG02175   KENDELL; HOPKINS
Which is a negotiated charter?
⚓ A. Fixture
B. Bill of Lading
C. Conference agreement
D. All of the above

012607/DG01441   MMOH
Dead freight is the charge for the _____.
A. carriage of demise cargo
B. cost of transshipment of over-carried cargo
C. difference in the amount of cargo loaded and the amount of cargo discharged
⚓ D. difference in the amount of cargo loaded and the amount of cargo booked, through no fault of the vessel

012608/DG01401   MARTIN
A clause in the charter party requires a vessel's owner to pay dispatch money when the vessel _____.
A. changes berths to expedite loading or discharging
B. does not load and discharge its cargo in the time specified
C. is not ready to load or discharge cargo
⚓ D. loads and discharges its cargo in less time than specified

012609/DG01421   HOPKINS
The charterer has completed loading the vessel in 3 days instead of the 5 days agreed to in the charter party. As a result of this, the _____.
A. shipowner may charge for two lay days
⚓ B. charterer may receive dispatch money
C. stevedore may collect demurrage
D. consignee may be required to pay a ceaser fee

012610/DG01371   MARTIN
Delivery of a vessel to a charterer is called _____.
A. chartering
B. dispatching
C. fixing
⚓ D. tendering

012611/DG01381 **MARTIN**

The Master of a vessel may tender a Notice of Readiness to the charterer when the vessel _____.

A. has completed the terms of the charter party
⚓ B. is in all respects ready to load
C. is in all respects ready to sail
D. is safely moored or at a suitable anchorage

DEVIATIONS

012612/DG01801 **NORRIS**

A vessel proceeding to London, England, from New York makes an unscheduled call at the port of Hamilton, Bermuda. What term is used to denote the voluntary departure from the usual course?

A. Alteration
⚓ B. Deviation
C. Liberty
D. Unscheduled stop

012613/DG01451 **THE LAW OF SEAMEN; NORRIS; HOPKINS**

The implied condition(s) with respect to the doctrine of deviation in a marine insurance policy is(are) _____.

A. that the cargo be discharged from the vessel with customary dispatch
B. that the voyage be commenced in a reasonable time
C. that the voyage be pursued over the usual and direct route
⚓ D. All of the above

MARINE INSURANCE

GENERAL AVERAGE

012614/DG01471 **MARTIN**

One of the requirements for a general average act is _____.

⚓ A. a successful venture
B. no imminent peril
C. no losses
D. All of the above

012615/DG02795 **HOPKINS**

The York-Antwerp Rules relate to the _____.

A. minimum required number of officers and crew
⚓ B. settlement of general average claims
C. ship owner's responsibilities to provide a well-found vessel in a charter party
D. navigation regulations that apply in the English Channel

012616/DG02919 **HOPKINS**

Which statement about general average is TRUE?

A. Damage to a ship must have been incurred while the ship and/or its machinery was being used for its intended purpose.
⚓ B. Property must have been sacrificed or an expenditure of money incurred.
C. The loss or damage to deck cargo due to heavy weather constitutes general average.
D. Of the ship, the freight, and the cargo interests, only one need be involved.

012617/DG01461 **MARTIN**

While a vessel is at sea, the mate on watch discovers a fire in one of the hatches. Fire hoses are used to put the fire out and some of the cargo is damaged by water. In marine insurance terms, this partial loss by water is called _____.

A. an Act of God
B. fire and water damage
⚓ C. general average
D. particular average

PARTICULAR AVERAGE

012618/DG01481 **MARTIN; ENCY. NAUT. KNOW.**

A fire has damaged 20 bales of cotton on a freighter loaded with general cargo. This claim would come under _____.

A. constructive total loss
B. general average
⚓ C. particular average
D. total loss of a part

012619/DG01501 **HOPKINS**

Particular average is _____.

A. the average distance steamed per day over the duration of the voyage
B. charges against all parties in a marine venture to pay for damages
⚓ C. loss sustained by only one party
D. claimed after all liens against the vessel are settled

012620/DG01491 **MARTIN**

While underway, part of your cargo is damaged by fire. In marine insurance terms this partial loss is called _____.

A. absolute total loss
B. constructive total loss
C. general average
⚓ D. particular average

MARINE INSURANCE TERMINOLOGY

012621/DG02166   **HOPKINS**
A ballasted vessel sinks enroute to a dry dock. Under these circumstances, the vessel's owner can claim _____.

A. actual total loss
B. constructive total loss
C. general average
D. particular average

012622/DG01511   **HOPKINS**
A vessel has been damaged by fire. The survey shows the cost of repairs will exceed the value of the repaired vessel. This is an example of a(n) _____.

A. constructive total loss
B. salvage loss
C. actual loss
D. preferred loss

012623/DG01521   **HOPKINS**
An underwriter is liable for _____.

A. loss arising from the subject itself because of its inherent qualities
B. loss caused by the ordinary evaporation of liquids
C. loss caused by heavy weather
D. the natural decay of the vessel due to the passage of time

012624/DG01297   **HOPKINS**
What is an example of the term "Restraint of Rulers, Princes, or Peoples" in a marine insurance policy?

A. A prohibition from loading a cargo from a country's government interference.
B. Arrest of a vessel by legal authorities to satisfy claims through exercise of a maritime lien.
C. Damage caused by riot of the population of a port.
D. Losses caused by fines from polluting the harbor after malfunction of a piping system.

012625/DG02529   **HOPKINS**
Which condition would NOT entitle a vessel to carry goods on deck?

A. The shipper agrees to deck stowage
B. The cargo will damage other cargoes by tainting or contamination
C. Deck stowage is required by law or regulation
D. Deck stowage is customary in the trade (i.e. timber cargoes)

MARITIME LIENS

012626/DG01965   **NORRIS**
A maritime lien may be placed against _____.

A. any assets that a ship's owner may have
B. a vessel, cargo, or freight
C. objects that are fixed and immovable, such as wharves
D. the vessel only

012627/DG01956   **HOPKINS**
Which lien against a vessel would be settled FIRST?

A. Maintenance and cure
B. Vessel mortgage
C. Salvage lien
D. Ship repairer's lien

MISCELLANEOUS

012628/DG01467   **KENDELL**
The type of carrier required to file a copy of freight tariffs would be the _____.

A. common carrier
B. tramp
C. public vessel
D. bulk carrier

012629/DG01321   **ENCY. NAUT. KNOW.**
Which type of carrier accepts without discrimination all legal cargoes of a shipper?

A. Common
B. Industrial
C. Private
D. Tramp

012630/DG01251   **INT. MARITIME DICTIONARY**
What is NOT a primary function of the freight forwarder?

A. To book cargo space in advance
B. To execute, approve, and submit all shipping documents necessary to the particular shipment
C. To provide financial assistance to the shipper when required
D. Clear the goods through customs

GENERAL MARINE REGULATIONS

PROCEDURES & TERMINOLOGY

012631/DG01531   ***46 CFR 97.10-5**
Maritime Administration personnel may be allowed in the pilothouse upon the responsibility of the _____.

A. Chief Officer
B. Navigator
C. most senior person present from the Maritime Administration
D. officer in charge of the watch

012632/DG01541   INT. MARITIME DICTIONARY
Which act would be considered barratry?
A. A criminal act committed by a crew member ashore in a foreign port
⚓ B. A criminal act committed by the ship Master in violation of his duty to the shipowner
C. Theft of cargo by longshoremen
D. Smuggling with the connivance of the shipowner

012633/DG02676   HOPKINS
Who cannot commit the crime of barratry?
A. Master
B. Ship's officer(s)
C. Ship's unlicensed crewmember(s)
⚓ D. Ship owner

SEAWORTHINESS

012634/DG01591   AMSM
A complaint of unseaworthiness by a majority of crew members to the American Consul is found to be justified after a survey is completed. Who must pay the cost of the survey?
A. Crew members requesting the survey
B. American Consul
⚓ C. Master
D. Vessel's owners

012635/DG01551   NORRIS; *46 USC 654;
**   *46 USC 10903 (b)**
A majority of the crew requests a survey from the American Consul to determine a vessel's seaworthiness. The vessel is found unfit to continue her intended voyage. The Consul allows the vessel to sail to another port where deficiencies can be corrected. The crew must _____.
A. be discharged and given first class passage back to the original port of signing on in lieu of one month's wages
B. be discharged by the American Consul with additional one month's wages until repairs are made
C. be furnished employment on another vessel returning to the United States which is satisfactory to that crew
⚓ D. comply with the judgment

012636/DG03589   *46 USC 10906
A vessel has been surveyed in a foreign port and found unseaworthy as a result of neglect. A seaman on this vessel is entitled to discharge and _____.
A. transportation to the port of engagement
B. one month's pay only
C. one month's pay or transportation to the nearest U.S. port, whichever is the least amount
⚓ D. one month's pay or transportation to the nearest U.S. port, whichever is the greater amount

012637/DG01581   *46 USC 10903
A vessel is found to be seaworthy after a complaint in writing to the American Consul by the Chief and Second Mates. The cost of the survey is to be paid by the _____.
A. American Consul
⚓ B. Chief and Second Mates
C. Vessel's agent
D. vessel's owners

012638/DG01571   USC
As Chief Officer of a vessel underway, it comes to your attention that the vessel is, in some manner, unseaworthy. Under such circumstances the Master is required to take action upon receiving _____.
A. information of such condition from yourself
⚓ B. notification of such condition from yourself and the Second Officer
C. notification of such condition from yourself and any other member of the crew
D. notification of such condition from yourself or the Second Officer

012639/DG01561   *46 USC 10902
The Master of any vessel bound on a voyage must apply to a district court when an allegation of unseaworthiness has been made to the Master by _____.
A. any member of the crew of the vessel
B. any two officers of the vessel and a majority of the crew
⚓ C. the First and Second Officers of the vessel or a majority of the crew
D. the First Officer of the vessel

012640/DG01601   *46 USC 653
What would be prima facie evidence of unseaworthiness?
⚓ A. Overloading
B. Overstowage
C. Overbooking
D. Overcarriage

U.S. COAST GUARD PLACARD POSTING
REQUIREMENTS

012641/DG01295   *46 CFR 97.19-1
What is required to be posted in the pilothouse of a vessel?
A. Official Crew List
B. Company Mission Statement
C. Certificate of Inspection
⚓ D. Maneuvering Characteristics

012642/DG01293   *46 CFR 131.350
What is required to be posted in the pilothouse of a vessel?
A. Certificate of Inspection
B. Officer's licenses
C. Company Mission Statement
⚓ D. Muster List ("Station Bill")

012643/DG01651   *46 CFR 35.12-5; MARTIN;
                    ARAGON; McFARLAND & WALLS
Which document is NOT required by law to be posted aboard a vessel?
⚓ A. Official Crew List
B. Certificate of Inspection
C. Officer's licenses
D. Muster List

012644/DG01661   *46 CFR 97.53;
              *46 CFR 97.13; *46 CFR 91.01-5
Which document is NOT required by law to be posted aboard a vessel?
A. Certificate of Inspection
⚓ B. Official Crew List
C. Officer's licenses
D. Muster list

PENALTY PROVISIONS UNDER U.S. CODE

012645/DG00011   *46 USCA 2302
A person is found operating a vessel while intoxicated. He is liable for _____.
A. imprisonment for up to one year
⚓ B. a civil penalty of not more than $5,000
C. seizure of his/her vessel and forfeiture of the title
D. a fine of not more than $1,000

012646/DG00415   *46 USCA 2302
A person is found operating a vessel while intoxicated. He/she is liable for _____.
A. imprisonment for up to one year
B. a civil penalty of not more than $1,000
C. a fine of not more than $2,000
⚓ D. a civil penalty of not more than $5,000

012647/DG00413   *46 USCA 2302
A person is found operating a vessel while under the influence of alcohol. He/she is liable for _____.
A. imprisonment for up to three years
⚓ B. a civil penalty of not more than $5,000
C. a fine of not more than $3,000
D. a fine of not more than $10,000

012648/DG02026   *46 USC 10313
After a seaman is discharged, at the end of the voyage, the final payment of wages due must be made, whichever is earliest, either within 24 hours after the cargo has been discharged, or _____.
⚓ A. within 4 days after the seaman's discharge
B. prior to the vessel's departure on the next voyage
C. prior to loading any out-bound cargo
D. prior to any change of Master

012649/DG02162   *46 USC 10313
A crew has signed on for a 3-month voyage. Fourteen days into the voyage a seaman is improperly discharged at the first port of call. How much pay is he entitled to receive?
A. 14 days
B. 1 month's
⚓ C. 14 days and one month's extra
D. double wages (28 days)

012650/DG02056   *46 USC 10315
A seaman may not make an allotment to his _____.
A. minor children
B. grandparents
C. brother
⚓ D. mother-in-law

012651/DG02504   *46 USC 10315
A seaman may have all or part of his wages deposited by allotment to a bank or savings institution. Which of the following is NOT a requirement for this type of allotment?
⚓ A. The account must be either a checking or savings account.
B. The institution must be insured by the FSLIC or FDIC.
C. The account must be opened by the seaman and maintained in the seaman's name.
D. All of the above are requirements.

012652/DG02123   *46 USC 11103
Your vessel is required to have a slop chest. Which of the following articles is NOT required by law to be carried in the slop chest?
A. Foul weather clothing
⚓ B. Candy
C. Tobacco products
D. Blankets

012653/DG02141   *46 USC 11105

You are Master of a vessel that is sold in a foreign country after discharge of cargo. What is your responsibility to the crew in regards to return to the United States?

A. You must provide air transportation to the nearest port of entry in the United States.

⚓ B. You must provide passage to the port of original engagement.

C. There is no requirement for return to the United States provided the voyage has exceeded 4 weeks duration.

D. The crew can be employed on another United States vessel, but only if it is returning to the port of original engagement.

012654/DG00597   *46 USC 11109

Wages due a seaman may be attached by the court for the _____.

A. payment of monthly bills

B. payment of creditors

⚓ C. support of a minor child

D. All of the above

012655/DG02536   *46 USCA 11109

Wages due a seaman may be attached by the court for the _____.

A. payment of any fines imposed by the court

B. payment of back taxes to the IRS

⚓ C. support of a spouse

D. All of the above

012656/DG03462   *46 USC 11501

Under U.S. law, what is the penalty for assaulting the Master?

A. Fine of not more than $1000

B. Fine of not more than $500 and/or imprisonment for not more than 1 year

⚓ C. Imprisonment for not more than 2 years

D. Revocation of the Merchant Mariner's Document (and license if applicable)

012657/DG03680   *46 USC 11501

What is the penalty for willfully damaging cargo?

⚓ A. Forfeiture of wages equal to the value of the damage and, if ordered by the court, imprisonment for not more than 12 months

B. Fine equal to the value of the damage plus a 1000 dollar penalty and/or imprisonment not to exceed 2 years

C. Fine not to exceed the value of the damage and/or imprisonment not to exceed 18 months

D. Revocation of Merchant Mariner's Document (and license if applicable), fine equal to the value of the damage or imprisonment for not more than 2 years

012658/DG03602   *46 USC 11501

What is the penalty for desertion?

A. Fine of not more than 2000 dollars and forfeiture of wages

B. Imprisonment for not more than 2 years and/or a fine of not more than 2000 dollars

C. Revocation of Merchant Mariner's Document (and license if applicable) and forfeiture of wages due

⚓ D. Forfeiture of money and property left on the vessel, and wages due

012659/DG02102   *46 USC 11505; NORRIS

A seaman deserts the vessel in a foreign port. What should the Master do with any of the deserter's personal effects remaining on board?

A. Sell them at auction and deposit the money in the ship's morale or welfare fund.

B. Donate them to a local charity upon return to the United States.

⚓ C. Transfer them to the appropriate district court of the U.S. at the end of the voyage.

D. Inventory them, make an appropriate entry in the Official Logbook and dispose of them at sea.

012660/DG00725   *46 USCA 7704

By law, a user of marijuana shall be subject to _____.

A. loss of pay during the period of such use

B. reprimand by the US Coast Guard

⚓ C. revocation of license or certificate

D. termination of employment

LICENSING & CERTIFICATE OF SEAMEN

012661/DG00756   68 Fed Register 116

A licensed Master of Towing Vessels may NOT serve as the Captain of which towing vessel?

A. 99 GRT towing vessel operating on Chesapeake Bay

B. 199 GRT towing vessel operating in the Gulf of Alaska

C. 400 GRT towboat operating on the Western Rivers

⚓ D. 375 GRT towing vessel operating between Texas and Puerto Rico

012662/DG00432   68 Fed Register 116

A licensed Master of Towing Vessels may NOT serve as the person in charge of which towing vessel?

A. 99 GRT towing vessel operating on Chesapeake Bay

B. 199 GRT towing vessel operating in the Gulf of Alaska

C. 480 GRT towboat operating on the Western Rivers

⚓ D. 405 GRT towing vessel operating between Florida and the US Virgin Islands

012663/DG03210　　　　　**68 Fed Register 116**
A licensed Master of Towing Vessels may NOT serve as the person in charge of which towing vessel?
A. 99 GRT towing vessel operating on Chesapeake Bay
B. 199 GRT towing vessel operating in the Gulf of Alaska
C. 500 GRT towboat operating on the Western Rivers
⚓ D. 349 GRT towing vessel operating between Florida and Puerto Rico

012664/DG03170　　　　　***46 CFR 10.209 (e)**
A license for apprentice mate (steersman) of uninspected towing vessels shall be renewed within what time period before or after the expiration date?
A. 30 days
B. 90 days
C. 6 months
⚓ D. 12 months

012665/DG03200　　　　　***46 CFR 10.209 (e)**
A license issued by the U.S. Coast Guard for apprentice mate (steersman) of Uninspected Towing Vessels is valid for _____.
A. 2 years and must be renewed
B. 3 years and must be renewed
⚓ C. 5 years and must be renewed
D. None of the above

012666/DG03180　　　　　***46 CFR 10.209 (e)**
A license issued by the U.S. Coast Guard for Master of Towing Vessels is valid for _____.
A. 2 years and must be renewed
B. 3 years and must be renewed
⚓ C. 5 years and must be renewed
D. life and need not be renewed

012667/DG00310　　　　　***46 CFR 26.20-1**
Operators of Uninspected Passenger Vessels are required to keep their Coast Guard License aboard _____.
A. only when operating more than one mile from shore
B. only when operating at night
⚓ C. only when carrying passengers for hire
D. At all times

012668/DG02616　　　***33 CFR 125.53; *33 CFR 125.09**
You are in charge of a towing vessel that operates exclusively on inland waters. You regularly tow barges that provide services (cargo lighters, fuel barges, etc.) to foreign flag vessels in port. What will be accepted as proper credentials for you and your crew?
A. No credentials are required since you operate on inland waters only
B. Social Security card
C. State driver's license with photo ID
⚓ D. Merchant Mariner's Document

012669/DG02674　　　***33 CFR 125.53; *33 CFR 125.09**
You operate a harbor craft on inland waters exclusively. If you regularly service or contact foreign flag vessels in the course of business, which statement is TRUE?
A. Your vessel must be inspected.
⚓ B. Your crew must have identification credentials.
C. A customs official must be on board when contacting a foreign flag vessel.
D. All contacts with a foreign flag vessel must be reported to the U.S. Coast Guard.

SUSPENSION & REVOCATION OF LICENSE

012670/DG00968　　　　　***46 USC 7703 (1) (b)**
The Master may have his/her license suspended or revoked for _____.
A. carrying stowaways
B. sailing shorthanded
⚓ C. being negligent
D. All of the above

012671/DG00978　　　　　***46 CFR 05.203**
Anyone voluntarily surrendering their license to a U.S. Coast Guard investigating officer signs a statement indicating that _____.
A. all title to the license is given up for 5 years
⚓ B. their rights to a hearing are waived
C. they may be issued a new license in 5 years after passing another written examination
D. All of the above

012672/DG01008　　　　　***46 CFR 05.203**
When anyone voluntarily deposits his/her license or document with a Coast Guard investigating officer _____.
A. he/she permanently gives up rights to the license or document
⚓ B. it may be for reasons of mental or physical incompetence
C. it must be for reason of addiction to narcotics
D. All of the above

012673/DG03220　　　　　***46 CFR 05.61**
If you are guilty of failure to properly perform your duties as Master of Uninspected Towing Vessels, which of the following actions may NOT be taken?
A. Issuance of a letter of warning
B. Suspension of your license
C. Revocation of your license
⚓ D. A fine placed against your license

012674/DG00136 *33 CFR 95.020 (b)

Under the federal regulations, what minimum level of Blood Alcohol Content (BAC) constitutes a violation of the laws prohibiting Boating Under the Influence of Alcohol (BUI) on commercial vessels?

A. .18% BAC
B. .10% BAC
C. .06% BAC
⚓ D. .04% BAC

SOLAS REGULATIONS

012675/DG03710 SOLAS IV/18; *46 CFR 199.180 (g)

A new crewman reports on board. He must be trained in the use of the ship's lifesaving appliances within what time period?

A. 2 months
B. 1 month
⚓ C. 2 weeks
D. Before sailing

012676/DG03740 *46 CFR 199.180 (g) (3)

Instructions to the crew in the use of all the ship's lifesaving equipment shall be completed _____.

A. before sailing
B. within one week of sailing
C. in one month and repeated quarterly
⚓ D. within any two month period

012677/DG03770 SOLAS IV/18

SOLAS requires a lifesaving training manual be provided in each crew cabin or in the _____.

A. bridge
B. engineering control station
⚓ C. recreation and messrooms
D. fire control room

012678/DG01443 McEWEN

The Safety of Life at Sea Convention was developed by the _____.

A. U.S. Coast Guard
B. American Bureau of Shipping
⚓ C. International Maritime Organization
D. American Institute of Maritime Shipping

ACCIDENT & CASUALTY REPORTING

REPORTING PROCEDURES

012679/DG00027 *46 USC 10104

Under Title 46 of the United States Code, the person in charge of a documented vessel who fails to report a complaint of a sexual offense may be _____.

⚓ A. fined up to $5,000
B. imprisoned for up to one year
C. charged with accessory to sexual assault
D. All of the above

012680/DG00065 *46 USC 10104

Under Title 46 of the United States Code, the person in charge of a documented vessel who fails to report a complaint of a sexual offense may be _____.

A. charged with accessory to sexual assault
B. imprisoned for up to one year
⚓ C. fined up to $5,000
D. All of the above

012681/DG00067 *46 USC 10104

You are in charge of a U.S. documented vessel. Under Title 46 of the United States Code, if you fail to report a complaint of a sexual offense, you may be _____.

⚓ A. civilly charged and fined
B. criminally charged and jailed
C. held personally liable by the victim and sued
D. All of the above are correct.

012682/DG00029 *46 USC 10104

You are in charge of a U.S. documented vessel. Under Title 46 of the United States Code, if you fail to report a complaint of a sexual offense, you may be _____.

A. criminally charged and jailed
⚓ B. civilly penalized
C. held personally liable by the victim and sued
D. All of the above are correct

012683/DG00055 *46 USC 10104

You are in charge of a U.S. documented vessel. Under Title 46 of the United States Code, if you fail to report a complaint of a sexual offense, you may be _____.

A. held personally liable by the victim and sued
B. criminally charged and jailed
⚓ C. civilly charged and fined
D. All of the above are correct.

012684/DG01078 *46 USC 2303

By law, the maximum penalty for failing (without reasonable cause) to give aid in the case of collision is _____.

A. one year imprisonment or $500
⚓ B. two years imprisonment or $1000
C. two years imprisonment or $1500
D. two years imprisonment or $2000

012685/DG03321 *46 USC 2303

By law, the maximum penalty for failing (without reasonable cause) to give aid in the case of collision is _____.

A. one year imprisonment or $500
B. two years imprisonment or $500
⚓ C. two years imprisonment or $1000
D. two years imprisonment or $2000

012686/DG01333   *46 CFR 4.03-2
What accident situation is considered a Serious Marine Incident?
A. An injury to a crewmember that renders that person unfit to continue working on the vessel
B. Damage to property in excess of $100,000
C. A discharge of 10,000 gallons or more of oil into navigable waters of the U.S.
⚓ D. All of the above

012687/DG00305   *46 CFR 4.03-2
What is considered a Serious Marine Incident?
A. an allision that results in $500 damage to a boat dock
⚓ B. an injury to a crewmember, passenger, or other person which requires professional medical treatment beyond first aid
C. grounding of a vessel on a sandbar that does not result in injuries and/or any damage to the vessel
D. None of the above

012688/DG00303   *46 CFR 4.03-2; *46 CFR 4.05-1
What requires a Report of Marine Accident, Injury or Death?
A. Collision with a bridge
B. Injury beyond first aid
C. loss of life
⚓ D. All of the above

012689/DG02293   *46 CFR 04.03-45
As defined in the regulations governing marine casualties a "marine employer" may be the _____.
A. owner
B. agent
C. Master
⚓ D. All of the above

012690/DG00557   *46 CFR 4.05-5
A report of casualty to a vessel must include _____.
A. the estimated cost of damage
B. an evaluation of who was at fault
C. the amount of ballast on board
⚓ D. the name of the owner or agent of the vessel

012691/DG01088   *46 CFR 04.05-1
As Master or person in charge, you must notify the U.S. Coast Guard if an injury leaves a crewman unfit to perform routine duties for more than _____.
A. 24 hours
B. 48 hours
C. 72 hours
⚓ D. Any amount of time

012692/DG01058   *46 CFR 04.05-1
The damage to a vessel is over $25,000. Who must notify the nearest Coast Guard Marine Safety or Marine Inspection Office as soon as possible?
A. The owner of the vessel
B. The Master of the vessel
C. The person in charge of the vessel at the time of casualty
⚓ D. Any one of the above

012693/DG00477   *46 CFR 04.05-1
When underway with a tow, you are required to notify the Coast Guard in which casualty situation?
A. An injury requiring first aid treatment
B. Damage of bridge-to-bridge radio capability
⚓ C. Accidental stranding or grounding
D. Damage to property amounting to $12,500

012694/DG03017   *46 CFR 4.03-1 (b)
Which situation requires you to furnish a notice of marine casualty to the Coast Guard?
A. Storm damage to the cargo winch motors requires repairs costing $19,000.
⚓ B. Your vessel is at anchor and grounds at low tide with no apparent damage.
C. You collide with a buoy and drag it off station with no apparent damage to the vessel or the buoy.
D. A seaman slips on ice on deck and sprains his ankle, requiring an ace bandage.

012695/DG01048   *46 CFR 04.05-1
You are the person in charge of a vessel involved in a marine casualty. You must notify the nearest Coast Guard Marine Inspection Office if the property damage is over _____.
A. $1,500
B. $10,000
⚓ C. $25,000
D. $50,000

012696/DG01632   *46 CFR 04.05-1
In which casualty case is it UNNECESSARY to notify the local Coast Guard Marine Safety Office?
⚓ A. Your vessel strikes a pier and does $1,500 damage to the pier but none to the vessel.
B. A nylon mooring line parts while the vessel is tied up and kills a harbor worker who was on the pier.
C. A seaman is injured and in the hospital for four days.
D. Your vessel is backing from a dock and runs aground, but is pulled off by tugs in 30 minutes.

012697/DG01699   ***46 CFR 4.05-1**

In which casualty case is it UNNECESSARY to notify the local Coast Guard Marine Safety Office?

A. Your vessel is backing from a dock and runs aground, but is pulled off by tugs in 30 minutes.

⚓ B. Your vessel strikes a pier and does $1,500 damage to the pier but no damage to the vessel.

C. A nylon mooring line parts while the vessel is tied up and kills a harbor worker who was on the pier.

D. A seaman is injured and in the hospital for four days.

012698/DG02707   ***46 CFR 4.05-1**

In which casualty case is it UNNECESSARY to notify the local Coast Guard Marine Safety Office?

A. Your vessel is backing from a dock and runs aground, but is pulled off by tugs in 30 minutes.

B. A seaman is injured and in the hospital for four days.

⚓ C. Your vessel strikes a pier and does $1,500 damage to the pier but no damage to the vessel.

D. A nylon mooring line parts while the vessel is tied up and kills a harbor worker who was on the pier.

012699/DG01315   ***46 CFR 04.05-1**

In which casualty case is it UNNECESSARY to notify the local Coast Guard Marine Safety Office?

A. A seaman is injured and in the hospital for four days.

B. Nylon mooring line parts while the vessel is tied up and kills a harbor worker who was on the pier.

C. Your vessel is backing from a dock and runs aground, but is pulled off by tugs in 30 minutes.

⚓ D. Your vessel strikes and sinks an anchored sailboat costing a total of $20,000 for salvage and repair.

012700/DG01403   ***46 CFR 04.05-1**

A vessel is involved in a casualty. The cost of property damage includes the _____.

A. loss of revenue while the vessel is being repaired, up to a maximum of $50,000

⚓ B. cost of labor and material to restore the vessel to the service condition which existed before the casualty

C. damage claims awarded to individuals or companies involved in the casualty, up to a maximum of $50,000

D. All of the above

012701/DG01959   ***46 CFR 4.05-1**

A vessel is involved in a casualty. The cost of property damage includes the _____.

A. damage claims awarded to individuals or companies involved in the casualty, up to a maximum of $50,000

B. loss of revenue while the vessel is being repaired, up to a maximum of $50,000

⚓ C. cost of labor and material to restore the vessel to the service condition which existed before the casualty

D. All of the above

012702/DG00001   ***46 CFR 04.05-1**

During the course of a voyage, a seaman falls on the main deck and injures his ankle. The Master should submit a Report of Marine Accident, Injury or Death if the _____.

A. injured needs first aid

⚓ B. injured is incapacitated

C. injury results in loss of life only

D. injury is the result of misconduct

012703/DG00115   ***46 CFR 04.05-1**

During the course of a voyage, a seaman falls on the main deck and injures his ankle. The Master should submit a Report of Marine Accident, Injury or Death if the _____.

A. injury is the result of misconduct

B. injury results in loss of life only

C. injured need first aid

⚓ D. injured is incapacitated

012704/DG01317   ***46 CFR 04.05-1**

The damage to a vessel is over $25,000. Who must notify the nearest Coast Guard Marine Safety or Marine Inspection Office as soon as possible?

A. The person in charge of the vessel

B. The operator of the vessel

C. The Master of the vessel

⚓ D. All of the above

012705/DG00863   ***46 CFR 4.05-1**

When underway with a tow, you are required to notify the Coast Guard in which casualty situation?

A. Damage to property amounting to $12,500

⚓ B. Accidental stranding or grounding

C. Loss of bridge-to-bridge radio capability

D. An injury requiring first aid treatment

012706/DG01562   *46 CFR 4.05-1

Which situation requires you to furnish a notice of marine casualty to the Coast Guard?

A. A seaman slips on ice on deck and sprains his ankle, requiring an ace bandage.

B. You collide with a buoy and drag it off station with no apparent damage to the vessel or the buoy.

C. Storm damage to the cargo winch motors requires repairs costing $19,000.

⚓ D. Your vessel is at anchor and grounds at low tide with no apparent damage.

012707/DG00230   *46 CFR 04.05-1

You are the Master of a 500-gross ton passenger vessel operating on rivers. Your vessel accidentally runs aground. Under the regulations for passenger vessels, you must notify the _____.

A. Coast Guard, only if the grounding results in damage to property in excess of $25,000

⚓ B. nearest Coast Guard Marine Safety or Marine Inspection Office as soon as possible

C. Coast Guard, only if the grounding results in a loss of life

D. Coast Guard, only if the grounding results in injury to personnel

012708/DG01262   *46 CFR 04.05-1

You are the Master of a 500-gross ton passenger vessel operating on rivers. Your vessel accidentally runs aground. Under the regulations for passenger vessels, you must notify the _____.

A. Coast Guard, only if the grounding results in damage to property in excess of $25,000

B. Coast Guard, only if the grounding results in a loss of life

C. Coast Guard, only if the grounding results in injury to personnel

⚓ D. nearest Coast Guard Marine Safety or Marine Inspection Office as soon as possible

012709/DG01327   *46 CFR 04.05-1

You shall notify the nearest Coast Guard Marine Inspection Office as soon as possible when your vessel has been damaged in excess of _____.

A. $15,000

⚓ B. $25,000

C. $50,000

D. $100,000

012710/DG02897   *46 CFR 4.05-10

Form 2692 (Notice of Marine Casualty), when required, must be filed to the U.S. Coast Guard within how many days?

A. 1 day

B. 3 days

⚓ C. 5 days

D. 7 days

012711/DG00300   *46 CFR 4.05-10 (a)

On which form do you provide a written report of Marine Casualty to the nearest Coast Guard Marine Safety Office?

A. DD 214

⚓ B. CG 2692

C. DOT 211

D. CG 5511

012712/DG03250   *46 CFR 04.05-20

You are operator of a towing vessel which collides with a buoy and drags it off station. What should you do if the damage to your vessel is not serious?

A. If the buoy is afloat, no action is necessary.

B. Wait one week and submit form GG-2692 to the nearest Coast Guard Marine Safety or Inspection Office.

⚓ C. Immediately notify the nearest Coast Guard Marine Safety or Inspection Office and no further action is necessary.

D. Immediately notify the nearest Coast Guard Marine Safety or Inspection Office and then submit form CG-2692.

012713/DG04007   *46 CFR 4.05-20

You are the operator of a towing vessel which collides with a buoy and drags it off station. What should you do if the damage to your vessel is not serious?

⚓ A, Immediately notify the nearest Coast Guard Marine Safety or Inspection Office and no further action is necessary.

B. If the buoy is afloat, no action is necessary.

C. You have 24 hours from time of incident to submit form CG-2692 to the nearest Coast Guard Marine Safety or Inspection Office.

D. Immediately notify the nearest Coast Guard Marine Safety or Inspection Office and then submit form CG-2692.

012714/DG01241   *46 CFR 4.05-5

A Notice of Marine Casualty to a vessel must include _____.

A. the estimated cost of damage

⚓ B. the name of the owner or agent of the vessel

C. an evaluation of who was at fault

D. the amount of ballast on board

012715/DG00307   *46 CFR Part 16

Which type of chemical testing is NOT required of merchant marine personnel?

A. Pre-employment

B. Periodic

C. Random

⚓ D. Annual

012716/DG01337   ***46 CFR 4.06-3***

Following a Serious Marine Incident, a mariner directly involved in the incident is required to submit to alcohol testing within _____.
A. 1 hour
B. 2 hours
C. 6 hours
D. 12 hours

012717/DG01342   ***46 CFR 4.06-5***

Following a Serious Marine Incident, a mariner involved in the incident is prohibited from consuming alcohol until after being tested or _____.
A. 2 hours following the incident
B. 4 hours following the incident
C. 8 hours following the incident
D. 12 hours following the incident

012718/DG01335   ***46 CFR 4.06-15***

Following a Serious Marine Incident, a mariner directly involved in the incident is required to submit a urine specimen for drug testing within _____.
A. 2 hours
B. 12 hours
C. 24 hours
D. 32 hours

012719/DG01345   ***46 CFR 4.06-15***

A vessel is not required to carry urine specimen collecting kits onboard the vessel only if the individuals directly involved in a Serious Marine Incident can be tested ashore within _____?
A. 12 hours
B. 24 hours
C. 32 hours
D. 48 hours

012720/DG01343   ***46 CFR 4.06-20***

Besides the chemical testing of a mariner's breath for alcohol, what other specimen testing for alcohol is acceptable to be taken onboard the vessel after a Serious Marine Incident?
A. Saliva
B. Blood
C. Hair
D. None of the above

012721/DG01625   ***46 CFR 04.06-20 (a)***

All inspected vessels on unrestricted ocean routes must have equipment on board for testing an individual's _____.
A. blood
B. breath
C. urine
D. All of the above

012722/DG00223   ***46 CFR 4.06-20 (b)***

Who is responsible for providing urine specimen collection kits to be used following a serious marine incident?
A. Qualified medical personnel
B. The marine employer
C. The U.S. Coast Guard
D. The local police department

012723/DG03587   ***46 CFR 04.06-20 (e)***

Following a serious marine incident, a device to test an individuals breath can be used by _____.
A. any individual trained to conduct such tests
B. the marine employer
C. qualified medical personnel only
D. any USCG licensed deck officer

012724/DG01318 ***46 CFR 26.03-5; *46 USC 2303***

The operator of an uninspected vessel MUST assist people affected by an accident if he or she can do so without _____.
A. serious danger to his or her own vessel
B. further damaging the other vessel
C. undue delay
D. creating a panic on either vessel

012725/DG00703   ***46 USC 2303***

The operator of an uninspected vessel MUST assist people affected by an accident if he or she can do so without _____.
A. serious danger to his or her own vessel
B. further damaging the other vessel
C. harming persons onboard
D. All of the above

012726/DG04051 ***46 CFR 26.03-5; *46 USC 2303***

You are the operator of an uninspected vessel which is involved in an accident. You are not required to assist people affected by the accident if _____.
A, the other vessel did not appear to be sinking
B. it would unduly delay your voyage
C. the other vessel was at fault
D. it would cause serious danger to your vessel

012727/DG00282   ***46 CFR 185.206***

The owner, agent, Master or person-in-charge of a "T-Boat" involved in a marine casualty causing injury that requires professional medical treatment must _____.
A. immediately notify the nearest USCG MSO, MIO, or Group Office
B. keep all voyage records and make them available to Coast Guard investigators
C. file a written report (CG2692) of the casualty within five days
D. All of the above

SHIP'S CONSTRUCTION & STABILITY

LOAD LINES

B10001/DG02762   ***46 CFR 45.15***

Which vessel is exempt from the load line and marking requirements for vessels operating on the Great Lakes System?
- A. A 300 GT tank barge operating exclusively on Lake Michigan
- B. A 200 GT passenger vessel operating between Duluth, MN and Munising, MI
- C. A 79-foot, 150 GT pleasure craft operating on the St. Lawrence River
- ⚓ D. A 500 GT dry cargo river barge operated continuously between Calumet Hbr Chicago, IL and Burns Hbr, IN

B10002/DG02718   ***46 CFR 45.35; *USCP 6***

On Great Lakes vessels, midsummer load lines apply _____.

- A. April 16 through April 30 and September 16 through September 30
- ⚓ B. May 1 through September 15
- C. July 16 through August 30
- D. June 16 through September 16

B10003/DG02929   ***46 CFR 45.5***

A vessel is loaded to her summer marks for a voyage from Montreal, Canada to Duluth, MN via the Great Lakes System. The voyage has been estimated to take nine (9) days. If the vessel departs Montreal on September 28th, which of the following statements is TRUE?
- A. The vessel must be at her summer marks when she arrives at Duluth.
- B. The vessel is in violation of the load line requirements.
- ⚓ C. The vessel's intermediate load line marks may not be submerged after September 30.
- D. The vessel must be at her winter marks by the evening of the third day.

DIAGRAM031DG

B10004/DG02802   ***46 CFR 45.31***

The single line located directly above the diamond is the _____. See Diagram D031DG
- A. load line
- B. water line
- C. freeboard line
- ⚓ D. deck line

B10005/DG02882   ***46 CFR 45.35***

What does the line labeled "MS" denote on the Great Lakes load line model shown? See Diagram D031DG
- A. Mean sea level
- B. Midseason
- C. Maximum submergence
- ⚓ D. Midsummer

B10006/DG02708   ***46 CFR 45.37***

Which statement is TRUE with respect to the load line markings shown. See Diagram D031DG
- ⚓ A. A vessel displaying these marks may load in the salt waters of the St. Lawrence River.
- B. Vessels engaged solely on Great Lakes voyages are not required to show these marks.
- C. U.S. flag vessels less than 100 feet in length and less than 200 gross tons are not required to show these marks.
- D. U.S. flag vessels of 100 gross tons and upward must show these marks.

B10007/DG02729   ***46 CFR 45.39***

The load line markings shown are inscribed on the vessel's _____. See Diagram D031DG
- A. port side
- B. starboard side
- ⚓ C. port and starboard sides
- D. stern

B10008/DG02692   ***46 CFR 45.5 (c)***

Your vessel is on a voyage from Ogdensburg, NY, to Chicago, IL, via the Great Lakes. The date is October 3 of the current year. If your vessel is subject to the load line requirements, to which of her marks should she be loaded? See Diagram D031DG
- A. Fresh water - Winter
- B. Salt water - Intermediate
- ⚓ C. Fresh water - Intermediate
- D. Salt water - Winter

LAKE AND RIVER NAVIGATION

INLAND NAVIGATION

B10009/DG02716   ***USCP 6***

A channel is stated as having a controlling depth of 38 feet. Which statement is TRUE?
- A. At least 80% of the channel is cleared to the charted depth.
- B. At least 50% of the channel is cleared to the charted depth.
- ⚓ C. 100% of the channel width is clear to 38 feet.
- D. The sides of the channel conform to at least 50% of the controlling depth.

B10010/DG02619   ***USCP 6**
On the Great Lakes, the term "controlling depth" means the _____.
A. designed dredging depth of a channel constructed by the Corps. of Engineers
B. minimum amount of tail water available behind a dam
C. distance in units of the chart (feet, meters or fathoms) from the reference datum to the bottom
⚓ D. least depth within the limits of the channel which restricts the navigation

B10011/DG02832   ***USCP 6**
You are transiting the Straits of Mackinac by way of an improved channel. You have information which indicates that the channel's Federal project depth is 28 ft. Which of the following statements is true with regards to this channel?
A. The least depth within the limits of the channel is 28 ft.
⚓ B. The design dredging depth of the channel is 28 ft.
C. The channel has 28 ft. in the center but lesser depths may exist in the remainder of the channel.
D. The maximum depth which may be expected within the limits of the channel is 28 ft.

B10012/DG02736   ***USCP 6**
Distances on the Great Lakes System are generally expressed in _____.
A. miles above the entrance to the St. Lawrence Seaway (MASLW)
B. miles above the head of the passes (AHP)
C. nautical miles
⚓ D. statute miles

B10013/DG02759   ***USCP 6**
Which of the Great Lakes is most affected by short-term Lake level fluctuations?
A. Lake Superior
B. Lake Michigan
C. Lake Huron
⚓ D. Lake Erie

B10014/DG02712   **GLWL; U.S.A.C.E.**
Which two Great Lakes are considered hydraulically as one?
A. Lakes Superior - Huron
⚓ B. Lakes Michigan - Huron
C. Lakes Erie - St. Clair
D. Lakes Erie - Ontario

B10015/DG02768   ***USCP 6**
Which of the Great Lakes lies entirely within the United States?
A. Lake Ontario
B. Lake St. Clair
⚓ C. Lake Michigan
D. Lake Superior

B10016/DG02819   ***USCP 6**
On which of the Great Lakes would shore ice be the most pronounced?
A. Lake Michigan
⚓ B. Lake Superior
C. Lake Huron
D. Lake Erie

B10017/DG02746   ***USCP 6**
Which of the Great Lakes experiences the least amount of water level fluctuation between seasonal high and low water marks?
A. Lake Huron
B. Lake Erie
⚓ C. Lake Superior
D. Lake Michigan

B10018/DG02784   ***USCP 6**
Which of the Great Lakes generally has the shortest navigation season?
A. Lake Erie
B. Lake Huron
C. Lake Michigan
⚓ D. Lake Superior

B10019/DG02836   ***USCP 6; GLWL**
Which of the Great Lakes is generally the last to reach its seasonal low and seasonal high water marks?
⚓ A. Lake Superior
B. Lake Michigan
C. Lake Huron
D. Lake Ontario

B10020/DG02666   ***USCP 6**
On the Great Lakes, short-term fluctuations in water levels may be a result of any of the following EXCEPT _____.
A. strong winds
B. sudden changes in barometric pressure
C. seiches
⚓ D. below normal rain fall

B10021/DG02902   ***USCP 6**
Which basic category of water level fluctuations on the Great Lakes is the most regular?
⚓ A. Seasonal fluctuations
B. Outflow fluctuations
C. Short-term fluctuations
D. Long-term fluctuations

B10022/DG02774   ***USCP 6**
There are basically three categories of water level fluctuations on the Great Lakes. What is NOT included as one of these?
A. Long range fluctuations
⚓ B. Controlled outflow fluctuations
C. Seasonal fluctuations
D. Short period fluctuations

B10023/DG02474   ***USCP 6**

Generally speaking, the more destructive storms occurring on the Great Lakes usually come from the _____.

   A. northeast or east

⚓ B. southwest or west

   C. northwest or north

   D. southeast or south

SAFETY

SAFETY INSPECTION

B10024/DG02499   ***46 CFR 91.40-3 (b)**

Single hull vessels operating exclusively on the Great Lakes must be dry docked at intervals not to exceed _____.

   A. 12 months

   B. 24 months

   C. 48 months

⚓ D. 60 months

SAFETY EQUIPMENT

B10025/DG02644   **AMSM**

The boat is stowed on the davit rather than on a cradle with which type of davit?

⚓ A. Crescent

   B. Sheath-screw boom

   C. Quadrantal

   D. Radial

B10026/DG02508   **WSM**

What is required to launch a boat stowed in a crescent davit?

   A. Hoist the boat clear of the cradle.

   B. Release the outboard part of the cradle.

   C. Rig the tricing lines.

⚓ D. Crank the crescent out.

B10027/DG02909   ***46 CFR 160**

A mechanical davit is designed to automatically _____.

   A. position the boat at the embarkation station

⚓ B. lift the boat off the inboard chocks

   C. energize the winch for the falls

   D. set the brake on the winch

B10028/DG04058   **AMSM**

Your vessel is equipped with mechanical davits. When stowing the lifeboat after a drill while underway, you should _____.

   A, leave the tricing pendants slack

⚓ B. ensure the falls are taut

   C. leave the outboard part of the cradle in the down position

   D. secure the inboard gripes only

B10029/DG02469   **WSM**

While cranking out a quadrantal davit, slippage of the quadrant due to excessive wear or failure of the teeth in the quadrant will cause the _____.

⚓ A. davit arm to pivot on the traveling nut and the head to fall outboard

   B. traveling nut to lock up in place on the worm gear

   C. limit switch to engage and hold the traveling nut in position

   D. winch brake to lock in position and prevent lowering the boat

B10030/DG02706   **AMSM**

Which type of davit is not considered to be a mechanical davit?

   A. Sheath-screw boom

⚓ B. Radial

   C. Crescent

   D. Quadrantal

B10031/DG02926   ***PUB 117; IKS**

Many sheath-screw davits have markings to indicate the maximum angle to which they should be cranked out. If the angle is exceeded, the davit _____.

   A. may jam against the stops

   B. will not automatically position the boat at the embarkation station

⚓ C. screw may come out of the sheath

   D. will chafe against the falls and may cause their failure

B10032/DG02726   **WSM**

The lifeboats on your vessel are stowed on cradles on deck and are handled by sheath-screw boom davits. Which of the following statements about launching a boat is TRUE?

   A. The boat should be hoisted a few inches clear of the cradle before cranking out the davits.

   B. The inboard gripes should be cast off before the outboard gripes.

⚓ C. The outboard section of the cradle must be released.

   D. The tricing pendants will automatically bring the boat alongside at the embarkation deck.

B10033/DG04032   **NVIC 6-81**

The pivot pin at the base of a sheath-screw boom davit must be _____.

   A, inserted each time before the booms are cranked out

⚓ B. periodically removed for inspection and lubricated

   C. replaced at each inspection for certification

   D. in the locked position after the boat is cradled and griped down

B10034/DG02607 *46 CFR 199.155 (d)
Which statement is TRUE concerning lifeboat installations on Great Lakes vessels?
A. All davit installations shall have 3 lifelines fitted to a davit span.
B. All vessels over 3,000 gross tons must be fitted with gravity davits.
C. All lifelines shall be able to reach the water at the vessel's lightest draft with a 20° list.
D. All of the above

B10035/DG02548 *46 CFR 94.33-10
What is the accepted standard for wire rope falls used in connection with the lifeboat gear?
A. Six by seven galvanized wire rope
B. Six by twenty-four improved plow steel wire rope
C. Six by thirty-seven preformed fiber-core wire rope
D. Six by nineteen regular-lay filler wire rope

B10036/DG04059 *46 CFR 94.43-10 (a)
A 750 foot passenger vessel operating on the Great Lakes, not subject to SOLAS regulations, is required to carry how many ring life buoys?
A. 24
B. 18
C. 12
D. 6

B10037/DG02559 *46 CFR 96.07-5
A vessel in Great Lakes service shall carry anchors in accordance with standards established by the _____.
A. American Bureau of Shipping
B. Canadian Coast Guard
C. U.S. Coast Guard
D. underwriter of the vessel

B10038/DG02754 *46 CFR 96.17
Which statement is TRUE concerning vessels over 1600 gross tons certificated for service solely on the Great Lakes?
A. They must have magnetic compasses.
B. They must have gyro compasses.
C. They must carry a deep-sea hand lead.
D. All of the above statements are TRUE.

B10039/DG02578 *46 CFR 97.15-20 (d)
According to regulations when, if ever, may cargo hatches on Great Lakes vessels, with more than 6 feet of freeboard, be left uncovered or open while the vessel is being navigated?
A. If a Mate deems it necessary for ship's maintenance
B. At the discretion of the Master, for reasonable purposes
C. On the authority of the Bosun
D. The hatch may never be uncovered

B10040/DG02598 *46 CFR 199.70 (b) (v)
Where, due to the arrangement of the vessel, lifejackets may become inaccessible, additional lifejackets shall be carried _____.
A. for the people on bridge watch
B. for the forward lifeboats
C. as determined by the OCMI
D. for 50% of the crew of the vessel, not including those assigned to engineering duties

B10041/DG01388 *46 CFR 199.610 (b), 199.211 (b)
If a passenger vessel navigating the Great Lakes is required to carry 8 life buoys, what is the allowable minimum number of these buoys that must have self-igniting lights attached?
A. 8
B. 6
C. 4
D. 2

B10042/DG01180 *46 CFR 199.60 (c)
The regulations require that inspected vessels on an international voyage, other than small passenger vessels, must carry which of the following distress signals on or near the navigating bridge?
A. 12 hand red flares
B. 12 rocket parachute flares
C. 12 hand combination flares and orange smoke signals
D. 6 hand red flares, and 6 hand orange smoke signals

B10043/DG02534 *46 CFR 199.640 (c)
Great Lakes vessels, using liferafts, must have sufficient liferaft capacity on each side of the vessel to accommodate at least _____.
A. 50% of the persons on board
B. 100% of the persons on board
C. 100% of the persons normally assigned to those spaces
D. 150% of the crew

B10044/DG02679 *46 CFR 199.640 (d) (2)
Great Lakes cargo vessels, having a liferaft stowed more than 100 meters from the bow or stern, must have at least how many liferafts?
A. One
B. Two
C. Three
D. Four

NAVIGATION GENERAL

CHARTS & BUOYAGE

B10045/DG02778   **LIGHT LIST; *USCP 6**
Assume that your vessel has just entered Lake Erie by way of the Welland Canal and is proceeding in a southwesterly direction. Which statement about the aids to navigation you can expect to encounter along the route is TRUE?

⚓ A. The characteristics of buoys and other aids are as if "returning from seaward" when proceeding in this direction.

B. All aids are maintained by the U.S. Coast Guard, 9th Coast Guard District, Cleveland, Ohio.

C. All red even-numbered buoys should be kept on your port side when proceeding in this direction.

D. Lighted aids, fog signals, and radio beacons maintained by Canada are not included in the Great Lakes Light List.

B10046/DG02738   **CG-159**
Assume that your vessel has just entered Lake Michigan via the Straits of Mackinac and is proceeding south to Chicago. Which statement is TRUE with respect to the aids to navigation you will encounter along this route?

A. Aids to navigation are serviced jointly by the U.S. and Canadian Coast Guard.

⚓ B. Red buoys should be passed down your starboard side.

C. Green buoys mark the location of wrecks or obstructions which must be passed by keeping the buoy on the right hand.

D. All solid colored buoys are numbered, the red buoys bearing odd numbers and green buoys bearing even numbers.

B10047/DG02776   **LIGHT LIST; *USCP 6**
How are aids to navigation on the Great Lakes arranged geographically?

A. In a westerly and northerly direction, except on Lake St. Clair

B. In an easterly and southerly direction, except on Lake Erie

⚓ C. In a westerly and northerly direction, except on Lake Michigan

D. In an easterly and southerly direction, except on the New York State Barge Canal

B10048/DG02848   ***USCP 6**
Nautical charts published by the Canadian Hydrographic service which are referenced in the United States Coast Pilot are identified by _____.

A. the abbreviation "can" preceding the chart number

B. the letter "c" in parentheses following the chart number

⚓ C. an asterisk preceding the chart number

D. a footnote number

B10049/DG02748   **GREAT LAKES CHART; *USCP 6**
The Lake Carriers Association and the Canadian Shipowners Association prescribe separation routes for upbound and downbound vessels on the Great Lakes. The recommended courses for these routes are shown on the Great Lakes Charts in the form of _____.

⚓ A. red or magenta figures over a segmented course line track

B. red figures over a solid course line track

C. black figures over a segmented course line track

D. green figures over a solid course line track

DATUM

B10050/DG02879   ***USCP 6**
The vertical reference for all water levels and bench marks on the Great Lakes - St. Lawrence River System is known as _____.

A. Mean Sea Level Datum

⚓ B. International Great Lakes Datum

C. Great Lakes Low Water Datum

D. North Central Reference Datum

B10051/DG02789   ***USCP**
Your vessel is approaching the International Bridge on the St. Mary's River. If the gage on the bridge, read from top to bottom, indicates 124 ft. and the IGLD (1955) is 600 ft., determine the actual vertical clearances between the existing water level and the lowest point of the bridge over the channel.

⚓ A. 124 feet

B. 476 feet

C. 724 feet

D. 840 feet

PUBLICATIONS

B10052/DG02794   ***46 CFR 97.05**
The Great Lakes Edition of the Notice to Mariners is published _____.

⚓ A. weekly by the 9th Coast Guard District

B. monthly by the Army Corps of Engineers

C. monthly by the Naval Oceanographic office

D. biweekly by the Commandant, U.S. Coast Guard

B10053/DG00295   ***USCP 6**
Which publication offers information on Great Lakes
ice services?
A. Light List volume VII
B. U.S. Coast Pilot #6
C. Marine Weather Log
D. National Weather Service, Ice Outlooks

B10054/DG02799   ***USCP 6**
Who publishes the "Canadian List of Lights, Buoys and
Fog Signals"?
A. The U.S. Coast Guard
B. The Canadian Coast Guard
C. The U.S. Hydrographic Service
D. The Canadian Hydrographic Service

B10055/DG02914   ***USCP 6**
Your vessel has been ordered to proceed to the United
Grain Growers Wharf at Thunder Bay, Lake Superior,
for the purpose of taking on a load of wheat. Which
publication(s) would you consult for such information
as the length of the wharf, the depth of the water
alongside, and the loading capacity at the facility?
A. The Navigational Chart and Light List Vol. VII
B. The International Guide to Canadian Ports and
     Facilities
C. The Lake Carriers Association Facilities Directory
D. The United States Coast Pilot #6

B10056/DG00290   BOWD; NATIONAL ICE CENTER
What is NOT a form used by ice support services to
disseminate information?
A. Ice Analyses
B. Ice Forecasts
C. Ice Outlooks
D. Ice Bulletins

LIGHT LIST

B10057/DG02969   ***USCP 6**
Fog can form in any season on the Great Lakes, but it is
most likely to occur over open waters in _____.
A. summer and early autumn
B. autumn and early winter
C. winter and early spring
D. spring and early summer

B10058/DG03082   **LIGHT LIST**
Which statement is FALSE with regards to the Great
Lakes Light List?
A. The Light List does not contain information on any
     of the navigational aids maintained by Canada.
B. Volume VII does not include information on Class
     III private aids to navigation.
C. The Light List does not include Coast Guard
     mooring buoys, special purpose buoys, or buoys
     marking fish net areas.
D. The Light List should be corrected each week from
     the appropriate Notice to Mariners.

WEATHER

B10059/DG03056   ***USCP 6**
Advection fog holds longest over which portions of the
lakes?
A. Northwest
B. Southeast
C. Northeast
D. Southwest

B10060/DG02996   ***USCP 6**
Advection fog, a common occurrence on the Great
Lakes, forms when _____.
A. air comes in contact with a rapidly cooling land
     surface
B. frigid arctic air moves across the lakes and
     becomes saturated
C. relatively warm air flows over cooler water
D. cool air contacts warm river currents

B10061/DG03026   ***USCP 6**
Which type of fog is the most dense and widely spread
of those that occur on the Great Lakes?
A. Steam fog
B. Advection fog
C. Radiation fog
D. Lake effect fog

B10062/DG02964   ***USCP 6**
Seiche is defined as a(n) _____.
A. unusually strong storm system which approaches
     the Great Lakes System generally from the
     Northeast
B. lake current which is predominant during the
     spring and fall navigation season on the Great
     Lakes
C. oscillation caused by the diminishing of forces
     which cause lake level fluctuations
D. higher than normal high water or lower than
     normal low water

B10063/DG03054   *USCP 6
The phenomenon known as a "seiche" is most likely to occur on Lake Erie _____.
A. during the passage of a rapidly moving warm front
B. when strong winds from the Northeast suddenly diminish
C. during the months of May through August
D. when the Moon and Sun are in alignment

B10064/DG02994   *USCP 6
Nearly half of all storms that enter the Great Lakes Basin during the period from October through May come from _____.
A. highs which originate in the east and east central USA
B. lows which originate in north central and western Canada
C. highs which originate in north eastern and eastern Canada
D. lows which originate in the central and western USA

B10065/DG02968   *USCP 6
On the Great Lakes, winter storms compound the ice threat by bringing a variety of wind, wave, and weather problems on an average of every _____.
A. two days
B. three days
C. four days
D. five days

B10066/DG02936   *USCP 6
Storms that enter the Great Lakes Basin from the west and northwest at a peak in October are the products of pressure systems known as _____.
A. Northwesters
B. Alberta lows
C. Fata morgana
D. Polar highs

B10067/DG01212   KOTSCH; DONN
What is NOT characteristic of the conditions which would be experienced by a vessel located southeast of an approaching eastward-moving storm center on the Great Lakes?
A. Falling barometer
B. A westerly wind
C. Lowering clouds
D. Rain or snow

B10068/DG04016   *USCP 6
Which statement is TRUE concerning weather conditions on the Great Lakes?
A, When a vessel is south of an eastward-moving storm center, the approach of the low is evidenced by winds from the north to northeast.
B. When a vessel is north of an eastward-moving storm center, changes in the weather are less distinctive than when sailing south of the center.
C. The most destructive storms usually come from the northwest or north.
D. Thunderstorms are most likely to develop from November through April.

B10069/DG02939   *USCP 6
A vessel operating on the Great Lakes, and whose position is south of an approaching eastward-moving storm center, would NOT experience _____.
A. a falling barometer
B. lowering clouds and drizzle
C. a southwest to west wind
D. rain or snow

B10070/DG02938   GLWL
Which statement concerning storm surges on the Great Lakes is FALSE?
A. They are common along the deeper areas of the lakes.
B. They cause rapid differences in levels between one end of the lake and the other.
C. The greatest water level difference occurs when the wind is blowing along the axis of the lake.
D. If the wind subsides rapidly, a seiche effect will most likely occur.

RULES OF THE ROAD

B10071/DG02894   INLAND RULE 3 (m)
The term "Great Lakes", as defined by the Inland Rules of the Road, includes part of the _____.
A. Calumet River
B. Chicago River
C. St. Lawrence River
D. All of the above

B10072/DG02854   INLAND RULE 3 (m)
The term "Great Lakes", as defined by the Inland Rules of the Road, does NOT include _____.
A. portions of the Chicago River
B. portions of the Calumet River
C. the St. Lawrence River to Trois Rivieres
D. Saginaw Bay

B10073/DG03028   **INLAND RULE 3 (o)**

The term "inland waters", as defined in the Rules of the Road, includes _____.

A. the Great Lakes in their entirety

B. the Mississippi River System

C. U.S. waters out to three miles offshore

D. the St. Lawrence River to Anticosti Island

B10074/DG02696   **INLAND RULE 9 (a) (ii)**

You are on a power-driven vessel proceeding down a channel, with the current, on a river on the Great Lakes System. If you meet another power-driven vessel who is upbound, your responsibilities include _____.

A. backing down to get out of the way of the other vessel

B. waiting for the other vessel to signal her intentions, and then answering promptly

C. proposing a safe way to pass

D. All of the above

B10075/DG02896   **INLAND RULE 9 (a) (ii)**

You are proceeding against the current on a river in the Great Lakes System. You are meeting a downbound vessel. Both vessels are power-driven. The other vessel sounds one short blast. You must _____.

A. change course to port

B. hold course and speed

C. sound three short blasts

D. sound one short blast

B10076/DG02855   **INLAND RULE 9 (c)**

A 150-meter vessel is proceeding down the course of a narrow channel in the Great Lakes System. A 60-meter vessel is starting to cross the channel. Which statement is TRUE?

A. If the smaller vessel is engaged in fishing, he shall not impede the passage of the other vessel.

B. The crossing vessel has the right of way.

C. The vessel in the channel must slow to her steerageway.

D. The larger vessel is considered to be a vessel restricted in her ability to maneuver.

B10077/DG02814   **INLAND RULE 15 (b)**

Your vessel is crossing a river on the Great Lakes System. A power-driven vessel is ascending the river, crossing your course from port to starboard. Which statement is TRUE?

A. The vessel ascending the river has the right of way.

B. Your vessel has the right of way, but you are directed not to impede the other vessel.

C. The other vessel must hold as necessary to allow you to pass.

D. You are required to propose the manner of passage.

B10078/DG02816   **INLAND RULE 23 (d)**

Which statement is TRUE concerning lighting requirements for Great Lakes vessels?

A. The showing of a forward masthead light is optional for vessels under 150 meters.

B. An all-round white light may be carried in lieu of the second masthead light and stern light.

C. Sidelights for vessels over 50 meters are required to have only a two-mile range of visibility.

D. Great Lakes vessels are exempted from the requirement to show yellow towing lights.

ICE NAVIGATION

B10079/DG03058   ***USCP 6**

Which type of ice is the most difficult to combat and presents the greatest hazard to shipping on the Great Lakes during the winter months?

A. Icebergs

B. Fast ice

C. Slow ice

D. Pack slush ice

B10080/DG00297   ***USCP 6**

Commercial ships or other persons or agencies requiring the assistance of Canadian Coast Guard icebreakers should first contact _____.

A. the Canadian Coast Guard

B. Ice Sarnia

C. the Ice Navigation Center

D. the icebreaker assigned to the area

B10081/DG02839   **GLIN**

Adequate horsepower is of great importance when a ship is navigating independently in ice. Adequate horsepower is generally considered to exist when the horsepower to length ratio is at least _____.

A. 4 to 1 or better

B. 5 to 1 or better

C. 6 to 1 or better

D. 8 to 1 or better

B10082/DG03089   **GLIN**

How does an icebreaker normally free a ship which has become beset while navigating independently?

A. By backing down the track and cutting out ice on either bow

B. By approaching from the stern and crossing ahead at an angle of 20° to 30° to the beset ship's course

C. By overtaking the beset ship, running ahead and then backing down the track to the beset vessel

D. By approaching the vessel from astern and towing the beset vessel stern first

B10083/DG02976   **GLIN**

Which statement is TRUE with respect to shiphandling procedures in ice?

A. Never go "full astern" at any time while in ice.

⚓ B. Go astern in ice with extreme care - always with rudder amidships.

C. Enter ice at medium speeds to reduce impact.

D. The presence of a snow cover on the ice assists a vessel's progress through an ice field.

B10084/DG02868   **GLIN**

Which vessel, if navigating independently in ice, is more likely to become beset due to inadequate horsepower?

A. A 254 ft. "Whaleback" tanker with 1800 H.P.

B. A 309 ft. cement carrier with 2000 H.P.

C. A 385 ft. shallow draft tanker with 2400 H.P.

⚓ D. A 630 ft. bulk ore carrier with 3500 H.P.

B10085/DG03004   **BOWD**

What is NOT a basic shiphandling rule for navigating in ice concentrations on the Great Lakes?

A. Keep moving - even very slowly, but keep moving.

B. Work with the ice movement, not against.

⚓ C. Transit ice along pressure ridges when possible.

D. Excessive speed means ice damage.

B10086/DG03036   **GLIN**

Which statement about ships operating in ice is FALSE?

A. Light and partly loaded ships should be ballasted as deeply as possible.

⚓ B. In brash-filled channels, operating with a shallow draft forward is most effective.

C. Traditionally, operating ships light in the ice has been effective in the spring.

D. Good searchlights should be available in the event of night navigation with or without icebreaker escort.

B10087/DG03086   **GLIN**

Which statement concerning the navigation of a vessel in ice is FALSE?

A. Anchoring in the presence of ice is not recommended except in an emergency.

B. Towing a vessel through an ice field is not recommended except in an emergency.

C. The "Free and Proceed" system of escorting a beset vessel cuts down on the number of freeing operations.

⚓ D. When anchoring in ice, it is advisable to increase the scope of the chain over what is normally used for non-icing conditions.

B10088/DG02944   **GLIN; CRENSHAW**

Your ship is navigating independently in heavy ice when it becomes beset. Which statement is FALSE?

A. The vessel will most likely require an icebreaker to free her.

B. The vessel may be able to free herself by pumping ballast from side to side.

⚓ C. The propeller is more susceptible to ice damage when turning slowly than when stopped.

D. It is advisable to clear the rudder area of ice by using ahead turns before backing down.

B10089/DG03032   ***USCP 6**

Ice is often strong enough to halt navigation through the St. Lawrence Seaway by mid-_____.

A. October

B. November

⚓ C. December

D. January

B10090/DG02719   ***USCP 6**

Which publication would give detailed information on the commercial vessel traffic reporting system for connecting waters from Lake Erie to Lake Huron?

A. United States Coast Pilot - Great Lakes #6

B. U.S. Coast Guard Light List - Vol. VII

⚓ C. Code of Federal Regulations - Title 33

D. The appropriate Great Lakes Navigation Chart

B10091/DG03059   ***H.O. 102**

A vessel which is being assisted by an icebreaker would display a flag hoist consisting of the code numeral "4" when the vessel _____.

A. speed begins to drop

B. stops

C. receives ice damage

⚓ D. becomes icebound

B10092/DG02869   **GLIN; *H.O. 102**

When more than one vessel is being assisted by an icebreaker, distances between vessels should be constant. Which signal should be given by a vessel which is ahead of another and whose speed suddenly begins to drop?

A. Four short blast on the whistle

B. A flag hoist consisting of the code figure "4"

⚓ C. A flag hoist consisting of the code figure "5"

D. A flag hoist consisting of the code letters "FE" (Foxtrot-Echo)

B10093/DG02978   *H.O. 102

An icebreaker assisting a vessel through an ice field would display a visual signal consisting of the code letter "E" (Echo) to signify that "_____".

⚓ A. I am altering my course to starboard
B. I am altering my course to port
C. I am operating astern propulsion
D. My vessel is stopped and making no way through the water

B10094/DG02744   *H.O. 102

An icebreaker assisting a vessel through an ice field would display a visual signal consisting of the code letter "I" (India) to signify that "_____".

A. I am altering my course to starboard
⚓ B. I am altering my course to port
C. I am operating astern propulsion
D. My vessel is stopped and making no way through the water

B10095/DG02826   *H.O. 102

An icebreaker may use the code letter "K" to remind ships of their obligation to listen continuously on their radio. This signal may be made by any of the following EXCEPT _____.

A. sound signal
B. light signal
C. visual signal
⚓ D. radiotelephone

B10096/DG02876   GLIN

A U.S. Coast Guard icebreaker may use all of the following distinctive lights when escorting ships in ice EXCEPT _____.

A. a single amber rotating light
B. a single red rotating light
C. red aircraft warning lights
⚓ D. a single blue rotating light

B10097/DG02859   *H.O. 102

An icebreaker assisting a vessel through an ice field would display a visual signal consisting of the code letter "M" (Mike) to signify that "_____".

A. I am altering my course to starboard
B. I am altering my course to port
C. I am operating astern propulsion
⚓ D. my vessel is stopped and making no way through the water

B10098/DG02946   *H.O. 102

Which single-letter signal, when used by icebreakers on the Great Lakes, may be made by using the ship's whistle?

A. E
B. I
⚓ C. M
D. None

B10099/DG04022   *H.O. 102

Your vessel is being assisted through an ice field in Thunder Bay by the Canadian Coast Guard icebreaker Alexander Henry. The starboard lookout reports that the icebreaker has run up the code flag "N" (November). What action should you take?

A, Reduce speed
⚓ B. Stop your engines
C. Reverse your engines
D. Stop your vessel instantly

B10100/DG02948   *H.O. 102

An icebreaker assisting a vessel through an ice field would display a visual signal consisting of the code letter "S" (Sierra) to signify that "_____".

A. I am altering my course to starboard
B. I am altering my course to port
⚓ C. I am operating astern propulsion
D. My vessel is stopped and making no way through the water

B10101/DG02824   *H.O. 102

While being assisted by an icebreaker on Lake Superior, you receive a single letter code instructing you to slow your vessel. Which signal could you use to signify that you are complying with the request?

A. Three blasts of the whistle
B. The code flag "A" (Alpha) displayed from a halyard
⚓ C. Four blasts of the whistle, namely 1 short 2 long and 1 short
D. The code flag "L" (Lima) displayed from a halyard

B10102/DG02838   *H.O. 102

A U.S. Coast Guard icebreaker, while escorting ships in ice, may sound four short and one long blasts on the whistle to indicate that the icebreaker _____.

⚓ A. has become beset in fast ice
B. is increasing speed; watch for broken ice
C. has its engines full astern
D. is increasing the distance between vessels

B10103/DG03064   *H.O. 102

What is the meaning of a flag hoist consisting of the code letters "WM" (Whiskey Mike) when displayed by an icebreaker?

A. I am going ahead; follow me.
B. You should stop your vessel instantly.
⚓ C. Icebreaker support is now commencing.
D. Icebreaker support is finished.

B10104/DG04024   *H.O. 102
An icebreaker displaying a flag hoist which consists of the code letters "WO" (Whiskey Oscar) is indicating that _____.
⚓ A, icebreaker support is finished
B. icebreaker support is commencing
C. the icebreaker is icebound
D. the icebreaker is beset

B10105/DG02949   *H.O. 102
A vessel which is being assisted by an icebreaker should indicate that he is ready to cast off the towline (if one is used) by _____.
⚓ A. displaying code letter "Y" (Yankee)
B. sounding five short blasts of his whistle
C. displaying code numeral "5"
D. sounding one prolonged blast of his whistle

B10106/DG02709   *H.O. 102
A vessel which is being assisted by an icebreaker should indicate that she is ready to cast off the towline by _____.
⚓ A. displaying code letter "Y" (Yankee)
B. sounding five short blasts on his whistle
C. displaying code numeral "5"
D. sounding one prolonged blast on his whistle

MISCELLANEOUS NAVIGATION GENERAL

B10107/DG03094   **MBLLF GREAT LAKES**
Your vessel is underway and approaching an overhead obstruction on Lake Superior. Given the following information, determine the clearance between your vessel and the obstruction. Highest point on vessel: 74 ft. Lowest point of obstruction: 126 (LWD). Monthly lake level: +2 (LWD). International Great Lakes Datum: 600.0 (182.88 meters). See Diagram D039DG
A. 474 feet
B. 400 feet
C. 175 feet
⚓ D. 50 feet

CARGO

BULK CARGO OPERATIONS

B10108/DG03068 MERCHANT SHIP CONSTRUCTION
While loading a cargo of grain, your vessel develops a list to starboard. This will be corrected by _____.
A. the compensating tanks on the high side
⚓ B. the list man changing the discharge location of the chutes
C. allowing the grain to level itself as the hold fills to the spar deck level
D. trimming the final loading cone by hand

B10109/DG03066 MERCHANT SHIP CONSTRUCTION
A list man would expect to see any of the following light signals EXCEPT _____.
A. two red lights
B. one green light
C. one white light
⚓ D. one amber light

B10110/DG03008 MERCHANT SHIP CONSTRUCTION
A list signal of one white light indicates that the vessel is _____.
A. on an even keel
⚓ B. listing about 1° to the side the light is displayed on
C. listing over 5° with the light displayed on the high side
D. listing, and the chutes should be directed to the side where the light is displayed

B10111/DG03009 MERCHANT SHIP CONSTRUCTION
While loading cargo, a white trimming light on the starboard side comes on. This indicates that _____.
⚓ A. the vessel has a list of about 1` to starboard
B. the chutes should be directed to the starboard side
C. the chutes in No. 1 hold should be directed to the starboard side
D. a severe list to starboard has developed and all loading should cease

MISCELLANEOUS CARGO OPERATIONS

B10112/DG03072 MERCHANT SHIP CONSTRUCTION
A Great Lakes bulk ore vessel would use an "Iron Deckhand" to assist in _____.
A. unloading bulk cargo
B. steering the vessel
C. making the vessel fast to a dock
⚓ D. removing hatch covers

B10113/DG03042   *46 CFR 93.20-20 (6)
A Great Lakes vessel bound for Anticosti Island is exempt from the IMO Grain Regulations if the vessel meets all of the following standards EXCEPT _____.
A. the metacentric height corrected for free surface must meet regulatory minimums throughout the voyage
⚓ B. slack surfaces should be in a mound
C. the longitudinal strength of the vessel must not be imperiled
D. the Master must ascertain the expected weather conditions enroute

KNOW YOUR CRANE SIGNALS

STOP (A)
Extend one arm and hold palm of hand vertical.
NOTE: EMERGENCY STOP is indicated by holding both arms up.

STOP (B)
Arm extended, palm down, move hand right and left.
Usually for different level operations.

HOLD EVERYTHING
Clasp hands in front of body.

HOIST
With forearm vertical, forefinger pointing up, move hand in horizontal circles.

LOWER
With arm extended down, move arm in horizontal circles.

MOVE SLOWLY
Place one arm motionless across chest in conjunction with or before giving any other directional signal. ("Hoist slowly" shown as example).

RAISE BOOM (LUFF UP)
Arm extended, fingers closed, thumb pointing upwards.

LOWER BOOM (LUFF DOWN)
Arm extended, fingers closed, thumb pointing downwards.

SLEW
Arm extended, point with finger in direction of swing of boom.
OVERHEAD GANTRY CRANE Arm extended, point with finger in the long travel or cross travel direction.

RAISE BOOM LOWER LOAD
One arm extended, finger closed, thumb pointing upwards. Other arm extended downward with forefinger pointing down, move arm in horizontal circles.

LOWER BOOM RAISE LOAD
One arm extended, fingers closed, thumb pointing downwards. Other arm vertical with forefinger pointing up, move arm in horizontal circles.

EXTEND BOOM or TROLLEY OUT (TOWER CRANE)
Both fists in front of body with thumbs pointing outward.

RETRACT BOOM or TROLLEY IN (TOWER CRANE)
Both fists in front of body with thumbs pointing toward each other.

USE MAIN HOIST
Tap fist on head, then use regular signals.

USE FLYLINE (AUXILIARY HOIST)
Tap elbow with one hand, then use regular signals.

FINISHED WITH CRANE
Place arms above head and cross hands.

TRAVEL
Arm bent at the elbows, fists clenched, rotate both forearms around each other then point in the direction of travel.

TRAVEL (One track-Crawler cranes only)
Lock the track on the side indicated by the closed fist. Travel opposite track in the direction indicated by circular motion of other fist rotated vertically in front of body

DIAGRAMS UTILIZED IN VOLUME 1, DECK GENERAL

1. Diagram 37
2. D001DG
3. D003DG
4. D008DG
5. D019DG
6. D022DG
7. D023DG
8. D024DG
9. D025DG
10. D029DG
11. D030DG
12. D031DG
13. D033DG
14. D034DG
15. D035DG
16. D038DG
17. D042DG
18. D043DG
19. D044DG
20. D045DG
21. D047DG
22. D049DG
23. D051DG
24. D058DG

CHAPTER 1
RULES OF THE ROAD

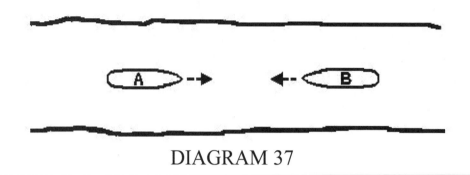

DIAGRAM 37

CHAPTER 2
DECK GENERAL

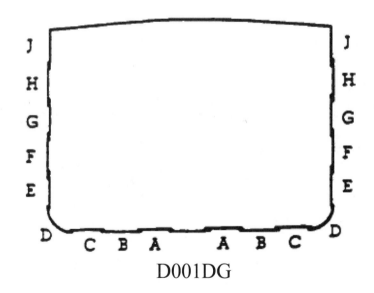

D001DG

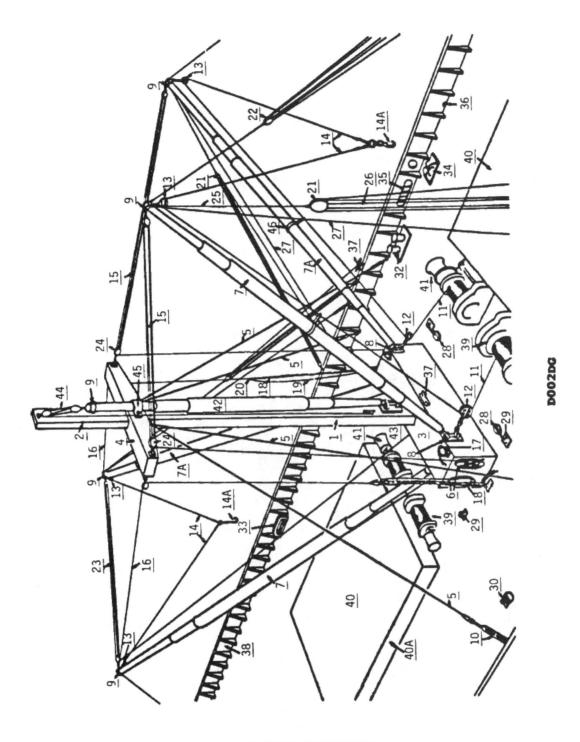

D002DC

DELETED

A

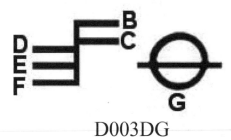

D003DG

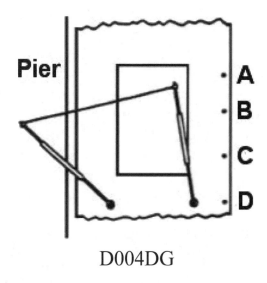

D004DG

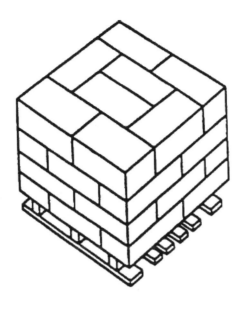

D005DG

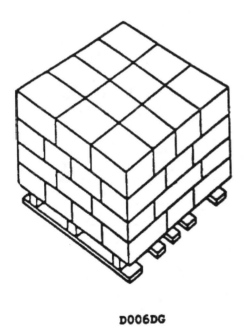

D006DG

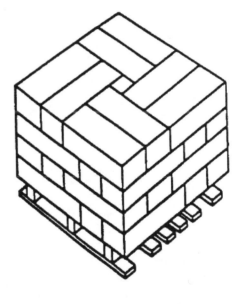

D007DG

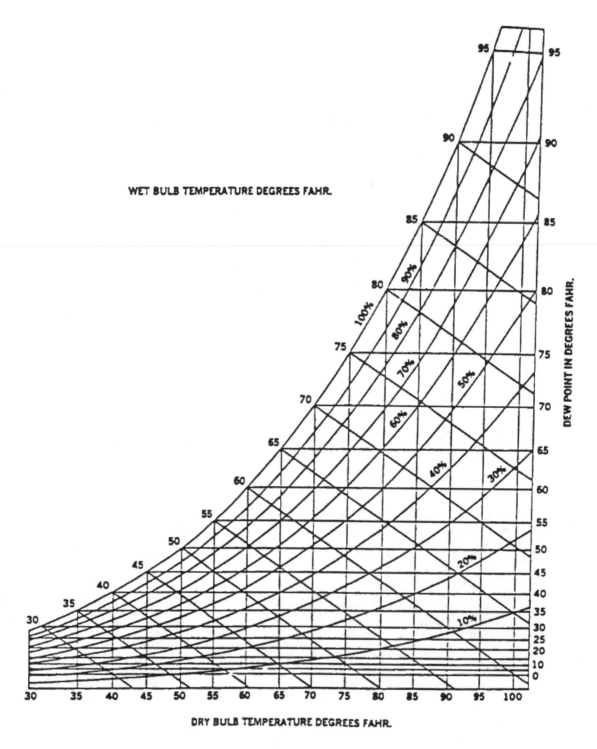

D008DG

D009DG THROUGH D018DG RESERVED

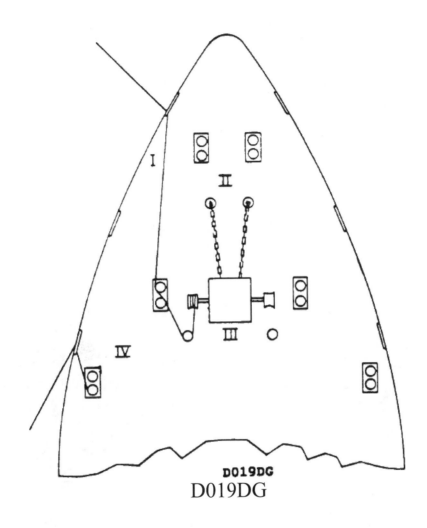

D019DG

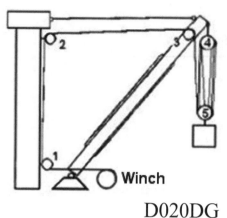

1, 2, 3 - Single sheave
fairlead blocks

4, 5 - Triple sheave
blocks

Winch

D020DG

D021DG RESERVED

D022DG

D023DG

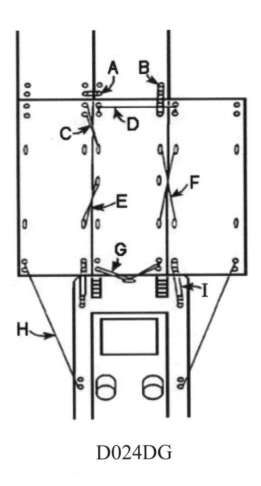

D024DG

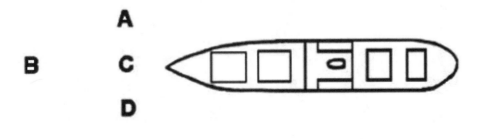

D025DG

D026DG THROUGH D028DG RESERVED

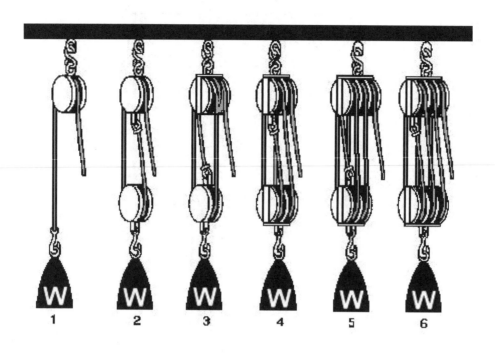

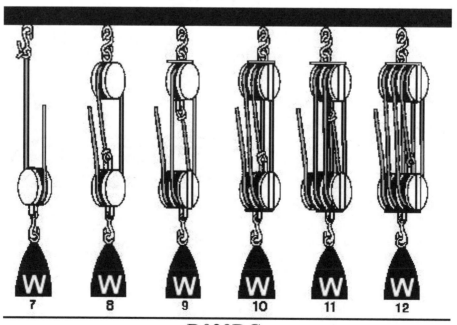

D029DG

D030DG

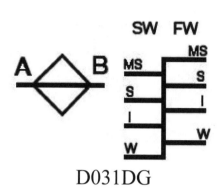

D031DG

12   12
11   11
10   10
9   9
8   8
7   7

AFT DRAFT   **FWD DRAFT**
MARKS   **MARKS**

D032DG

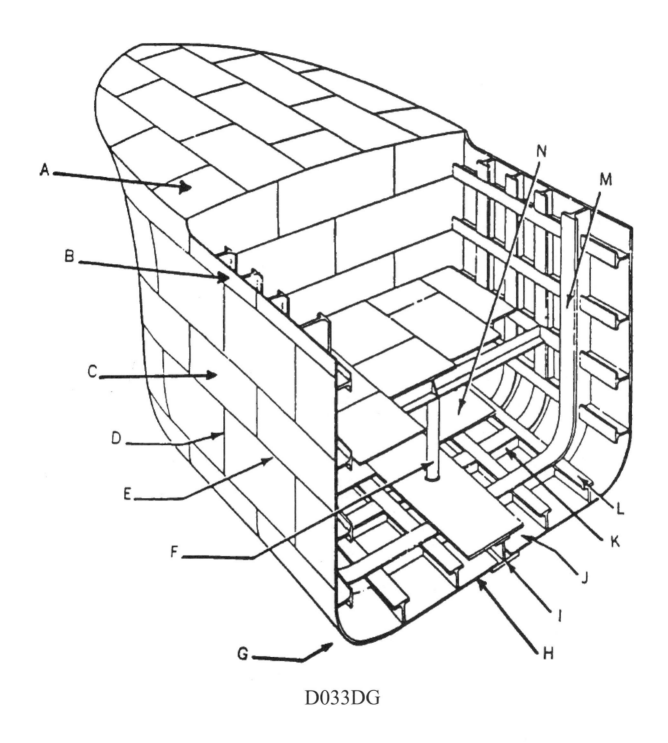

D033DG

HEADING (TRUE)	BEARING (TRUE)	RANGE (YDS)	REMARKS
228°			INITIAL HEADING
228°	232°	2260	ON INITIAL COURSE
228°	234°	1700	RIGHT FULL RUDDER ORDERED
230°	236°	1490	
252°	235°	1275	
275°	231°	1000	
316°	214°	850	
352°	198°	975	
022°	194°	1210	
053°	197°	1430	
087°	202°	1600	
115°	209°	1690	
151°	217°	1700	
183°	225°	1600	
218°	232°	1350	RUDDER AMIDSHIPS
228°	235°	1125	STEADY ON 228°

D034DG

HEADING (TRUE)	BEARING (TRUE)	RANGE (YDS)	REMARKS
333°			INITIAL HEADING
333°	315°	2125	ON INITIAL COURSE
333°	310°	1650	LEFT FULL RUDDER ORDERED
327°	307°	1475	
310°	303°	1250	
278°	302°	1050	
268°	305°	900	
236°	318°	750	
196°	337°	800	
157°	344°	1100	
113°	340°	1350	
079°	332°	1525	
050°	324°	1575	
022°	318°	1550	
343°	308°	1400	RUDDER AMIDSHIPS
333°	302°	1175	STEADY ON 333°

D035DG

U.S. Department
of Transportation

**United States
Coast Guard**

Commandant
United States Coast Guard

Washington. D.C. 20593-0001
Staff Symbol.
Phone.

16710
8 Apr 87

Master, M/V HUDSON, O.N. 666666

Subj: M/V HUDSON
        Stability

Dear Sir:

A stability test, supervised by the U.S. Coast Guard, was conducted on the M/V HUDSON at San Diego, California on 08 April 1987. On the basis of this test, stability calculations have been performed. Results indicate that the stability of the M/V HUDSON, as presently outfitted and equipped, is satisfactory for operation in Ocean Service as indicated on the Certificate of Inspection, provided the following restrictions are strictly observed:

1. a.   The vessel shall only be loaded according to the instructions on the attached LOADING DIAGRAM bearing U.S. Coast Guard approval stamp dated 8 April 1986.

   b.   Drilling fluids may be carried. The maximum specific gravity of the fluids shall not exceed 2.60.

   c.   The vessel may engage in towing operations when loaded in accordance with the attached LOADING DIAGRAM.

2. The height above the main deck of the center of gravity of the deck cargo shall not exceed the value shown on the LOADING DIAGRAM (3.0 feet). Such cargo must be positively secured against shifting prior to leaving protected waters.

3. Permanent ballast, in the form of 64.4 long tons of high density fluids (sg. = 2.87), is to be maintained in the after peak tank. No permanent ballast shall be added, removed, altered and/or relocated without the authorization and supervision of the cognizant Officer in Charge, Marine Inspection.

4. The maximum summer load line draft is 13 feet 8 3/8 inches. Trim shall be minimized and shall always result in a freeboard of at least 22 inches at the stern.

5. No more than one centerline or P/S pair of the following tanks may be partially filled at any one time: fuel oil, lube oil, potable water, ballast/cargo water, fuel oil day tanks, drilling fluid. Cross-connections between all port and starboard tank pairs shall be kept closed at all times when underway.

D036DG

6. Main deck hatches and weather doors to the forecastle and machinery spaces shall be kept closed and fully secured at all times when underway, except when actually used for transit under safe conditions.

7. Main deck freeing ports shall be maintained operable and completely unobstructed at all times.

8. Bilges shall be kept pumped to minimum content at all times.

9. Suitable tables or curves for determining the capacities of full or partially full tanks shall be maintained aboard the vessel.

10. The Master should make every effort to determine the cause of any list of the vessel before taking corrective action.

It shall be the Master's responsibility to maintain the vessel in a satisfactory stability condition at all times.

This stability letter shall be posted under suitable transparent material in the pilothouse of the vessel so that all pages and the diagram are visible. It supersedes any stability information previously furnished the vessel.

Sincerely,

A. B. SEA
Lieutenant Commander
U.S. Coast Guard

Attachment: LOADING DIAGRAM for the subject vessel bearing U.S. Coast Guard approval stamp dated 8 April 1987

SEE NEXT PAGE FOR ATTACHMENT

D036DG continued

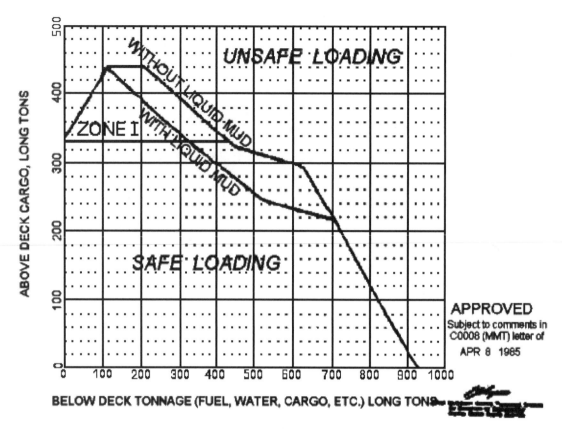

USCG STABILITY
LOADING INSTRUCTIONS

1. DRAW A VERTICAL LINE UP FROM 'BELOW DK' LOAD. DRAW HORIZONTAL LINE ACROSS FROM 'ABOVE DK' LOAD. IF THEY MEET BELOW THE CURVE THEN THE LOADING IS OK. IF THEY MEET ABOVE THE CURVE THEN YOU MUST CHANGE THE LOADING.

2. MAX. DECK CARGO VCG 3.00 FT. ABOVE DECK.

3. WHEN OPERATING IN ZONE 1 (I.E. MORE THAN 334 LONG TONS OF DECK CARGO) THE FOREPEAK BALLAST TANK SHALL BE PRESSED FULL.

D036DG continued

U.S. Department
of Transportation

**United States
Coast Guard**

Commandant
United States Coast Guard

Washington, D C 20593-0001
Staff Symbol
Phone

16710
13 May 87

Master, M/V SURVEYOR, O.N. 678678

Subj: M/V SURVEYOR
        Stability

Dear Sir:

A stability test, supervised by the U.S. Coast Guard, was conducted on
the M/V SURVEYOR at New Orleans, Louisiana, on 7 May 1987. On the
basis of this test, stability calculations have been performed.
Results indicate that the stability of the M/V SURVEYOR, as presently
outfitted and equipped, is satisfactory for operation in Ocean Service
as indicated on the Certificate of Inspection, provided the following
restrictions are strictly observed:

1. A maximum of 78 persons may be carried. In no case shall the
   number of persons exceed that allowed on the Certificate of
   Inspection.

2. The drafts as read on the draft marks shall not exceed 6 feet 3
   inches forward or 7 feet 1 inch aft. Trim should be minimized.
   A loadline is not authorized.

3. The height above the main deck of the center of gravity of deck
   cargo shall not exceed 2.0 feet. Such cargo must be positively
   secured before leaving protected waters.

4. A maximum of 50 long tons of deck cargo may be carried when no
   other below deck ballast or cargo is carried. When rig water
   is carried, a maximum of 35 long tons of deck cargo may be
   carried, and no other below deck cargo or ballast is permitted.

5. No permanent ballast or other such weights shall be added,
   removed, altered, and/or relocated without the authorization
   and supervision of the cognizant Officer in Charge, Marine
   Inspection.

6. No watertight bulkheads shall be removed or altered without the
   authorization and supervision of the cognizant Officer in
   Charge, Marine Inspection.

7. The watertight door in the bulkhead at frame 18 shall be closed
   and properly dogged at all times when underway except when
   actually used for transit under safe conditions.

D037DG

8. Cross-connections between all tank sets shall be kept closed at all times when underway.

9. Bilges shall be kept pumped to minimum content at all times.

10. Jet fuel may be carried on deck in eight DOT tanks. The total weight of the fuel and tanks shall not exceed 23.16 long tons and the vertical center of gravity shall not exceed 3 feet 6 inches above the deck. Such tanks must be positively secured against shifting in a seaway prior to leaving protected waters. Neither passengers nor other deck cargo shall be carried when such tanks are aboard the vessel.

11. The Master should make every effort to determine the cause of any list of the vessel before taking corrective action.

It shall be the Master's responsibility to maintain the vessel in a satisfactory stability condition at all times.

This temporary stability letter shall be posted under suitable transparent material in the pilothouse of the vessel so that all pages are visible. It supersedes any stability information previously furnished the vessel.

Sincerely,

W. T. DOOR
Lieutenant Commander
U.S. Coast Guard

D037DG continued

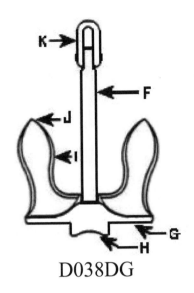

D038DG

D039DG

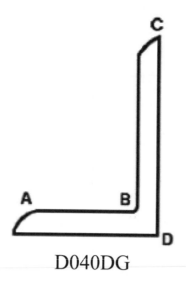

D040DG

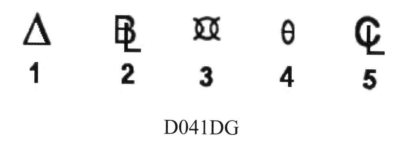

D041DG

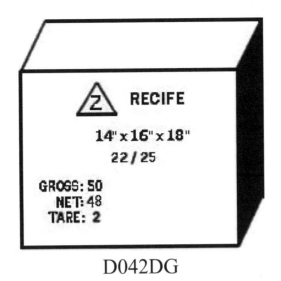

D042DG

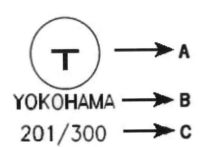

D043DG

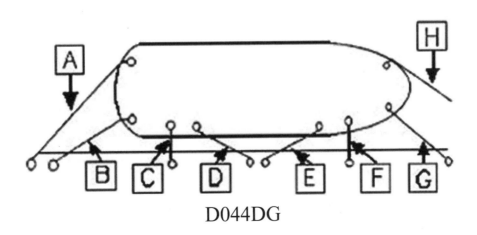

D044DG

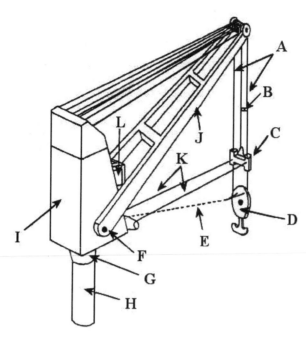

D045DG

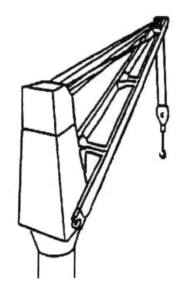

D046DG

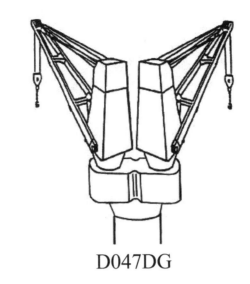

D047DG

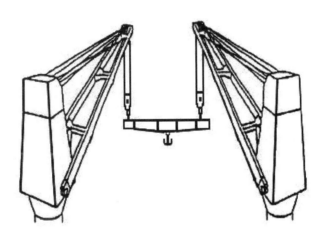

D048DG

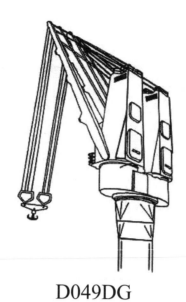

D049DG

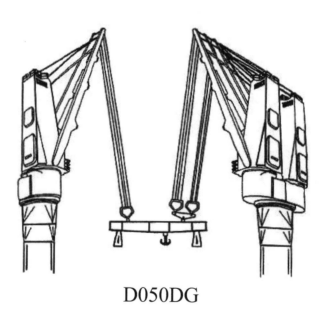

D050DG

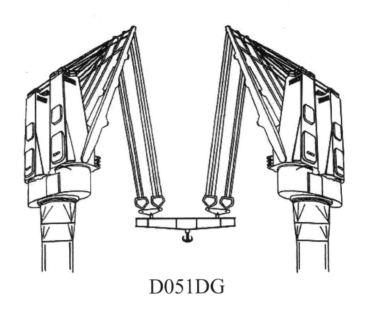

D051DG

D052DG THROUGH D057DG RESERVED

A.

B.

C.

D.

D058DG